THE WORLD'S GREAT CLASSICS

Homer

THE ILIAD

Done into English prose by ANDREW LANG, M.A.,
WALTER LEAF, Litt.D., and ERNEST MYERS, M.A.;
with a critical and biographical profile of the author
by HERBERT J. ROSE, Emeritus Professor of Greek, United College
of St. Salvator and St. Leonard, St. Andrews, Scotland

 Grolier
INCORPORATED
NEW YORK

Standard Book Number 7172–0000–0

Set in Grolier Ultratype®

PRINTED IN THE UNITED STATES OF AMERICA

A critical and biographical profile of
Homer by HERBERT J. ROSE,
Emeritus Professor of Greek, United College
of St. Salvator and St. Leonard,
St. Andrews, Scotland.

H omer is the traditional name of the author of the two
oldest and greatest epics in any European language,
the *Iliad* and the *Odyssey*. Nothing whatever is known of
his life, save that his technical skill shows that he was a
professional poet; and certain linguistic and other evidences
point to his having composed in Ionia, not in Greece
proper. His surviving biographies are mere collections of
folklore, centuries later than any possible date for him,
and are of no historical value whatever. Even the meaning
of his name (Greek names regularly have a meaning) is
unknown; its identity in sound with the word for hostage
probably is accidental. The tradition that he was blind
comes from one of the *Hymns* which, along with various
other works, were attributed to him in antiquity but now,
on the basis of evidence collected by the best critics, ancient
and modern, are known to be later. In one of these, the
Hymn to Apollo, the author bids the singers tell anyone
asking who their best poet is that he is "a blind man, and
dwells in craggy Chios." This assertion of blindness is con-
tradicted by the many instances of keen visual observation
in the epics. His date is variously estimated, the arguments

Reprinted from The Encyclopedia Americana, 1968 copyright, by per-
mission of the Americana Corporation, New York.

vii

being based on probabilities rather than certainties; the most reasonable datings put him not earlier than the tenth nor later than the eighth century B.C.

For a long while, especially from 1795, when Friedrich August Wolf (1759–1824) published his *Prolegomena ad Homerum,* it was held by many excellent and industrious scholars that the epics as we have them could not have been composed by one man (the theory still survives in places, especially in Continental Europe). The fundamental reasons for it were advanced by Wolf, who stated that writing was unknown to the Greeks of "Homer's" day and that without writing no one could compose such long works. Both these propositions are now known to be false. Therefore, the arguments based consciously or unconsciously on them are futile. Writing of a kind was known at least to some Greeks centuries before any likely date for Homer, and professional poets in illiterate societies are capable of remembering a prodigious amount of poetry, their own or another's. The search for the shorter poems supposedly put together to make the epics led to curious analyses of the epics and the supposed discovery of all manner of inconsistencies, "later" additions, and so on, as well as to the finding of something that is really there: older and newer forms of words. These, however, are distributed fairly evenly throughout the poems and fail entirely to coincide with the "earlier" and "later" portions. The inconsistencies are few and slight, and very few of the supposed additions still appear to be such when the structure of the poems as wholes and the ancient manner of telling a long story are duly considered. The assembling of the supposed shorter pieces was commonly ascribed to Pisistratus (d. 527 B.C.), tyrant of Athens, on late and slender evidence. The truth seems to be that, in his time, regulations were made for the public recital of the poems in their proper order, not of random selections made by the reciters to suit their own tastes or capabilities.

A modification of the ballad theory, as it may be called, was upheld by the historian George Grote (1794–1871), among others. This was to the effect that the *Iliad* grew out of successive additions, by unknown hands, to a shorter epic, about half the length of the poem as we have it. This, too, is backed by no really cogent arguments; and all these theories tend to lose sight of the fact that Homer did not live in a primitive community, but in one that still retained memories of the brilliant Mycenaean civilization and, futhermore, was on the fringes of, and in at least occasional contact with, great cultures—Oriental and Egyptian—given to the composition of long and elaborate poems and other works and to their preservation in writing.

The only problem which is really alive today is the old one (it goes back to the Alexandrian critics) of whether Homer—meaning by that the author of the *Iliad*—also composed the *Odyssey*. Though differences in language and tone do exist, it cannot be said that the arguments for separate authorship are cogent, for these may be reasonably accounted for by the difference in subject: the *Iliad* describes an important episode in a long war, and the *Odyssey* the adventures of a man trying, under great difficulties, to return home, being mostly concerned with conditions of peace, or at least not with open and regular warfare.

All this does not mean that the poems have come down to us precisely as Homer composed them. Apart from modernizations of language here and there, certain passages, mostly quite short, may be additions made by reciters for one reason or another. Nor does it mean that Homer made no use of, or did not quote from, earlier poems that are lost to us. On the contrary, his frequent use of stock epithets, recurrent descriptions of natural phenomena, such as sunrise, formulas introducing a speech, and the like, make it clear that he inherited not only a vocabulary but a supply of ready-made metrical tags which he had no hesitation in using whenever it suited him; probably his hearers would have been surprised and disappointed if he had not done so.

The high poetical quality of his work is vouched for by the consensus of the best literary criticism, ancient and modern.

HERBERT J. ROSE

Emeritus Professor of Greek, United College of
   St. Salvator and St. Leonard, St. Andrews,
   Scotland

The Iliad of Homer

BOOK I

How Agamemnon and Achilles fell out at the siege of Troy; and
Achilles withdrew himself from battle, and won from Zeus a
pledge that his wrong should be avenged on Agamemnon and
the Achaians.

SING, goddess, the wrath of Achilles Peleus' son, the
ruinous wrath that brought on the Achaians woes innumerable, and hurled down into Hades many strong souls
of heroes, and gave their bodies to be a prey to dogs and
all winged fowls; and so the counsel of Zeus wrought out its
accomplishment from the day when first strife parted
Atreides king of men and noble Achilles.

Who among the gods set the twain at strife and variance?
Apollo, the son of Leto and of Zeus; for he in anger at the
king sent a sore plague upon the host, so that the folk began
to perish, because Atreides had done dishonour to Chryses
the priest. For the priest had come to the Achaians' fleet
ships to win his daughter's freedom, and brought a ransom
beyond telling; and bare in his hands the fillet of Apollo the
Far-darter upon a golden staff; and made his prayer unto all
the Achaians, and most of all to the two sons of Atreus,
orderers of the host: "Ye sons of Atreus and all ye well-
greaved Achaians, now may the gods that dwell in the
mansions of Olympus grant you to lay waste the city of
Priam, and to fare happily homeward; only set ye my dear

1

child free, and accept the ransom in reverence to the son of Zeus, far-darting Apollo."

Then all the other Achaians cried assent, to reverence the priest and accept his goodly ransom; yet the thing pleased not the heart of Agamemnon son of Atreus, but he roughly sent him away, and laid stern charge upon him, saying: "Let me not find thee, old man, amid the hollow ships, whether tarrying now or returning again hereafter, lest the staff and fillet of the god avail thee naught. And her will I not set free; nay, ere that shall old age come on her in our house, in Argos, far from her native land, where she shall ply the loom and serve my couch. But depart, provoke me not, that thou mayest the rather go in peace."

So said he, and the old man was afraid and obeyed his word, and fared silently along the shore of the loud-sounding sea. Then went that aged man apart and prayed aloud to king Apollo, whom Leto of the fair locks bare: "Hear me, god of the silver bow! If ever I built a temple gracious in thine eyes, or if ever I burnt to thee fat flesh of thighs of bulls or goats, fulfil thou this my desire; let the Danaans pay by thine arrows for my tears."

So spake he in prayer, and Phoebus Apollo heard him, and came down from the peaks of Olympus wroth at heart, bearing on his shoulders his bow and covered quiver. And the arrows clanged upon his shoulders in his wrath, as the god moved; and he descended like to night. Then he sate him aloof from the ships, and let an arrow fly; and there was heard a dread clanging of the silver bow. First did he assail the mules and fleet dogs, but afterward, aiming at the men his piercing dart, he smote; and the pyres of the dead burnt continually in multitude.

Now for nine days ranged the god's shafts through the host; but on the tenth Achilles summoned the folk to assembly, for in his mind did goddess Hera of the white arms put the thought, because she had pity on the Danaans when she beheld them perishing. Now when they had gathered and were met in assembly, then Achilles fleet of foot stood up and spake among them: "Son of Atreus, now deem I that we shall return wandering home again if war at once and pestilence must indeed ravage the Achaians. But come, let us now inquire of some soothsayer or priest, yea, or an interpreter of dreams—seeing that a dream too is of Zeus— who shall say wherefore Phoebus Apollo is so wroth, whether he blame us by reason of vow or hecatomb; if perchance he would accept the savour of lambs or unblemished goats, and so would take away the pestilence from us."

So spake he and sate him down; and there stood up before them Kalchas son of Thestor, most excellent far of augurs, who knew both things that were and that should be and that had been before, and guided the ships of the Achaians to Ilios by his soothsaying that Phoebus Apollo bestowed on him. He made harangue and spake amid them: "Achilles, dear to Zeus, thou biddest me tell the wrath of Apollo, the king that smiteth afar. Therefore will I speak; but do thou make covenant with me, and swear that verily with all thy heart thou wilt aid me both by word and deed. For of a truth I deem that I shall provoke one that ruleth all the Argives with might, and whom the Achaians obey. For a king is more of might when he is wroth with a meaner man; even though for the one day he swallow his anger, yet doth he still keep his displeasure thereafter in his breast till he accomplish it. Consider thou, then, if thou wilt hold me safe."

And Achilles fleet of foot made answer and spake to him: "Yea, be of good courage, speak whatever soothsaying thou knowest; for by Apollo, dear to Zeus, him by whose worship thou, O Kalchas, declarest thy soothsaying to the Danaans, no man while I live and behold light on earth shall lay violent hands upon thee amid the hollow ships; no man of all the Danaans, not even if thou mean Agamemnon, that now avoweth him to be greatest far of the Achaians."

Then was the noble seer of good courage, and spake: "Neither by reason of a vow is he displeased, nor for any hecatomb, but for his priest's sake to whom Agamemnon did despite, and set not his daughter free and accepted not the ransom; thereforth hath the Far-darter brought woes upon us, yea, and will bring. Nor will he ever remove the loathly pestilence from the Danaans till we have given the bright-eyed damsel to her father, unbought, unransomed, and carried a holy hecatomb to Chryse; then might we propitiate him to our prayer."

So said he and sate him down, and there stood up before them the hero son of Atreus, wide-ruling Agamemnon, sore displeased; and his dark heart within him was greatly filled with anger, and his eyes were like flashing fire. To Kalchas first spake he with look of ill: "Thou seer of evil, never yet hast thou told me the thing that is pleasant. Evil is ever the joy of thy heart to prophesy, but never yet didst thou tell any good matter nor bring it to pass. And now with sooth-saying thou makest harangue among the Danaans, how that the Far-darter bringeth woes upon them because, forsooth, I would not take the goodly ransom of the damsel Chryseis, seeing I am the rather fain to keep her own self within mine house. Yea, I prefer her before Klytaimnestra my wedded wife; in no wise is she lacking beside her, neither in favour nor stature, nor wit nor skill. Yet for all this will I give her back, if that is better; rather would I see my folk whole than perishing. Only make ye me ready a prize of honour forth-with, lest I alone of all the Argives be disprized, which thing beseemeth not; for ye all behold how my prize is departing from me."

To him then made answer fleet-footed goodly Achilles: "Most noble son of Atreus, of all men most covetous, how shall the great-hearted Achaians give thee a meed of hon-our? We know naught of any wealth of common store, but what spoil soe'er we took from captured cities hath been apportioned, and it beseemeth not to beg all this back from the folk. Nay, yield thou the damsel to the god, and we Achaians will pay thee back threefold and fourfold, if ever Zeus grant us to sack some well-walled town of Troy-land."

To him lord Agamemnon made answer and said: "Not in this wise, strong as thou art, O godlike Achilles, beguile thou me by craft; thou shalt not outwit me nor persuade me. Dost thou wish, that thou mayest keep thy meed of honour, for me to sit idle in bereavement, and biddest me give her back? Nay, if the great-hearted Achaians will give me a meed suited to my mind, that the recompense be equal—but if they give it not, then I myself will go and take a meed of

honour, thine be it or Aias', or Odysseus' that I will take
unto me; wroth shall he be to whomsoever I come. But for
this we will take counsel hereafter; now let us launch a
black ship on the great sea, and gather picked oarsmen, and
set therein a hecatomb, and embark Chryseis of the fair
cheeks herself, and let one of our counsellors be captain,
Aias or Idomeneus or goodly Odysseus, or thou, Peleides,
most redoubtable of men, to do sacrifice for us and propitiate the Far-darter."

Then Achilles fleet of foot looked at him scowling and
said: "Ah me, thou clothed in shamelessness, thou of crafty
mind, how shall any Achaian hearken to thy bidding with
all his heart, be it to go a journey or to fight the foe amain?
Not by reason of the Trojan spearmen came I hither to
fight, for they have not wronged me; never did they harry
mine oxen nor my horses, nor ever waste my harvest in deep-
soiled Phthia, the nurse of men; seeing there lieth between
us long space of shadowy mountains and sounding sea; but
thee, thou shameless one, followed we hither to make thee
glad, by earning recompense at the Trojans' hands for Menelaos and for thee, thou dog-face! All this thou reckonest
not nor takest thought thereof; and now thou threatenest
thyself to take my meed of honour, wherefor I travailed
much, and the sons of the Achaians gave it me. Never win I
meed like unto thine, when the Achaians sack any populous
citadel of Trojan men; my hands bear the brunt of furious
war, but when the apportioning cometh then is thy meed far
ampler, and I betake me to the ships with some small thing
when I have fought to weariness. Now will I depart to
Phthia, seeing it is far better to return home on my beaked

ships; nor am I minded here in dishonour to draw thee thy fill of riches and wealth."

Then Agamemnon king of men made answer to him: "Yea, flee, if thy soul be set thereon. It is not I that beseech thee to tarry for my sake; I have others by my side that shall do me honour, and above all Zeus, lord of counsel. Most hateful art thou to me of all kings, fosterlings of Zeus; thou ever lovest strife and wars and fightings. Though thou be very strong, yet that I ween is a gift to thee of God. Go home with thy ships and company and lord it among thy Myrmidons; I reck not aught of thee nor care I for thine indignation; and this shall be my threat to thee: seeing Phoebus Apollo bereaveth me of Chryseis, her with my ship and my company will I send back; and mine own self will I go to thy hut and take Briseis of the fair cheeks, even that thy meed of honour, that thou mayest well know how far greater I am than thou, and so shall another hereafter abhor to match his words with mine and rival me to my face."

So said he, and grief came upon Peleus' son, and his heart within his shaggy breast was divided in counsel, whether to draw his keen blade from his thigh and set the company aside and so slay Atreides, or to assuage his anger and curb his soul. While yet he doubted thereof in heart and soul, and was drawing his great sword from his sheath, Athene came to him from heaven, sent forth of the white-armed goddess Hera, whose heart loved both alike and had care for them. She stood behind Peleus' son and caught him by his golden hair, to him only visible, and of the rest no man beheld her. Then Achilles marvelled, and turned him about, and straightway knew Pallas Athene; and terribly shone her

eyes. He spake to her winged words, and said: "Why now
art thou come hither, thou daughter of aegis-bearing Zeus?
Is it to behold the insolence of Agamemnon, son of Atreus?
Yea, I will tell thee what I deem shall even be brought to
pass: by his own haughtinesses shall he soon lose his life."

Then the bright-eyed goddess Athene spake to him again:
"I came from heaven to stay thine anger, if perchance thou
wilt hearken to me, being sent forth of the white-armed
goddess Hera, that loveth you twain alike and careth for
you. Go to now, cease from strife, and let not thine hand
draw the sword; yet with words indeed revile him, even as it
shall come to pass. For thus will I say to thee, and so it shall
be fulfilled; hereafter shall goodly gifts come to thee, yea in
three-fold measure, by reason of this despite; hold thou
thine hand, and hearken to us."

And Achilles fleet of foot made answer and said to her:
"Goddess, needs must a man observe the saying of you
twain, even though he be very wroth at heart; for so is the
better way. Whosoever obeyeth the gods, to him they gladly
hearken."

He said, and stayed his heavy hand on the silver hilt, and
thrust the great sword back into the sheath, and was not
disobedient to the saying of Athene; and she forthwith was
departed to Olympus, to the other gods in the palace of
aegis-bearing Zeus.

Then Peleus' son spake again with bitter words to Atreus'
son, and in no wise ceased from anger: "Thou heavy with
wine, thou with face of dog and heart of deer, never didst
thou take courage to arm for battle among thy folk or to lay
ambush with the princes of the Achaians; that to thee were

even as death. Far better booteth it, forsooth, to seize for thyself the meed of honour of every man through the wide host of the Achaians that speaketh contrary to thee. But I will speak my word to thee, and swear a mighty oath therewith: verily by this staff that shall no more put forth leaf or twig, seeing it hath for ever left its trunk among the hills, verily shall longing for Achilles come hereafter upon the sons of the Achaians one and all; and then wilt thou in no wise avail to save them, for all thy grief, when multitudes fall dying before manslaying Hector. Then shalt thou tear thy heart within thee for anger that thou didst in no wise honour the best of the Achaians."

So said Peleides and dashed to earth the staff studded with golden nails, and himself sat down; and over against him Atreides waxed furious. Then in their midst rose up Nestor, pleasant of speech, the clear-voiced orator of the Pylians, he from whose tongue flowed discourse sweeter than honey. Two generations of mortal men already had he seen perish, that had been of old time born and nurtured with him in goodly Pylos, and he was king among the third. He made harangue to them and said: "Alas, of a truth sore lamentation cometh upon the land of Achaia. Verily Priam would be glad and Priam's sons, and all the Trojans would have great joy of heart, were they to hear all this tale of strife between you twain that are chiefest of the Danaans in counsel and chiefest in battle. Nay, hearken to me; ye are younger both than I. Of old days held I converse with better men even than you, and never did they make light of me. Even so hearken ye also, for better is it to hearken. Neither do thou, though thou art very great, seize from him his damsel, but leave her as she was given at the first by the sons of the Achaians to be a meed of honour; nor do thou, son of Peleus, think to strive with a king, might against might; seeing that no common honour pertaineth to a sceptred king to whom Zeus apportioneth glory. Though thou be strong, and a goddess mother bare thee, yet his is the greater place, for he is king over more. And thou, Atreides, abate thy fury; nay, it is even I that beseech thee to let go thine anger with Achilles, who is made unto all the Achaians a mighty bulwark of evil war."

Then lord Agamemnon answered and said: "Yea verily, old man, all this thou sayest is according unto right. But this fellow would be above all others, he would be lord of all and king among all and captain to all; wherein I deem none will hearken to him. Though the immortal gods made him a spearman, do they therefore put revilings in his mouth for him to utter?"

Then goodly Achilles brake in on him and answered: "Yea, for I should be called coward and man of naught, if I yield to thee in every matter, howsoe'er thou bid. To others give now thine orders, not to me. This, moreover, will I say to thee, and do thou lay it to thy heart. Know that not by violence will I strive for the damsel's sake, neither with thee nor any other; ye gave and ye have taken away. But of all else that is mine beside my fleet black ship, thereof shalt thou not take anything or bear it away against my will. Yea, go to now, make trial, that all these may see; forthwith thy dark blood shall gush about my spear."

Now when the twain had thus finished the battle of violent words, they stood up and dissolved the assembly beside the Achaian ships. Peleides went his way to his huts and trim ships with Menoitios' son and his company; and Atreides launched a fleet ship on the sea, and picked twenty oarsmen therefor, and embarked the hecatomb for the god, and brought Chryseis of the fair cheeks and set her therein; and Odysseus of many devices went to be their captain.

So these embarked and sailed over the wet ways; and Atreides bade the folk purify themselves. So they purified themselves, and cast the defilements into the sea and did sacrifice to Apollo, even unblemished hecatombs of bulls and goats, along the shore of the unvintaged sea; and the sweet savour arose to heaven eddying amid the smoke.

Thus were they busied throughout the host; but Agamemnon ceased not from the strife wherewith he threatened Achilles at the first; he spake to Talthybios and Eurybates that were his heralds and nimble squires: "Go ye to the tent of Achilles Peleus' son, and take Briseis of the fair cheeks by the hand and lead her hither; and if he give her not, then will I myself go, and more with me, and seize her; and that will be yet more grievous for him."

So saying he sent them forth, and laid stern charge upon them. Unwillingly went they along the beach of the unvintaged sea, and came to the huts and ships of the Myrmidons. Him found they sitting beside his hut and black ship; nor when he saw them was Achilles glad. So they in dread and reverence of the king stood, and spake to him no word, nor questioned him. But he knew in his heart, and spake to them: "All hail, ye heralds, messengers of Zeus and men, come near; ye are not guilty in my sight, but Agamemnon that sent you for the sake of the damsel Briseis. Go now, heaven-sprung Patroklos, bring forth the damsel, and give them her to lead away. Moreover, let the twain themselves be my witnesses before the face of the blessed gods and mortal men, yea and of him, that king untoward, against the day when there cometh need of me hereafter to save them all from shameful wreck. Of a truth he raveth with baleful mind, and hath not knowledge to look before and after, that so his Achaians might battle in safety beside their ships."

So said he, and Patroklos hearkened to his dear comrade, and led forth from the hut Briseis of the fair cheeks, and gave them her to lead away. So these twain took their way back along the Achaians' ships, and with them went the woman all unwilling. Then Achilles wept anon, and sat him down apart, aloof from his comrades on the beach of the grey sea, gazing across the boundless main; he stretched forth his arms and prayed instantly to his dear mother: "Mother, seeing thou didst of a truth bear me to so brief span of life, honour at the least ought the Olympian to have granted me, even Zeus that thundereth on high; but now doth he not honour me, no, not one whit. Verily Atreus' son, wide-ruling Agamemnon, hath done me dishonour; for he hath taken away my meed of honour and keepeth her of his own violent deed."

So spake he weeping, and his lady mother heard him as she sate in the sea-depths beside her aged sire. With speed arose she from the grey sea, like a mist, and sate her before the face of her weeping son, and stroked him with her hand, and spake and called on his name: "My child, why weepest thou? What sorrow hath entered into thy heart? Speak it forth, hide it not in thy mind, that both may know it."

Then with heavy moan Achilles fleet of foot spake to her:
"Thou knowest it; why should I tell this to thee that knowest all! If indeed thou canst, guard thine own son; betake
thee to Olympus and beseech Zeus by any deed or word
whereby thou ever didst make glad his heart. For oft have I
heard thee proclaiming in my father's halls and telling that
thou alone amid the immortals didst save the son of Kronos,
lord of the storm-cloud, from shameful wreck, when all the
other Olympians would have bound him, even Hera and
Poseidon and Pallas Athene. Then didst thou, O goddess,
enter in and loose him from his bonds, having with speed
summoned to high Olympus him of the hundred arms whom
gods call Briareus, and the blessed gods feared him withal
and bound not Zeus. This bring thou to his remembrance
and sit by him and clasp his knees, if perchance he will give
succour to the Trojans; and for the Achaians, hem them
among their ships' sterns about the bay, given over to
slaughter; that they may make trial of their king and that
even wide-ruling Agamemnon may perceive his blindness,
in that he honoured not at all the best of the Achaians."

Then Thetis weeping made answer to him: "Ah me, my
child, why reared I thee, cursed in my motherhood? Would
thou hadst been left tearless and griefless amid the ships,
seeing thy lot is very brief and endureth no long while; but
now art thou made short-lived alike and lamentable beyond
all men; in an evil hour I bare thee in our halls. But I will go
myself to snow-clad Olympus to tell this thy saying to Zeus,
whose joy is in the thunder, if perchance he may hearken to
me. But tarry thou now amid thy fleet-faring ships, and con-
tinue wroth with the Achaians, and refrain utterly from

battle: for Zeus went yesterday to Okeanos, unto the noble Ethiopians for a feast, and all the gods followed with him; but on the twelfth day will he return to Olympus, and then will I fare to Zeus' palace of the bronze threshold, and will kneel to him and think to win him."

So saying she went her way and left him there, vexed in spirit for the fair-girdled woman's sake, whom they had taken perforce despite his will: and meanwhile Odysseus came to Chryse with the holy hecatomb. When they were now entered within the deep haven, they furled their sails and laid them in the black ship, and lowered the mast by the forestays and brought it to the crutch with speed, and rowed her with oars to the anchorage. Then they cast out the mooring stones and made fast the hawsers, and so themselves went forth on to the sea-beach, and forth they brought the hecatomb for the Far-darter Apollo, and forth came Chryseis withal from the seafaring ship. Then Odysseus of many counsels brought her to the altar and gave her into her father's arms, and spake unto him: "Chryses, Agamemnon king of men sent me hither to bring thee thy daughter, and to offer to Phoebus a holy hecatomb on the Danaans' behalf, wherewith to propitiate the king that hath now brought sorrow and lamentation on the Argives."

So saying he gave her to his arms, and he gladly took his dear child; and anon they set in order for the god the holy hecatomb about his well-builded altar; next washed they their hands and took up the barley meal. Then Chryses lifted up his hands and prayed aloud for them: "Hearken to me, god of the silver bow! Even as erst thou heardest my prayer, and didst me honour, and mightily afflictedst the

people of the Achaians, even so now fulfil me this my
desire: remove thou from the Daanans forthwith the loathly
pestilence."

So spake he in prayer, and Phoebus Apollo heard him.
Now when they had prayed and sprinkled the barley meal,
first they drew back the victims' heads and slaughtered them
and flayed them, and cut slices from the thighs and wrapped
them in fat, making a double fold, and laid raw collops
thereon, and the old man burnt them on cleft wood and
made libation over them of gleaming wine. Now when the
thighs were burnt and they had tasted the vitals, then sliced
they all the rest and pierced it through with spits, and
roasted it carefully, and drew all off again. So when they
had rest from the task and had made ready the banquet,
they feasted, nor was their heart aught stinted of the fair
banquet. But when they had put away from them the desire
of meat and drink, the young men crowned the bowls with
wine, and gave each man his portion after the drink-offering
had been poured into the cups. So all day long worshipped
they the god with music, singing the beautiful paean, the
sons of the Achaians making music to the Far-darter; and
his heart was glad to hear. And when the sun went down
and darkness came on them, they laid them to sleep beside
the ship's hawsers; and when rosy-fingered Dawn appeared,
the child of morning, then set they sail for the wide camp of
the Achaians; and Apollo the Far-darter sent them a fa-
vouring gale. They set up their mast and spread the white
sails forth, and the wind filled the sail's belly and the dark
wave sang loud about the stem as the ship made way, and
she sped across the wave, accomplishing her journey. So

when they were now come to the wide camp of the Achaians, they drew up their black ship to land high upon the
sands, and set in line the long props beneath her; and themselves were scattered amid their huts and ships.

But he sat by his swift-faring ships, still wroth, even the
heaven-sprung son of Peleus, Achilles fleet of foot; he betook him neither to the assembly that is the hero's glory,
neither to war, but consumed his heart in tarrying in his
place, and yearned for the war-cry and for battle.

Now when the twelfth morn thereafter was come, then
the gods that are for ever fared to Olympus all in company,
led of Zeus. And Thetis forgat not her son's charge, but rose
up from the sea-wave, and at early morn mounted up to
great heaven and Olympus. There found she Kronos' son of
the farsounding voice sitting apart from all on the topmost
peak of many-ridged Olympus. So she sat before his face
and with her left hand clasped his knees, and with her right
touched him beneath his chin, and spake in prayer to king
Zeus son of Kronos: "Father Zeus, if ever I gave thee aid
amid the immortal gods, whether by word or deed, fulfil
thou this my desire; do honour to my son, that is doomed to
earliest death of all men: now hath Agamemnon king of
men done him dishonour, for he hath taken away his meed
of honour and keepeth her of his own violent deed. But
honour thou him, Zeus of Olympus, lord of counsel; grant
thou victory to the Trojans the while, until the Achaians do
my son honour and exalt him with recompense."

So spake she; but Zeus the cloud-gatherer said no word to
her, and sat long time in silence. But even as Thetis had
clasped his knees, so held she by him clinging, and ques-

tioned him yet a second time: "Promise me now this thing verily, and bow thy head thereto; or else deny me, seeing there is naught for thee to fear; that I may know full well how I among all gods am least in honour."

Then Zeus the cloud-gatherer, sore troubled, spake to her: "Verily it is a sorry matter, if thou wilt set me at variance with Hera, whene'er she provoketh me with taunting words. Even now she upbraideth me ever amid the immortal gods, and saith that I aid the Trojans in battle. But do thou now depart again, lest Hera mark aught; and I will take thought for these things to fulfil them. Come now, I will bow my head to thee, that thou mayest be of good courage; for that, of my part, is the surest token amid the immortals; no word of mine is revocable nor false nor unfulfilled when the bowing of my head hath pledged it."

Kronion spake, and bowed his dark brow, and the ambrosial locks waved from the king's immortal head; and he made great Olympus quake.

Thus the twain took counsel and parted; she leapt therewith into the deep sea from glittering Olympus, and Zeus fared to his own palace. All the gods in company arose from their seats before their father's face; neither ventured any to await his coming, but they stood up all before him. So he sate him there upon his throne; but Hera saw, and was not ignorant how that the daughter of the Ancient of the sea, Thetis the silver-footed, had devised counsel with him. Anon with taunting words spake she to Zeus the son of Kronos: "Now who among the gods, thou crafty of mind, hath devised counsel with thee? It is ever thy good pleasure to hold aloof from me and in secret meditation to give thy judgments, nor of thine own good will hast thou ever brought thyself to declare unto me the thing thou purposest."

Then the father of gods and men made answer to her: "Hera, think not thou to know all my sayings; hard they are for thee, even though thou art my wife. But whichsoever it is seemly for thee to hear, none sooner than thou shall know, be he god or man. Only when I will to take thought aloof from the gods, then do not thou ask of every matter nor make question."

Then Hera the ox-eyed queen made answer to him: "Most dread son of Kronos, what word is this thou hast spoken? Yea, surely of old I have not asked thee nor made question, but in very quietness thou devisest all thou wilt. But now is my heart sore afraid lest thou have been won over by silver-footed Thetis, daughter of the Ancient of the sea, for she at early morn sat by thee and clasped thy knees. To her I deem thou gavest a sure pledge that thou wilt do honour to Achilles, and lay many low beside the Achaians' ships."

To her made answer Zeus the cloud-gatherer: "Lady, good lack! ever art thou imagining, nor can I escape thee. Abide thou in silence and hearken to my bidding, lest all the gods that are in Olympus keep not off from thee my visitation, when I put forth my hands unapproachable against thee."

He said, and Hera the ox-eyed queen was afraid, and sat in silence, curbing her heart; but throughout Zeus' palace the gods of heaven were troubled. Then Hephaistos the famed craftsman began to make harangue among them, to do kindness to his dear mother, white-armed Hera: "Verily this will be a sorry matter, neither any more endurable, if ye twain thus fight for mortals' sakes, and bring wrangling among the gods; neither will there any more be joy of the goodly feast, seeing that evil triumpheth. So I give counsel to my mother, though herself is wise, to do kindness to our dear father Zeus, that our father upbraid us not again and cast the banquet in confusion. What if the Olympian, the lord of the lightning, will to dash us from our seats! for he is strongest far. Nay, approach thou him with gentle words, then will the Olympian forthwith be gracious unto us."

So speaking he rose up and set in his dear mother's hand the two-handled cup, and spake to her: "Be of good courage, mother mine, and endure, though thou art vexed, lest I behold thee, that art so dear, chastised before mine eyes, and then shall I not be able for all my sorrow to save thee; for the Olympian is a hard foe to face. Yea, once ere this, when I was fain to save thee, he caught me by my foot and hurled me from the heavenly threshold; all day I flew, and at the set of sun I fell in Lemnos, and little life was in me."

He spake, and the white-armed goddess Hera smiled, and smiling took the cup at her son's hand. Then he poured wine to all the other gods from right to left, ladling the sweet nectar from the bowl. And laughter unquenchable arose amid the blessed gods to see Hephaistos bustling through the palace.

So feasted they all day till the setting of the sun; nor was their soul aught stinted of the fair banquet, nor of the beauteous lyre that Apollo held, and the Muses singing alternately with sweet voice.

Now when the bright light of the sun was set, these went

each to his own house to sleep, where each one had his palace made with cunning device by famed Hephaistos the lame god; and Zeus the Olympian, the lord of lightning, departed to his couch where he was wont of old to take his rest, whenever sweet sleep visited him. There went he up and slept, and beside him was Hera of the golden throne.

BOOK II

How Zeus beguiled Agamemnon by a dream; and of the assembly of the Achaians and their marching forth to battle.

Now all other gods and chariot-driving men slept all night long, only Zeus was not holden of sweet sleep; rather was he pondering in his heart how he should do honour to Achilles and destroy many beside the Achaians' ships. And this design seemed to his mind the best, to wit, to send a baneful dream upon Agamemnon son of Atreus. So he spake, and uttered to him winged words: "Come now, thou baneful Dream, go to the Achaians' fleet ships, enter into the hut of Agamemnon son of Atreus, and tell him every word plainly as I charge thee. Bid him call to arms the flowing-haired Achaians with all speed, for now he may take the wide-wayed city of the Trojans. For the immortals that dwell in the halls of Olympus are no longer divided in counsel, since Hera hath turned the minds of all by her beseeching, and over the Trojans sorrows hang."

So spake he, and the Dream went his way when he had heard the charge. With speed he came to the Achaians' fleet ships, and went to Agamemnon son of Atreus, and found him sleeping in his hut, and ambrosial slumber poured over him. So he stood over his head in seeming like unto the son of Neleus, even Nestor, whom most of all the elders Agamemnon honoured; in his likeness spake to him the heavenly Dream:

21

"Sleepest thou, son of wise Atreus tamer of horses? To sleep all night through beseemeth not one that is a counsellor, to whom peoples are entrusted and so many cares belong. Now hearken straightway to me, for I am a messenger to thee from Zeus, who though he be afar yet hath great care for thee and pity. He biddeth thee call to arms the flowing-haired Achaians with all speed, for now thou mayest take the wide-wayed city of the Trojans. For the immortals that dwell in the halls of Olympus are no longer divided in counsel, since Hera hath turned the minds of all by her beseeching, and over the Trojans sorrows hang by the will of Zeus. But do thou keep this in thy heart, nor let forgetfulness come upon thee when honeyed sleep shall leave thee."

So spake the Dream, and departed and left him there, deeming in his mind things that were not to be fulfilled. For indeed he thought to take Priam's city that very day; fond man, in that he knew not the plans that Zeus had in mind, who was willed to bring yet more grief and wailing on Trojans alike and Danaans throughout the course of stubborn fights. Then woke he from sleep, and the heavenly voice was in his ears. So he rose up sitting, and donned his soft tunic, fair and bright, and cast around him his great cloak, and beneath his glistering feet he bound his fair sandals, and over his shoulder cast his silver-studded sword, and grasped his sires' sceptre, imperishable for ever, wherewith he took his way amid the mail-clad Achaians' ships.

Now went the goddess Dawn to high Olympus, foretelling daylight to Zeus and all the immortals; and the king bade the clear-voiced heralds summon to the assembly the flowing-haired Achaians. So did those summon, and these gathered with speed.

But first the council of the great-hearted elders met beside the ship of king Nestor the Pylos-born. And he that had assembled them told them his dream and framed this cunning counsel: "Come, let us now call to arms as we may the sons of the Achaians. But first I will speak to make trial of them as is fitting, and will bid them flee with their benched ships; only do ye from this side and from that speak to hold them back."

So spake he and sate him down; and there stood up among them Nestor, who was king of sandy Pylos. He made harangue to them and said: "My friends, captains and rulers of the Argives, had any other of the Achaians told us this dream we might deem it a false thing, and rather turn away therefrom; but now he hath seen it who of all Achaians avoweth himself far greatest. So come, let us call to arms as we may the sons of the Achaians."

So spake he, and led the way forth from the council, and all the other sceptred chiefs rose with him and obeyed the shepherd of the host; and the people hastened to them. Even as when the tribes of thronging bees issue from some hollow rock, ever in fresh procession, and fly clustering among the flowers of spring, and some on this hand and some on that fly thick; even so from ships and huts before the low beach marched forth their many tribes by companies to the place of assembly. And in their midst blazed forth Rumour, messenger of Zeus, urging them to go; and so they gathered. And the place of assemblage was in an uproar, and the earth echoed again as the hosts sate them

down, and there was turmoil. Nine heralds restrained them
with shouting, if perchance they might refrain from clamour, and hearken to their kings, the fosterlings of Zeus. And
hardly at the last would the people sit, and keep them to
their benches and cease from noise. Then stood up lord
Agamemnon bearing his sceptre, that Hephaistos had
wrought curiously. Thereon he leaned and spake his saying
to the Argives:

"My friends, Danaan warriors, men of Ares' company,
Zeus hath bound me with might in grievous blindness of
soul; hard of heart is he, for that erewhile he promised me
and pledged his nod that not till I had wasted well-walled
Ilios should I return; but now see I that he planned a cruel
wile and biddeth me return to Argos dishonoured, with the
loss of many of my folk. Shame is this even for them that
come after to hear; how so goodly and great a folk of the
Achaians thus vainly warred a bootless war, and fought
scantier enemies, and no end thereof is yet seen. Already
have nine years of great Zeus passed away, and our ships'
timbers have rotted and the tackling is loosed; while there
our wives and little children sit in our halls awaiting us; yet
is our task utterly unaccomplished wherefor we came
hither. So come, even as I shall bid let us all obey. Let us flee
with our ships to our dear native land; for now shall we
never take wide-wayed Troy."

So spake he, and stirred the spirit in the breasts of all
throughout the multitude, as many as had not heard the
council. And the assembly swayed like high sea-waves of
the Icarian Main that east wind and south wind raise, rushing upon them from the clouds of father Zeus; and even as

when the west wind cometh to stir a deep cornfield with violent blast, and the ears bow down, so was all the assembly stirred, and they with shouting hasted toward the ships; and the dust from beneath their feet rose and stood on high. And they bade each man his neighbour to seize the ships and drag them into the bright salt sea, and cleared out the launching-ways, and the noise went up to heaven of their hurrying homewards; and they began to take the props from beneath the ships.

Then would the Argives have accomplished their return against the will of fate, but that Hera spake a word to Athene: "Out on it, daughter of aegis-bearing Zeus, unwearied maiden! Shall the Argives thus indeed flee homeward to their dear native land over the sea's broad back? But they would leave to Priam and the Trojans their boast, even Helen of Argos, for whose sake many an Achaian hath perished in Troy, far away from his dear native land. But go thou now amid the host of the mail-clad Achaians; with thy gentle words refrain thou every man, neither suffer them to draw their curved ships down to the salt sea."

So spake she, and the bright-eyed goddess Athene disregarded not; but went darting down from the peaks of Olympus, and came with speed to the fleet ships of the Achaians. There found she Odysseus standing, peer of Zeus in counsel, neither laid he any hand upon his decked black ship, because grief had entered into his heart and soul. And bright-eyed Athene stood by him and said: "Heaven-sprung son of Laertes, Odysseus of many devices, will ye indeed fling yourselves upon your benched ships to flee homeward to your dear native land? But ye would leave to Priam and the Trojans their boast, even Helen of Argos, for whose sake many an Achaian hath perished in Troy, far from his dear native land. But go thou now amid the host of the Achaians, and tarry not; and with thy gentle words refrain every man, neither suffer them to draw their curved ships down to the salt sea."

So said she, and he knew the voice of the goddess speaking to him, and set him to run, and cast away his mantle, the which his herald gathered up, even Eurybates of Ithaca, that waited on him. And himself he went to meet Agamemnon son of Atreus, and at his hand received the sceptre of his sires, imperishable for ever, wherewith he took his way amid the ships of the mail-clad Achaians.

Whenever he found one that was a captain and a man of mark, he stood by his side, and refrained him with gentle words: "Good sir, it is not seemly to affright thee like a coward, but do thou sit thyself and make all thy folk sit down. For thou knowest not yet clearly what is the purpose of Atreus' son; now is he but making trial, and soon he will afflict the sons of the Achaians."

But whatever man of the people he saw and found him shouting, him he drave with his sceptre and chode him with loud words: "Good sir, sit still and hearken to the words of others that are thy betters; but thou art no warrior, and a weakling, never reckoned whether in battle or in council. In no wise can we Achaians all be kings here. A multitude of masters is no good thing; let there be one master, one king, to whom the son of crooked-counselling Kronos hath granted it."

So masterfully ranged he the host; and they hasted back

to the assembly from ships and huts, with noise as when a wave of the loud-sounding sea roareth on the long beach and the main resoundeth.

Now all the rest sat down and kept their place upon the benches, only Thersites still chattered on, the uncontrolled of speech, whose mind was full of words many and disorderly, wherewith to strive against the chiefs idly and in no good order, but even as he deemed that he should make the Argives laugh. And he was ill-favoured beyond all men that came to Ilios. Bandy-legged was he, and lame of one foot, and his two shoulders rounded, arched down upon his chest; and over them his head was warped, and a scanty stubble sprouted on it. Hateful was he to Achilles above all and to Odysseus, for them he was wont to revile. But now with shrill shout he poured forth his upbraidings upon goodly Agamemnon. With him the Achaians were sore vexed and had indignation in their souls. But he with loud shout spake and reviled Agamemnon: "Atreides, for what art thou now ill content and lacking? Surely thy huts are full of bronze and many women are in thy huts, the chosen spoils that we Achaians give thee first of all, whene'er we take a town. Can it be that thou yet wantest gold as well, such as some one of the horse-taming Trojans may bring from Ilios to ransom his son, whom I perchance or some other Achaian have led captive? It is not seemly for one that is their captain to bring the sons of the Achaians to ill. Soft fools, base things of shame, ye women of Achaia and men no more, let us depart home with our ships, and leave this fellow here in Troy-land to gorge him with meeds of honour, that he may see whether our aid avail him aught or no;

even he that hath now done dishonour to Achilles, a far
better man than he; for he hath taken away his meed of
honour and keepeth it by his own violent deed. Of a very
surety is there no wrath at all in Achilles' mind, but he is
slack; else this despite, thou son of Atreus, were thy last."

So spake Thersites, reviling Agamemnon shepherd of the
host. But goodly Odysseus came straight to his side, and
looking sternly at him with hard words rebuked him:
"Thersites, reckless in words, shrill orator though thou art,
refrain thyself, nor aim to strive singly against kings. For I
deem that no mortal is baser than thou of all that with the
sons of Atreus came before Ilios. Therefore were it well that
thou shouldest not have kings in thy mouth as thou talkest,
and utter revilings against them and be on the watch for
departure. We know not yet clearly how these things shall
be, whether we sons of the Achaians shall return for good or
for ill. Therefore now dost thou revile continually Agamemnon son of Atreus, shepherd of the host, because the
Danaan warriors give him many gifts, and so thou talkest
tauntingly. But I will tell thee plain, and that I say shall
even be brought to pass: if I find thee again raving as now
thou art, then may Odysseus' head no longer abide upon his
shoulders, nor may I any more be called father of Tele-
machos, if I take thee not and strip from thee thy garments,
thy mantle and tunic that cover thy nakedness, and for
thyself send thee weeping to the fleet ships, and beat thee
out of the assembly with shameful blows."

So spake he, and with his staff smote his back and shoulders: and he bowed down and a big tear fell from him, and a
bloody weal stood up from his back beneath the golden

sceptre. Then he sat down and was amazed, and in pain with helpless look wiped away the tear. But the rest, though they were sorry, laughed lightly at him, and thus would one speak, looking at another standing by: "Go to, of a truth Odysseus hath wrought good deeds without number ere now, standing foremost in wise counsels and setting battle in array, but now is this thing the best by far that he hath wrought among the Argives, to wit, that he hath stayed this prating railer from his harangues. Never again, forsooth, will his proud soul henceforth bid him revile the kings with slanderous words."

So said the common sort; but up rose Odysseus waster of cities, with the sceptre in his hand. And by his side bright-eyed Athene in the likeness of a herald bade the multitude keep silence, that the sons of the Achaians, both the nearest and the farthest, might hear his words together and give heed to his counsel. He made harangue to them and said: "Now surely are the Achaians for making thee, O king, most despised among all mortal men, nor will they fulfil the promise that they pledged thee when they still were marching hither from horse-pasturing Argos; that thou shouldest not return till thou hadst laid well-walled Ilios waste. For like young children or widow women do they wail each to the other of returning home. Yea, here is toil to make a man depart disheartened. For he that stayeth away but one single month far from his wife in his benched ship fretteth himself when winter storms and the furious sea imprison him; but for us, the ninth year of our stay here is upon us in its course. Therefore do I not marvel that the Achaians should fret beside their beaked ships; yet nevertheless is it shameful to wait long and to depart empty. Be of good heart, my friends, and wait a while, until we learn whether Kalchas be a true prophet or no. For he foretold that we should war here nine years, but in the tenth year we should take the wide-wayed city. So spake the seer; and now are all these things being fulfilled. So come, abide ye all, ye well-greaved Achaians, even where ye are, until we have taken the great city of Priam."

So spake he, and the Argives shouted aloud, and all round the ships echoed terribly to the voice of the Achaians as they praised the saying of godlike Odysseus. And then spake among them knightly Nestor of Gerenia: "Out on it; in very truth ye hold assembly like silly boys that have no care for deeds of war. If any man is overmuch desirous to depart homewards, let him lay his hand upon his decked black ship, that before all men he may encounter death and fate. But do thou, my king, take good counsel thyself, and hearken to another that shall give it; the word that I speak, whate'er it be, shall not be cast away. Separate thy warriors by tribes and by clans, Agamemnon, that clan may give aid to clan and tribe to tribe. If thou do thus and the Achaians hearken to thee, then wilt thou know who among thy captains and who of the common sort is a coward, and who too is brave; for they will fight each after their sort. So wilt thou know whether it is even by divine command that thou shalt not take the city, or by the baseness of thy warriors and their ill skill in battle."

And lord Agamemnon answered and said to him: "Verily hast thou again outdone the sons of the Achaians in speech, old man. Ah, father Zeus and Athene and Apollo, would that among the Achaians I had ten such councillors; then would the city of king Priam soon bow beneath our hands, captive and wasted. But aegis-bearing Zeus, the son of Kronos, hath brought sorrows upon me, in that he casteth my lot amid fruitless wranglings and strifes. For in truth I and Achilles fought about a damsel with violent words, and I was first to be angry; but if we can only be at one in council, then will there no more be any putting off the day of evil for the Trojans, no not for an instant. But now go ye to your meal that we may join battle. Let each man sharpen well his spear and bestow well his shield, and let him well give his fleet-footed steeds their meal, and look well to his chariot on every side and take thought for battle, that all day long we may contend in hateful war. For of respite shall there intervene no, not a whit, only that the coming of night shall part the fury of warriors. On each man's breast shall the baldric of his covering shield be wet with sweat, and his hand shall grow faint about the spear, and each man's horse shall sweat as he draweth the polished chariot. And whomsoever I perceive minded to tarry far from the fight beside the beaked ships, for him shall there be no hope hereafter to escape the dogs and birds of prey."

So spake he, and the Argives shouted aloud, like to a wave on a steep shore, when the south wind cometh and stirreth it; even on a jutting rock, that is never left at peace by the waves of all winds that rise from this side and from that. And they stood up and scattered in haste throughout the ships, and made fires in the huts and took their meal. And they did sacrifice each man to one of the everlasting gods, praying for escape from death and the tumult of battle. But Agamemnon king of men slew a fat bull of five years to most mighty Kronion, and called the elders, the princes of the Achaian host, Nestor first and king Idomeneus, and then the two Aiantes and Tydeus' son, and sixthly Odysseus peer of Zeus in counsel. And Menelaos of the loud war-cry came to him unbidden, for he knew in his heart how his brother toiled. Then stood they around the bull and took the barley meal. And Agamemnon made his prayer in their midst and said: "Zeus, most glorious, most great, god of the storm-cloud, that dwellest in the heaven, vouchsafe that the sun set not upon us nor the darkness come near, till I have laid low upon the earth Priam's palace smirched with smoke, and burnt the doorways thereof with consuming fire, and rent on Hector's breast his doublet cleft with the blade; and about him may full many of his comrades prone in the dust bite the earth."

So spake he, but not as yet would Kronion grant him fulfilment; he accepted the sacrifice, but made toil to wax unceasingly.

So when they had rest from the task and had made ready the banquet, they feasted, nor was their heart aught stinted of the fair banquet. But when they had put away from them the desire of meat and drink, then did knightly Nestor of Gerenia open his saying to them: "Most noble son of Atreus, Agamemnon king of men, let us not any more hold long converse here, nor for long delay the work that god putteth in our hands; but come, let the heralds of the mail-clad Achaians make proclamation to the folk and gather them throughout the ships; and let us go thus in concert through the wide host of the Achaians, that the speedier we may arouse keen war."

So spake he and Agamemnon king of men disregarded not. Straightway he bade the clear-voiced heralds summon to battle the flowing-haired Achaians. So those summoned and these gathered with all speed. And the kings, the fosterlings of Zeus that were about Atreus' son, eagerly marshalled them, and bright-eyed Athene in the midst, bearing the holy aegis that knoweth neither age nor death, whereon wave an hundred tassels of pure gold, all deftly woven and each one an hundred oxen worth. Therewith she passed dazzling through the Achaian folk, urging them forth; and in every man's heart she roused strength to battle without ceasing and to fight. So was war made sweeter to them than to depart in their hollow ships to their dear native land. Even as ravaging fire kindleth a boundless forest on a mountain's peaks, and the blaze is seen from afar, even so as they marched went the dazzling gleam from the innumerable bronze through the sky even unto the heavens.

And as the many tribes of feathered birds, wild geese or cranes or long-necked swans, on the Asian mead by Kaystrios' stream, fly hither and thither joying in their plumage, and with loud cries settle ever onwards, and the mead resounds; even so poured forth the many tribes of warriors from ships and huts into the Skamandrian plain. And the earth echoed terribly beneath the tread of men and horses. So stood they in the flowery Skamandrian plain, unnumbered as are leaves and flowers in their season. Even as the many tribes of thick flies that hover about a herdsman's steading in the spring season, when milk drencheth the pails, even in like number stood the flowing-haired Achaians upon the plain in face of the Trojans, eager to rend them asunder. And even as the goatherds easily divide the ranging flocks of goats when they mingle in the pasture, so did their captains marshal them on this side and on that, to enter into the fray, and in their midst lord Agamemnon, his head and eyes like unto Zeus whose joy is in the thunder, and his waist like unto Ares and his breast unto Poseidon. Even as a bull standeth out far foremost amid the herd, for he is pre-eminent amid the pasturing kine, even such did Zeus make Atreides on that day, pre-eminent among many and chief amid heroes.

But Achilles lay idle among his seafaring ships, in sore wrath against Agamemnon Atreus' son, shepherd of the host; and his folk along the sea-shore sported with quoits and with casting of javelins and archery; and the horses each beside his own chariot stood idle, champing clover and parsley of the marsh, and their lords' chariots lay well covered up within the huts, while the men yearned for their warrior chief, and wandered hither and thither through the camp and fought not.

Now fleet Iris the wind-footed went to the Trojans, a messenger from aegis-bearing Zeus, with a grievous message. These were holding assembly at Priam's gate, being gathered all together both young men and old. And fleet-footed Iris stood hard by and spake to them; and she made her voice like to the voice of Polites son of Priam, who was the sentinel of the Trojans and was wont to sit trusting in his fleetness upon the barrow of Aisyetes of old, and on the top thereof wait the sallying of the Achaians forth from their ships. Even in his likeness did fleet-footed Iris speak to Priam: "Old man, words beyond number are still pleasant to thee as erst in the days of peace; but war without respite is upon us. Of a truth have I very oft ere now entered into battles of the warriors, yet have I never seen so goodly a host and so great; for in the very likeness of the leaves of the forest or the sands of the sea are they marching along the plain to fight against the city. But, Hector, thee do I charge beyond all to do even as I shall say. Seeing that the allies are very many throughout Priam's great city, and diverse men, being scattered abroad, have diverse tongues; therefore let each one give the word to those whose chieftain he is, and them let him lead forth and have the ordering of his coun-trymen."

So spake she, and Hector failed not to know the voice of the goddess, and straightway dismissed the assembly, and they rushed to arms. And the gates were thrown open wide, and the host issued forth, footmen and horsemen, and mighty din arose.

BOOK III

How Menelaos and Paris fought in single combat; and Aphrodite
rescued Paris. And how Helen and Priam beheld the Achaian
host from the walls of Troy.

Now when they were arrayed, each company with their
captains, the Trojans marched with clamour and
with shouting like unto birds, even as when there goeth up
before heaven a clamour of cranes which flee from the
coming of winter and sudden rain, and fly with clamour
towards the streams of ocean, bearing slaughter and fate to
the Pigmy men, and in early morn offer cruel battle. But
on the other side marched the Achaians in silence breathing courage, eager at heart to give succour man to man.

Even as when the south wind sheddeth mist over the
crests of a mountain, mist unwelcome to the shepherd, but
to the robber better than night, and a man can see no
further than he casteth a stone; even so thick arose the
gathering dustclouds at their tread as they went; and with
all speed they advanced across the plain.

So when they were now come nigh in onset on each other,
godlike Alexandros played champion to the Trojans, wearing upon his shoulders panther-skin and curved bow and
sword; and he brandished two bronze-headed spears and
challenged all the chieftains of the Argives to fight him man

to man in deadly combat. But when Menelaos dear to Ares marked him coming in the forefront of the multitude with long strides, then even as a lion is glad when he lighteth upon a great carcase, a horned stag, or a wild goat that he hath found, being anhungered; and so he devoureth it amain, even though the fleet hounds and lusty youths set upon him; even thus was Menelaos glad when his eyes beheld godlike Alexandros; for he thought to take vengeance upon the sinner. So straightway he leapt in his armour from his chariot to the ground.

But when godlike Alexandros marked him appear amid the champions, his heart was smitten, and he shrank back into the host of his comrades, avoiding death. And even as a man that hath seen a serpent in a mountain glade starteth backward and trembling seizeth his feet beneath him, and he retreateth back again, and paleness hath hold of his cheeks, even so did godlike Alexandros for fear of Atreus' son shrink back into the throng of lordly Trojans. But Hector beheld and upbraided him with scornful words: "Ill Paris, most fair in semblance, thou deceiver woman-mad, would thou hadst been unborn and died unwed. Yea, that were my desire, and it were far better than thus to be our shame and looked at askance of all men. I ween that the flowing-haired Achaians laugh, deeming that a prince is our champion only because a goodly favour is his; but in his heart is there no strength nor any courage. Art thou indeed such an one that in thy seafaring ships thou didst sail over the deep with the company of thy trusted comrades, and in converse with strangers didst bring back a fair woman from

a far country, one that was by marriage daughter to warriors that bear the spear, that she might be a sore mischief to
thy father and city and all the realm, but to our foes a rejoicing, and to thyself a hanging of the head? And canst thou
not indeed abide Menelaos dear to Ares? Thou mightest see
what sort of warrior is he whose lovely wife thou hast. Thy
lyre will not avail thee nor the gifts of Aphrodite, those thy
locks and fair favour, when thou grovellest in the dust. But
the Trojans are very cowards: else ere this hadst thou
donned a robe of stone for all the ill thou hast wrought."

And godlike Alexandros made answer to him again:
"Cast not in my teeth the lovely gifts of golden Aphrodite;
not to be flung aside are the gods' glorious gifts that of their
own good will they give; for by his desire can no man win
them. But now if thou wilt have me do battle and fight,
make the other Trojans sit down and all the Achaians, and
set ye me in the midst, and Menelaos dear to Ares, to fight
for Helen and all her wealth. And whichsoever shall vanquish and gain the upper hand, let him take all the wealth
aright, and the woman, and bear them home. And let the
rest pledge friendship and sure oaths; so may ye dwell in
deep-soiled Troy, and let them depart to Argos pasture-land
of horses, and Achaia home of fair women."

So spake he, and Hector rejoiced greatly to hear his
saying, and went into the midst and restrained the battalions of the Trojans, with his spear grasped by the middle;
and they all sate them down. But the flowing-haired Achaians kept shooting at him, aiming with arrows and casting
stones. But Agamemnon king of men cried aloud: "Refrain, ye Argives; shoot not, ye sons of the Achaians; for

Hector of the glancing helm hath set himself to say somewhat."

So spake he, and they refrained from battle and made
silence speedily. And Hector spake between the two hosts:
"Hear of me, Trojans and well-greaved Achaians, the saying of Alexandros, for whose sake strife hath come about.
He biddeth the other Trojans and all the Achaians to lay
down their goodly armour on the bounteous earth, and himself in the midst and Menelaos dear to Ares to fight alone
for Helen and all her wealth. And whichsoever shall vanquish and gain the upper hand, let him take all the wealth
aright, and the woman, and bear them home; but let all of
us pledge friendship and sure oaths."

So spake he, and they all kept silence and were still. Then
in their midst spake Menelaos of the loud war-cry: "Bring
ye two lambs, one white ram and one black ewe, for earth
and sun; and let us bring one for Zeus. And call hither great
Priam, that he may pledge the oath himself, seeing he hath
sons that are overweening and faithless, lest any by transgression do violence to the oath of Zeus; for young men's
hearts are ever lifted up. But wheresoever an old man entereth in, he looketh both before and after, whereby the best
issue shall come for either side."

So spake he, and Achaians and Trojans were glad, deeming that they should have rest from grievous war. So they
refrained their chariots to the ranks, and themselves
alighted and doffed their arms. And these they laid upon the
earth each close to each, and there was but small space
between. And Hector sent two heralds to the city with all
speed, to bring the lambs, and to call Priam. And lord

Agamemnon sent forth Talthybios to go to the hollow ships, and bade him bring a ram; and he was not disobedient to noble Agamemnon.

Now Iris went with a message to white-armed Helen in the likeness of her husband's sister, Laodike fairest favoured of Priam's daughters. And in the hall she found Helen weaving a great purple web of double fold, and embroidering thereon many battles of horse-taming Trojans and mail-clad Achaians, that they had endured for her sake at the hands of Ares. So fleet-footed Iris stood by her side and said: "Come hither, dear sister, that thou mayest see the wondrous doings of horse-taming Trojans and mail-clad Achaians. They that erst waged tearful war upon each other in the plain, eager for deadly battle, even they sit now in silence, and the battle is stayed, and they lean upon their shields, and the tall spears are planted by their sides. But Alexandros and Menelaos dear to Ares will fight with their tall spears for thee; and thou wilt be declared the dear wife of him that conquereth."

So spake the goddess, and put into her heart sweet longing for her former husband and her city and parents.

Forthwith she veiled her face in shining linen, and hastened from her chamber, letting fall a round tear; not unattended, for there followed with her two handmaidens, Aithre daughter of Pittheus and ox-eyed Klymene. Then came she straightway to the place of the Skaian gates. And the elders of the people sat at the Skaian gates. These had now ceased from battle for old age, yet were they right good orators, like grasshoppers that in a forest sit upon a tree and utter their lily-like voice; even so sat the elders of the Trojans upon the tower. Now when they saw Helen coming to the tower they softly spake winged words one to the other: "Small blame is it that Trojans and well-greaved Achaians should for such a woman long time suffer hardships; marvellously like is she to the immortal goddesses to look upon. Yet even so, though she be so goodly, let her go upon their ships and not stay to vex us and our children after us."

So said they, and Priam lifted up his voice and called to Helen: "Come hither, dear child, and sit before me, that thou mayest see thy former husband and thy kinsfolk and thy friends. I hold thee not to blame; nay, I hold the gods to blame who brought on me the dolorous war of the Achaians —so mayest thou now tell me who is this huge hero, this Achaian warrior so goodly and great. Of a truth there are others even taller by a head; yet did mine eyes never behold a man so beautiful nor so royal; for he is like unto one that is a king."

And Helen, fair among women, spake and answered him: "Reverend art thou to me and dread, dear father of my lord; would that sore death had been my pleasure when I followed thy son hither, and left my home and my kinsfolk and my daughter in her girlhood and the lovely company of mine age-fellows. But that was not so, wherefore I pine with weeping. Now will I tell thee that whereof thou askest me and inquirest. This is wide-ruling Agamemnon, one that is both a goodly king and mighty spearman. And he was husband's brother to me, ah, shameless me."

And next the old man saw Odysseus, and asked: "Come now, tell me of this man too, dear child, who is he, shorter by a head than Agamemnon son of Atreus, but broader of shoulder and of chest to behold? His armour lieth upon the bounteous earth, and himself like a bell-wether rangeth the ranks of warriors. Yea, I liken him to a thick-fleeced ram ordering a great flock of white ewes."

Then Helen sprung of Zeus made answer to him: "Now this is Laertes' son, crafty Odysseus, that was reared in the realm of Ithaka, rugged though it be, and is skilled in all the ways of wile and cunning device."

Then sage Antenor made answer to her: "Lady, verily the thing thou sayest is true indeed, for erst came goodly Odysseus hither also on an embassage for thee, in the company of Menelaos dear to Ares; and I gave them entertainment and welcomed them in my halls, and learnt the aspect of both and their wise devices. Now when they mingled with the Trojans in the assembly, while all stood up Menelaos overpassed them all by the measure of his broad shoulders; but when both sat down, Odysseus was the more stately. And when they began to weave the web of words and counsel in the face of all, then Menelaos haranged fluently, in few words, but very clearly, seeing he was not long of speech, neither random, though in years he was the younger. But whenever Odysseus full of wiles rose up, he stood and looked down, with eyes fixed upon the ground, and waved not his staff whether backwards or forwards, but held it stiff, like to a man of no understanding; one would deem him to be churlish, and naught but a fool. But when he uttered his great voice from his chest, and words like unto the snowflakes of winter, then could no mortal man contend with Odysseus; then marvelled we not thus to behold Odysseus' aspect."

And thirdly the old man saw Aias, and asked: "Who then is this other Achaian warrior, goodly and great, pre-eminent among the Argives by the measure of his head and broad shoulders?"

And long-robed Helen, fair among women, answered: "This is huge Aias, bulwark of the Achaians. And on the other side amid the Cretans standeth Idomeneus like a god, and about him are gathered the captains of the Cretans. Oft did Menelaos dear to Ares entertain him in our house whene'er he came from Crete. And now behold I all the other glancing-eyed Achaians, whom well I could discern and tell their names; but two captains of the host can I not see, even Kastor tamer of horses and Polydeukes the skilful boxer, mine own brethren, whom the same mother bare. Either they came not in the company from lovely Lakedaimon; or they came hither indeed in their seafaring ships, but now will not enter into the battle of the warriors, for fear of the many scornings and revilings that are mine."

So said she; but them the life-giving earth held fast there in Lakedaimon, in their dear native land.

Meanwhile were the heralds bearing through the city the holy oath-offerings, two lambs and strong-hearted wine, the fruit of the earth, in a goat-skin bottle. And the herald Idaios bare the shining bowl and golden cups; and came to the old man and summoned him and said: "Rise, thou son of Laomedon. The chieftains of the horse-taming Trojans and mail-clad Achaians call on thee to go down into the plain, that ye may pledge a trusty oath. But Alexandros and Menelaos dear to Ares will fight with their long spears for the lady's sake; and let lady and treasure go with him that shall conquer. And may we that are left pledge friendship and trusty oaths and dwell in deep-soiled Troy, and they shall depart to Argos pasture-land of horses and Achaia home of fair women."

So said he, and the old man shuddered and bade his companions yoke the horses; and they with speed obeyed. Then Priam mounted and drew back the reins, and by his side Antenor mounted the splendid chariot. So the two drave the fleet horses through the Skaian gates to the plain. And when they had come even to the Trojans and Achaians, they went down from the chariots upon the bounteous earth, and marched into the midst of Trojans and Achaians. Then forthwith rose up Agamemnon king of men, and up rose Odysseus the man of wiles; and the lordly heralds gathered together the holy oath-offerings of the gods, and mingled the wine in a bowl, and poured water over the princes' hands. And Atreides put forth his hand and drew his knife that hung ever beside his sword's great sheath, and cut the hair from off the lambs' heads; and then the heralds portioned it among the chief of the Trojans and Achaians. Then in their midst Atreus' son lifted up his hands and prayed aloud: "Father Zeus, that rulest from Ida, most glorious, most great, and thou Sun that seest all things and hearest all things, and ye Rivers and thou Earth, and ye that in the underworld punish men outworn, whosoever sweareth falsely; be ye witnesses, and watch over the faithful oath. If Alexandros slay Menelaos, then let him have Helen to himself and all her possessions; and we will depart on our seafaring ships. But if golden-haired Menelaos slay Alexandros, then let the Trojans give back Helen and all her possessions and pay the Argives the recompense that is seemly, such as shall live among men that shall be hereafter. But if so be that Priam and Priam's sons will not pay the recompense unto me when Alexandros falleth, then will I fight on thereafter for the price of sin, and abide here till I compass the end of war."

So said he, and cut the lambs' throats with the pitiless knife. Them he laid gasping upon the ground, failing of breath, for the knife had taken their strength from them; and next they drew the wine from the bowl into the cups, and poured it forth and prayed to the gods that live for ever. And thus would say many an one of Achaians and Trojans: "Zeus most glorious, most great, and all ye immortal gods, which folk soe'er be first to sin against the oaths, may their brains be so poured forth upon the earth even as this wine, theirs and their children's; and let their wives be made subject unto strangers."

So spake they, but the son of Kronos vouchsafed not yet fulfilment. And in their midst Priam of the seed of Dardanos uttered his saying: "Hearken to me, Trojans and well-greaved Achaians. I verily will return back to windy Ilios, seeing that I can in no wise bear to behold with mine eyes my dear son fighting with Menelaos dear to Ares. But Zeus knoweth, and all the immortal gods, for whether of the twain the doom of death is appointed."

So spake the godlike man, and laid the lambs in his chariot, and entered in himself, and drew back the reins; and by his side Antenor mounted the splendid chariot. So they departed back again to Ilios; and Hector son of Priam and goodly Odysseus first meted out a space, and then they took the lots, and shook them in a bronze-bound helmet, to know whether of the twain should first cast his spear of bronze. And the people prayed and lifted up their hands to the gods; and thus would say many an one of the Achaians and Trojans: "Father Zeus, that rulest from Ida, most glorious, most great; whichsoe'er it be that brought this trouble upon both peoples, vouchsafe that he may die and enter the house of Hades; that so for us peace may be assured and trusty oaths."

So said they; and great Hector of the glancing plume shook the helmet, looking behind him; and quickly leapt forth the lot of Paris. Then the people sat them down by ranks where each man's high-stepping horses and inwrought armour lay. And upon his shoulders goodly Alexandros donned his beauteous armour, even he that was lord to Helen of the lovely hair. First upon his legs set he his greaves, beautiful, fastened with silver ankle-clasps; next upon his breast he donned the corslet of his brother Lykaon, and fitted it upon himself. And over his shoulders cast he his silver-studded sword of bronze, and then a shield great and sturdy. And on his mighty head he set a wrought helmet of horse-hair crest, whereover the plume nodded terribly, and he took him a strong spear fitted to his grasp. And in like wise warlike Menelaos donned his armour.

So when they had armed themselves on either side in the throng, they strode between Trojans and Achaians, fierce of aspect, and wonder came on them that beheld, both on the Trojans tamers of horses and on the well-greaved Achaians. Then took they their stand near together in the measured space, brandishing their spears in wrath each against other.

First Alexandros hurled his far-shadowing spear, and smote on Atreides' round shield; but the bronze brake not through, for its point was turned in the stout shield. Next Menelaos son of Atreus lifted up his hand to cast, and made prayer to father Zeus: "King Zeus, grant me revenge on him that was first to do me wrong, even on goodly Alexandros, and subdue thou him at my hands; so that many an one of men that shall be hereafter may shudder to wrong his host that hath shown him kindness.

So said he, and poised his far-shadowing spear, and hurled, and smote on the round shield of the son of Priam. Through the bright shield went the ponderous spear and through the inwrought breastplate it pressed on; and straight beside his flank the spear rent the tunic, but he swerved and escaped black death. Then Atreides drew his silver-studded sword, and lifted up his hand and smote the helmet-ridge; but the sword shattered upon it into three, yea four, and fell from his hand. Thereat Atreides looked up to the wide heaven and cried: "Father Zeus, surely none of the gods is crueller than thou. Verily I thought to have gotten vengeance on Alexandros for his wickedness, but now my sword breaketh in my hand, and my spear sped from my grasp in vain, and I have not smitten him."

So saying, he leapt upon him and caught him by his horse-hair crest, and swinging him round dragged him towards the well-greaved Achaians; and he was strangled by the embroidered strap beneath his soft throat, drawn tight below his chin to hold his helm. Now would Menelaos have dragged him away and won glory unspeakable, but that Zeus' daughter Aphrodite was swift to mark, and tore asunder for him the strap of slaughtered ox's hide; so the helmet came away empty in his stalwart hand. Thereat Menelaos cast it with a swing toward the well-greaved Achaians, and his trusty comrades took it up; and himself sprang back again eager to slay him with spear of bronze. But Aphrodite snatched up Paris, very easily as a goddess may, and hid him in thick darkness, and set him down in his fragrant perfumed chamber; and herself went to summon Helen. Her she found on the high tower, and about her the Trojan women thronged. So with her hand she plucked her perfumed raiment and shook it and spake to her in the likeness of an aged dame, a woolcomber that was wont to work for her fair wool when she dwelt in Lakedaimon, whom too she greatly loved. Even in her likeness fair Aphrodite spake: "Come hither; Alexandros summoneth thee to go homeward. There is he in his chamber and inlaid bed, radiant in beauty and vesture; nor wouldst thou deem him to be come from fighting his foe, but rather to be faring to the dance, or from the dance to be just resting and set down."

So said she, and stirred Helen's soul within her breast; and when now she marked the fair neck and lovely breast and sparkling eyes of the goddess, she marvelled straightway and spake a word and called upon her name: "Strange queen, why art thou desirous now to beguile me? Verily thou wilt lead me further on to some one of the peopled cities of Phrygia or lovely Maionia, if there too thou hast perchance some other darling among mortal men, because even now Menelaos hath conquered goodly Alexandros, and will lead me, accursed me, to his home. Therefore thou comest hither with guileful intent. Go and sit thou by his side, and depart from the way of the gods; neither let thy feet ever bear thee back to Olympus, but still be vexed for his sake and guard him till he make thee his wife or perchance his slave. But thither will I not go; all the women of Troy will blame me hereafter; and I have griefs untold within my soul."

Then in wrath bright Aphrodite spake to her: "Provoke me not, rash woman, lest in mine anger I desert thee, and hate thee even as now I love thee beyond measure, and lest I devise grievous enmities between both, even betwixt Trojans and Achaians, and so thou perish in evil wise."

So said she, and Helen sprung of Zeus was afraid, and went wrapped in her bright radiant vesture, silently, and the Trojan women marked her not; and the goddess led the way.

Now when they were come to the beautiful house of Alexandros the handmaidens turned straightway to their tasks, and the fair lady went to the high-roofed chamber; and laughter–loving Aphrodite took for her a chair and brought it, even she the goddess, and set it before the face of Paris. There Helen took her seat, the child of aegis-bearing Zeus, and with eyes turned askance spake and chode her lord: "Thou comest back from battle; would thou hadst perished there, vanquished of that great warrior that was my former husband. Verily it was once thy boast that thou wast a better man than Menelaos dear to Ares, in the might of thine arm and thy spear. But go, now, challenge Menelaos dear to Ares to fight thee again face to face. Nay, but I, even I, bid thee refrain, nor fight a fight with golden-haired

Menelaos man to man, neither attack him recklessly, lest perchance thou fall to his spear anon."

And Paris made answer to her and said: "Chide not my soul, lady, with cruel taunts. For now indeed hath Menelaos vanquished me with Athene's aid, but another day may I do so unto him; for we too have gods with us."

But Atreides the while strode through the hosts like to a wild beast, if anywhere he might set eyes on godlike Alexandros. But none of the Trojans or their famed allies could discover Alexandros to Menelaos dear to Ares. Yet surely did they in no wise hide him for kindliness, could any have seen him; for he was hated of all even as black death. So Agamemnon king of men spake among them there: "Hearken to me, Trojans and Dardanians and allies. Now is victory declared for Menelaos dear to Ares; give ye back Helen of Argos and the possessions with her, and pay ye the recompense such as is seemly, that it may live even among men that shall be hereafter." So said Atreides, and all the Achaians gave assent.

BOOK IV

How Pandaros wounded Menelaos by treachery; and Agamemnon exhorted his chief captains to battle.

Now the gods sat by Zeus and held assembly on the golden floor, and in the midst the lady Hebe poured them their nectar: they with golden goblets pledged one another, and gazed upon the city of the Trojans. Then did Kronos' son essay to provoke Hera with vexing words, and spake maliciously: "Twain goddesses hath Menelaos for his helpers, even Hera and Athene. Yet these sit apart and take their pleasure in beholding; but beside that other ever standeth laughter-loving Aphrodite and wardeth off fate from him, and now hath she saved him as he thought to perish. But of a truth the victory is to Menelaos dear to Ares; so let us take thought how these things shall be; whether once more we shall arouse ill war and the dread battle din, or put friendship between the foes. Moreover if this were welcome to all and well pleasing, may the city of king Priam yet be an habitation, and Menelaos take back Helen of Argos."

So said he, but Athene and Hera murmured thereat, who were sitting by him and devising ills for the Trojans. Now Athene held her peace and said not anything, for wrath at father Zeus, and fierce anger gat hold upon her: but Hera's breast contained not her anger, and she spake: "Most dread

51

son of Kronos, what word is this thou hast spoken? How hast thou the will to make my labour void and of none effect, and the sweat of my toil that I sweated, when my horses were wearied with my summoning of the host, to be the plague of Priam and his sons? Do as thou wilt; but we other gods do not all approve thee."

Then in sore anger Zeus the cloud-gatherer spake to her: "Good lack, how have Priam and Priam's sons done thee such great wrong that thou art furiously minded to sack the established citadel of Ilios? Perchance wert thou to enter within the gates and long walls and devour Priam raw, and Priam's sons and all the Trojans, then mightest thou assuage thine anger. Do as thou art minded, only let not this quarrel hereafter be to me and thee a sore strife between us both. And this moreover will I say to thee, and do thou lay it to thy heart; whene'er I too be of eager mind to lay waste a city where is the race of men that are dear to thee, hinder thou not my wrath, but let me be, even as I yield to thee of free will, yet with soul unwilling. For of all cities beneath sun and starry heaven that are the dwelling of mortal men, holy Ilios was most honoured of my heart, and Priam and the folk of Priam of the good ashen spear. For never did mine altar lack the seemly feast, even drink-offering and burnt-offering, the worship that is our due."

Then Hera the ox-eyed queen made answer to him: "Of a surety three cities are there that be dearest far to me, Argos and Sparta and wide-wayed Mykene; these lay thou waste whene'er they are found hateful to thy heart; not for them will I stand forth, nor do I grudge thee them. For even if I be jealous and would forbid thee to overthrow them, yet will my jealousy not avail, seeing that thou art stronger far than I. Still must my labour too not be made of none effect; for I also am a god, and my lineage is even as thine, and Kronos the crooked counsellor begat me to the place of honour in double wise, by birthright, and because I am named thy spouse, and thou art king among all the immortals. Let us indeed yield each to other herein, I to thee and thou to me, and the rest of the immortal gods will follow with us; and do thou with speed charge Athene to betake her to the fierce battle din of Trojans and Achaians, and to essay that the Trojans may first take upon them to do violence to the Achaians in their triumph, despite the oaths."

So said she, and the father of men and gods disregarded not and roused Athene that already was set thereon; and from Olympus' heights she darted down. Even as the son of Kronos the crooked counsellor sendeth a star, a portent for mariners or a wide host of men, bright shining, and therefrom are scattered sparks in multitude; even in such guise sped Pallas Athene to earth, and leapt into their midst; and astonishment came on them that beheld, on horse-taming Trojans and well-greaved Achaians. Then the goddess entered the throng of Trojans in the likeness of a man, even Antenor's son Laodokos, a stalwart warrior, and sought for godlike Pandaros the son of Lykaon, if haply she might find him. Him found she, the noble and stalwart, standing, and about him the stalwart ranks of the shield-bearing host that followed him. So she came near and spake winged words: "Wilt thou now hearken to me, thou wise son of Lykaon? Then wouldst thou take heart to shoot a swift arrow at

Menelaos, and wouldst win favour and glory before all the Trojans, and before king Alexandros most of all. Surely from him first of any wouldst thou receive glorious gifts, if perchance he see Menelaos, Atreus' warrior son, vanquished by thy dart and brought to the grievous pyre. Go to now, shoot at glorious Menelaos, and vow to Apollo, the son of light, the lord of archery, to sacrifice a goodly hecatomb of firstling lambs when thou art returned to thy home."

So spake Athene, and persuaded his fool's heart. Forthwith he unsheathed his polished bow of horn of a wild ibex. He laid it down when he had well strung it, by resting it upon the ground; and his staunch comrades held their shields before him, lest the warrior sons of the Achaians should first set on them, ere Menelaos, Atreus' warrior son, were smitten. Then opened he the lid of his quiver and took forth a feathered arrow, never yet shot, a source of grievous pangs; and anon he laid the bitter dart upon the string and vowed to Apollo, the son of light, the lord of archery, to sacrifice a goodly hecatomb of firstling lambs when he should have returned to his home. Then he took the notch and string of ox's-sinew together, and drew, bringing to his breast the string, and to the bow the iron head. So when he had now bent the great bow into a round, the horn twanged, and the string sang aloud, and the keen arrow leapt eager to wing his way amid the throng.

But the blessed gods immortal forgat not thee, Menelaos; and before all the daughter of Zeus, the driver of the spoil, who stood before thee and warded off the piercing dart. She turned it just aside from the flesh, even as a mother driveth a fly from her child that lieth in sweet slumber; and with her own hand guided it where the golden buckles of the belt were clasped and the doubled breastplate met them. So the bitter arrow lighted upon the firm belt; through the in-wrought belt it sped and through the curiously wrought breastplate it pressed on and through the taslet he wore to shield his flesh, a barrier against darts; and this best shielded him, yet it passed on even through this. Then did the arrow graze the warrior's outermost flesh, and forthwith the dusky blood flowed from the wound.

As when some woman of Maionia or Karia staineth ivory with purple, to make a cheek-piece for horses, and it is laid up in the treasure chamber, and many a horseman prayeth for it to wear; but it is laid up to be a king's boast, alike an adornment for his horse and a glory for his charioteer; even in such wise, Menelaos, were thy shapely thighs stained with blood and thy legs and thy fair ankles beneath.

Thereat shuddered Agamemnon king of men when he saw the black blood flowing from the wound. And Mene-laos dear to Ares likewise shuddered; but when he saw how thread and barbs were without, his spirit was gathered in his breast again. Then lord Agamemnon moaned deep, and spake among them, holding Menelaos by the hand; and his comrades made moan the while: "Dear brother, to thy death, meseemeth, pledged I these oaths, setting thee forth to fight the Trojans alone before the face of the Achaians; seeing that the Trojans have so smitten thee, and trodden under foot the trusty oaths. I shall have sore sorrow for thee, Menelaos, if thou die and fulfil the lot of life. Yea in utter shame should I return to thirsty Argos, seeing that the

Achaians will forthwith bethink them of their native land, and so should we leave to Priam and the Trojans their boast, even Helen of Argos."

But golden-haired Menelaos encouraged him and said: "Be of good courage, neither dismay at all the host of the Achaians. The keen dart lighted not upon a deadly spot; my glistering belt in front stayed it, and the kirtle of mail beneath, and the taslet that the coppersmiths fashioned."

Then lord Agamemnon answered him and said: "Would it may be so, dear Menelaos. But the leech shall feel the wound, and lay thereon drugs that shall assuage thy dire pangs."

So saying he spake to godlike Talthybios, his herald: "Talthybios, with all speed call Machaon hither, the hero son of Asklepios the noble leech, to see Menelaos, Atreus' warrior son, whom one well skilled in archery, some Trojan or Lykian, hath wounded with a bow-shot, to his glory and our grief."

And when Machaon was come where was golden-haired Menelaos wounded, and all as many as were chieftains gathered around him in a circle, the godlike hero came and stood in their midst, and anon drew forth the arrow from the clasped belt; and as it was drawn forth the keen barbs were broken backwards. Then he loosed the glistering belt and the kirtle of mail beneath and taslet that the copper-smiths fashioned; and when he saw the wound where the bitter arrow had lighted, he sucked out the blood and cun-ningly spread thereon soothing drugs.

While these were tending Menelaos of the loud war-cry, the ranks of shield-bearing Trojans came on; so the

Achaians donned their arms again, and bethought them of
the fray. Now wouldest thou not see noble Agamemnon
slumbering, nor cowering, nor unready to fight, but very
eager for glorious battle. He left his horses and his chariot
adorned with bronze; and his squire kept apart the snorting
steeds; and he straitly charged him to have them at hand
whenever weariness should come upon his limbs with mar-
shalling so many; and thus on foot ranged he through the
ranks of warriors. And whomsoever of all the fleet-horsed
Danaans he found eager, he stood by them and by his words
encouraged them: "Ye Argives, relax not in any wise your
impetuous valour; for father Zeus will be no helper of liars,
but as these were first to transgress against the oaths, so
shall their own tender flesh be eaten of the vultures, and we
shall bear away their dear wives and little children in our
ships, when once we take the stronghold."

But whomsoever he found shrinking from hateful battle,
these he chode sore with angry words: "Ye Argives, warriors of the bow, ye men of dishonour, have ye no shame?
Why stand ye thus dazed like fawns that are weary with
running over the long plain and so stand still, and no valour
is found in their hearts at all? Even thus stand ye dazed, and
fight not. Is it that ye wait for the Trojans to come near
where your good ships' sterns are drawn up on the shore of
the grey sea, to see if Kronion will stretch his arm over you
indeed?"

As when on the echoing beach the sea-wave lifteth up
itself in close array before the driving of the west wind; out
on the deep doth it first raise its head, and then breaketh
upon the land and belloweth aloud and goeth with arching

crest about the promontories, and speweth the foaming brine afar; even so in close array moved the battalions of the Danaans without pause to battle. Each captain gave his men the word, and the rest went silently; thou wouldest not deem that all the great host following them had any voice within their breasts; in silence feared they their captains. On every man glittered the inwrought armour wherewith they went clad. But for the Trojans, like sheep beyond number that stand in the courtyard of a man of great substance, to be milked of their white milk, and bleat without ceasing to hear their lambs' cry, even so arose the clamour of the Trojans through the wide host. For they had not all like speech nor one language, but their tongues were mingled, and they were brought from many lands. These were urged on of Ares, and those of bright-eyed Athene, and Terror and Rout, and Strife whose fury wearieth not, sister and friend of murderous Ares. She now cast common discord in their midst, as she fared through the throng and made the lamentation of men to wax.

Now when they were met together and come unto one spot, then clashed they targe and spear and fury of bronze-clad warrior; the bossed shields pressed each on each and mighty din arose. Then were heard the voice of groaning and the voice of triumph together of the slayers and the slain, and the earth streamed with blood. As when two winter torrents flow down the mountains to a watersmeet and join their furious flood within the deep ravine from their great springs, and the shepherd heareth the roaring far off among the hills: even so from the joining of battle came there forth shouting and travail. Antilochos first slew a

Trojan warrior in full array, valiant amid the champions, Echepolos son of Thalysios; him was he first to smite upon the ridge of his crested helmet, and he drave the spear into his brow and the point of bronze passed within the bone; darkness clouded his eyes, and he crashed like a tower amid the press of fight. As he fell lord Elephenor caught him by the foot, Chalkodon's son, captain of the great-hearted Abantes, and dragged him from beneath the darts, eager with all speed to despoil him of his armour. Yet but for a little endured his essay; great-hearted Agenor saw him haling away the corpse, and where his side was left uncovered of his buckler as he bowed him down, there smote he him with bronze-tipped spear-shaft and unstrung his limbs. So his life departed from him, and over his corpse the task of Trojans and Achaians grew hot; like wolves leapt they one at another, and man lashed at man.

Next Telamonian Aias smote Anthemion's son. Scanty was his span of life by reason of the spear of great-hearted Aias that laid him low. For as he went he first was smitten on his right breast beside the pap; straight through his shoulder passed the spear of bronze, and he fell to the ground in the dust like a poplar-tree, that hath grown up smooth in the lowland of a great marsh, and its branches grow upon the top thereof. In such fashion did heaven-sprung Aias slay Simoeisios son of Anthemion; then at him Antiphos of the glancing corslet, Priam's son, made a cast with his keen javelin across the throng. Him he missed, but smote Odysseus' valiant comrade Leukos in the groin as he drew the corpse his way, so that he fell upon it and the body dropped from his hands. Then Odysseus was very wroth at heart for the slaying of him, and strode through the forefront of the battle harnessed in flashing bronze, and went and stood hard by and glanced around him, and cast his bright javelin; and the Trojans shrank before the casting of the hero. He sped not the dart in vain, but smote Demokoon, Priam's bastard son that had come to him from tending his fleet mares in Abydos. Him Odysseus, being wroth for his comrade's sake, smote with his javelin on one temple; and through both temples passed the point of bronze, and darkness clouded his eyes, and he fell with a crash and his armour clanged upon him. Then the forefighters and glorious Hector yielded, and the Argives shouted aloud, and drew the bodies unto them, and pressed yet further onward. But Apollo looked down from Pergamos, and had indignation, and with a shout called to the Trojans: "Arise, ye Trojans, tamers of horses; yield not to the Argives in fight; not of stone nor iron is their flesh that it should resist the piercing bronze when they are smitten. Moreover Achilles, son of Thetis of the fair tresses, fighteth not, but amid the ships broodeth on his bitter anger."

So spake the dread god from the city; and the Achaians likewise were urged on of Athene, most glorious, as she passed through the throng wheresoever she beheld them slackening.

Next was Diores son of Amarynkeus caught in the snare of fate; for he was smitten by a jagged stone on the right leg hard by the ankle, and the caster thereof was captain of the men of Thrace, Peiroos son of Imbrasos that had come from Ainos. The pitiless stone crushed utterly the two sinews and the bones; back fell he in the dust, and stretched out both his hands to his dear comrades, gasping out his soul. Then he that smote him, even Peiroos, sprang at him and pierced him with a spear beside the navel; so all his bowels gushed forth upon the ground, and darkness clouded his eyes. But even as Peiroos departed from him Thoas of Aitolia smote with a spear his chest above the pap, and the point fixed in his lung. Then Thoas came close, and plucked out from his breast the ponderous spear, and drew his sharp sword, wherewith he smote his belly in the midst, and took his life. Yet he stripped not off his armour; for his comrades, the men of Thrace that wear the top-knot, stood around, their long spears in their hands, and albeit he was great and valiant and proud they drave him off from them and he gave ground reeling. So were the two captains stretched in the dust side by side, he of the Thracians and he of the mail-clad Epeians; and around them were many others likewise slain. Many Trojans that day and many Achaians were laid side by side upon their faces in the dust.

BOOK V

How Diomedes by his great valour made havoc of the Trojans, and wounded even Aphrodite and Ares by the help of Athene.

B UT now to Tydeus' son Diomedes Athene gave might and courage, for him to be pre-eminent amid all the Argives and win glorious renown. She kindled flame unwearied from his helmet and shield, like to the star of summer that above all others glittereth bright after he hath bathed in the ocean stream. In such wise kindled she flame from his head and shoulders and sent him into the midst, where men thronged the thickest.

Now there was amid the Trojans one Dares, rich and noble, priest of Hephaistos; and he had two sons, Phegeus and Idaios, well skilled in all the art of battle. These separated themselves and assailed him face to face, they setting on him from their car and he on foot upon the ground. And when they were now come near in onset on each other, first Phegeus hurled his far-shadowing spear; and over Tydeides' left shoulder the spear point passed, and smote not his body. Then next Tydeides made a spear-cast, and the javelin sped not from his hand in vain, but smote his breast between the nipples, and thrust him from the chariot. So Idaios sprang away, leaving his beautiful car, and dared not to bestride his slain brother; else had neither he himself escaped black fate: but Hephaistos guarded him and saved him in a veil of darkness, that he might not have his aged priest all broken with sorrow. And the son of great-hearted Tydeus drave away the horses and gave them to his men to take to the hollow ships. But when the great-hearted Trojans beheld the sons of Dares, how one was fled, and one was slain beside his chariot, the spirit of all was stirred. But bright-eyed Athene took impetuous Ares by the hand and spake to him and said: "Ares, Ares, blood-stained bane of mortals, thou stormer of walls, can we not now leave the Trojans and Achaians to fight, on whichsoever it be that father Zeus bestoweth glory? But let us twain give place, and escape the wrath of Zeus."

So saying she led impetuous Ares from the battle. Then she made him sit down beside loud Skamandros, and the Danaans pushed the Trojans back.

So they laboured in the violent melee; but of Tydeides man could not tell with whom he were joined, whether he consorted with Trojans or with Achaians. For he stormed across the plain like a winter torrent at the full, that in swift course scattereth the causeys; neither can the long lines of causeys hold it in, nor the fences of fruitful orchards stay its sudden coming when the rain of heaven driveth it; and before it perish in multitudes the fair works of the sons of men. Thus before Tydeides the serried battalions of the Trojans were overthrown, and they abode him not for all they were so many.

But when Lykaon's glorious son marked him storming across the plain, overthrowing battalions before him, anon he bent his crooked bow against Tydeides, and smote him as he sped onwards, hitting hard by his right shoulder the plate of his corslet; the bitter arrow flew through and held straight upon its way, and the corslet was dabbled with blood. Over him then loudly shouted Lykaon's glorious son: "Bestir you, great-hearted Trojans, urgers of horses; the best man of the Achaians is wounded, and I deem that he shall not for long endure the violent dart."

So spake he boasting; yet was the other not vanquished of the swift dart, only he gave place and stood before his horses and his chariot and spake to Sthenelos son of Kapaneus: "Haste thee, dear son of Kapaneus; descend from thy chariot, to draw me from my shoulder the bitter arrow."

So said he, and Sthenelos leapt from his chariot to earth and stood beside him and drew the swift shaft right through, out of his shoulder; and the blood darted up through the pliant tunic. Then Diomedes of the loud war-cry prayed thereat: "Hear me, daughter of aegis-bearing Zeus, unwearied maiden! If ever in kindly mood thou stoodest by my father in the heat of battle, even so now be thou likewise kind to me, Athene. Grant me to slay this man, and bring within my spear-cast him that took advantage to shoot me, and boasteth over me, deeming that not for long shall I see the bright light of the sun."

So spake he in prayer, and Pallas Athene heard him, and made his limbs nimble, his feet and his hands withal, and came near and spake winged words: "Be of good courage now, Diomedes, to fight the Trojans; for in thy breast I have set thy father's courage undaunted, even as it was in knightly Tydeus, wielder of the buckler. Moreover I have taken from thine eyes the mist that erst was on them, that thou mayest well discern both god and man. Therefore if any god come hither to make trial of thee, fight not thou face to face with any of the immortal gods; save only if Aphrodite daughter of Zeus enter into the battle, her smite thou with the keen bronze."

So saying bright-eyed Athene went her way and Tydeides returned and entered the forefront of the battle; even though erst his soul was eager to do battle with the Trojans, yet now did threefold courage come upon him, as upon a lion whom some shepherd in the field guarding his fleecy sheep hath wounded, being sprung into the fold, yet hath not vanquished him; he hath roused his might, and then cannot beat him back, but lurketh amid the steading, and his forsaken flock is affrighted; so the sheep are cast in heaps, one upon the other, and the lion in his fury leapeth out of the high fold; even so in fury mingled mighty Diomedes with the Trojans.

Him Aineias beheld making havoc of the ranks of warriors, and went his way along the battle and amid the hurtling of spears, seeking godlike Pandaros, if haply he might find him. Lykaon's son he found, the noble and stalwart, and stood before his face, and spake a word unto him. "Pandaros, where now are thy bow and thy winged arrows, and the fame wherein no man of this land rivalleth thee, nor any in Lykia boasteth to be thy better? Go to now, lift thy hands in prayer to Zeus and shoot thy dart at this fellow, whoe'er he be that lordeth it here and hath already wrought the Trojans much mischief, seeing he hath unstrung the knees of many a brave man; if indeed it be not some god wroth with the Trojans, in anger by reason of sacrifices; the wrath of god is a sore thing to fall on men."

And Lykaon's glorious son made answer to him: "Aineias, counsellor of the mail-clad Trojans, in everything liken I him to the wise son of Tydeus; I discern him by his shield and crested helmet, and by the aspect of his horses; yet know I not surely if it be not a god. But if it be the man I deem, even the wise son of Tydeus, then not without help of a god is he thus furious, but some immortal standeth beside him with a cloud wrapped about his shoulders and turned aside from him my swift dart even as it lighted. For already have I shot my dart at him and smote his right shoulder right through the breastplate of his corslet, yea and I thought to hurl him headlong to Aidoneus, yet I vanquished him not; surely it is some wrathful god. Already have I aimed at two princes, Tydeus' and Atreus' sons, and both I smote and surely drew forth blood, yet only roused them the more. Therefore in an evil hour I took from the peg my curved bow on that day when I led my Trojans to lovely Ilios, to do noble Hector pleasure. But if I return and mine eyes behold my native land and wife and great palace lofty-roofed, then may an alien forthwith cut my head from me if I break not this bow with mine hands and cast it upon the blazing fire; worthless is its service to me as air."

Then Aineias captain of the Trojans answered him: "Nay, talk not thus; naught shall be mended before that we with horses and chariot have gone to face this man, and made trial of him in arms. Come then, mount upon my car that thou mayest see of what sort are the steeds of Tros, well skilled for following or for fleeing hither or thither very fleetly across the plain; they will e'en bring us to the city safe and sound, even though Zeus hereafter give victory to

Diomedes son of Tydeus. Come therefore, take thou the lash and shining reins, and I will stand upon the car to fight; or else withstand thou him, and to the horses will I look."

To him made answer Lykaon's glorious son: "Aineias, take thou thyself the reins and thine own horses; better will they draw the curved car for their wonted charioteer, if perchance it hap that we must flee from Tydeus' son; lest they go wild for fear and will not take us from the fight, for lack of thy voice, and so the son of great-hearted Tydeus attack us and slay us both and drive away the whole-hooved horses. So drive thou thyself thy chariot and thy horses, and I will await his onset with my keen spear." So saying mounted they upon the well-dight chariot, and eagerly drave the fleet horses against Tydeides. And Sthenelos, the glorious son of Kapaneus, saw them, and anon spake to Tydeides winged words: "Diomedes son of Tydeus, dear to mine heart, I behold two stalwart warriors eager to fight against thee, endued with might beyond measure. The one is well skilled in the bow, even Pandaros, and he moreover boasteth aim to be Lykaon's son; and Aineias boasteth himself to be born son of great-hearted Anchises, and his mother is Aphrodite. Come now, let us give place upon the chariot, neither rage thou thus, I pray thee, in the forefront of battle, lest perchance thou lose thy life."

Then stalwart Diomedes looked sternly at him and said: "Speak to me no word of flight, for I ween that thou shalt not at all persuade me; not in my blood is it to fight a skulking fight or cower down; my force is steadfast still. I have no mind to mount the chariot, nay, even as I am will I go to face them; Pallas Athene biddeth me not be afraid. And as for these, their fleet horses shall not take both back from us again, even if one or other escape. And this moreover tell I thee, and lay thou it to heart: if Athene rich in counsel grant me this glory, to slay them both, then refrain thou here these my fleet horses, and bind the reins tight to the chariot rim; and be mindful to leap upon Aineias' horses, and drive them forth from the Trojans amid the well-greaved Achaians. For they are of that breed whereof far-seeing Zeus gave to Tros recompense for Ganymede his child, because they were the best of all horses beneath the daylight and the sun."

In such wise talked they one to the other, and anon those other twain came near, driving their fleet horses. First to him spake Lykaon's glorious son: "O thou strong-souled and cunning, son of proud Tydeus, verily my swift dart vanquished thee not, the bitter arrow; so now will I make trial with my spear if I can hit thee."

He spake and poised and hurled his far-shadowing spear, and smote upon Tydeides' shield; right through it sped the point of bronze and reached the breastplate. So over him shouted loudly Lykaon's glorious son: "Thou art smitten on the belly right through, and I ween thou shalt not long hold up thine head; so thou givest me great renown."

But mighty Diomedes unaffrighted answered him: "Thou hast missed, and not hit; but ye twain I deem shall not cease till one or other shall have fallen and glutted with blood Ares the stubborn god of war."

So spake he and hurled; and Athene guided the dart upon his nose beside the eye, and it pierced through his white teeth. So the hard bronze cut through his tongue at the root and the point issued forth by the base of the chin. He fell from his chariot, and his splendid armour gleaming clanged upon him, and the fleet-footed horses swerved aside; so there his soul and strength were unstrung.

Then Aineias leapt down with shield and long spear, fearing lest perchance the Achaians might take from him the corpse; and strode over him like a lion confident in his strength, and held before him his spear and the circle of his shield, eager to slay whoe'er should come to face him, crying his terrible cry. Then Tydeides grasped in his hand a stone—a mighty deed—such as two men, as men now are, would not avail to lift; yet he with ease wielded it all alone. Therewith he smote Aineias on the hip where the thigh turneth in the hip-joint, and this men call the "cup-bone." So he crushed his cup-bone, and brake both sinews withal, and the jagged stone tore apart the skin. Then the hero stayed fallen upon his knees and with stout hand leant upon the earth; and the darkness of night veiled his eyes. And now might Aineias king of men have perished, but that Aphrodite daughter of Zeus was swift to mark. About her dear son wound she her white arms, and spread before his face a fold of her radiant vesture, to be a covering from the darts, lest any of the fleet-horsed Danaans might hurl the spear into his breast and take away his life.

So was she bearing her dear son away from battle; but the son of Kapaneus forgat not the behest that Diomedes of the loud war-cry had laid upon him; he refrained his own whole-hooved horses away from the tumult, binding the reins tight to the chariot-rim, and leapt on the sleek-coated horses of Aineias, and drave them from the Trojans to the well-

greaved Achaians, and gave them to Deïpylos his dear comrade whom he esteemed above all that were his age-fellows,
because he was like-minded with himself; and bade him
drive them to the hollow ships. Then did the hero mount his
own chariot and take the shining reins and forthwith drive
his strong-heaved horses in quest of Tydeides, eagerly. Now
Tydeides had made onslaught with pitiless weapon on
Kypris, knowing how she was a coward goddess and none of
those that have mastery in battle of the warriors. Now when
he had pursued her through the dense throng and come on
her, then great-hearted Tydeus' son thrust with his keen
spear, and leapt on her and wounded the skin of her weak
hand; straight through the ambrosial raiment that the
Graces themselves had woven her pierced the dart into
the flesh, above the springing of the palm. Then flowed the
goddess's immortal blood, such ichor as floweth in the
blessed gods; for they eat no bread neither drink they
gleaming wine, wherefore they are bloodless and are named
immortals. And she with a great cry let fall her son: him
Phoebus Apollo took into his arms and saved him in a
dusky cloud, lest any of the fleet-horsed Danaans might hurl
the spear into his breast and take away his life. But over her
Diomedes of the loud war-cry shouted afar: "Refrain thee,
thou daughter of Zeus, from war and fighting. Is it not
enough that thou beguilest feeble women? But if in battle
thou wilt mingle, verily I deem that thou shalt shudder at
the name of battle, if thou hear it even afar off."

So spake he, and she departed in amaze and was sore
troubled: and wind-footed Iris took her and led her from
the throng tormented with her pain, and her fair skin was

stained. There found she impetuous Ares sitting, on the battle's left; and his spear rested upon a cloud, and his fleet steeds. Then she fell on her knees and with instant prayer besought of her dear brother his golden-frontleted steeds: "Dear brother, save me and give me thy steeds, that I may win to Olympus, where is the habitation of the immortals. Sorely am I afflicted with a wound wherewith a mortal smote me, even Tydeides, who now would fight even with father Zeus."

So spake she, and Ares gave her his golden-frontleted steeds, and she mounted on the chariot sore at heart. By her side mounted Iris, and in her hands grasped the reins and lashed the horses to start them; and they flew onward nothing loth. Thus soon they came to the habitation of the gods, even steep Olympus. There wind-footed fleet Iris loosed the horses from the chariot and stabled them, and set ambrosial forage before them; but fair Aphrodite fell upon Dione's knees that was her mother. She took her daughter in her arms and stroked her with her hand, and spake and called upon her name: "Who now of the sons of heaven, dear child, hath entreated thee thus wantonly, as though thou wert a wrong-doer in the face of all?"

Then laughter-loving Aphrodite made answer to her: "Tydeus' son wounded me, high-hearted Diomedes, because I was saving from the battle my dear son Aineias, who to me is dearest far of all men. For no more is the fierce battle-cry for Trojans and Achaians, but the Danaans now are fighting even the immortals."

Then the fair goddess Dione answered her: "Be of good heart, my child, and endure for all thy pain; for many of us that inhabit the mansions of Olympus have suffered through men, in bringing grievous woes one upon another."

So saying with both hands she wiped the ichor from the arm; her arm was comforted, and the grievous pangs assuaged. But Athene and Hera beheld, and with bitter words provoked Zeus the son of Kronos. Of them was the bright-eyed goddess Athene first to speak: "Father Zeus, wilt thou indeed be wroth with me whate'er I say? Verily I ween that Kypris was urging some woman of Achaia to join her unto the Trojans whom she so marvellously loveth; and stroking such an one of the fair-robed women of Achaia, she tore upon the golden brooch her delicate hand."

So spake she, and the father of gods and men smiled, and called unto him golden Aphrodite and said: "Not unto thee my child, are given the works of war; but follow thou after the loving tasks of wedlock, and to all these things shall fleet Ares and Athene look."

Now while they thus spake in converse one with the other, Diomedes of the loud war-cry leapt upon Aineias, knowing full well that Apollo himself had spread his arms over him; yet reverenced he not even the great god, but still was eager to slay Aineias and strip from him his glorious armour. So thrice he leapt on him, fain to slay him, and thrice Apollo beat back his glittering shield. And when the fourth time he sprang at him like a god, then Apollo the Far-darter spake to him with terrible shout: "Think, Tydeides, and shrink, nor desire to match thy spirit with gods; seeing there is no comparison of the race of immortal gods and of men that walk upon the earth."

So said he, and Tydeides shrank a short space backwards,

to avoid the wrath of Apollo the Far-darter. Then Apollo set Aineias away from the throng in holy Pergamos where his temple stood. There Leto and Archer Artemis healed him in the mighty sanctuary, and gave him glory; but Apollo of the silver bow made a wraith like unto Aineias' self, and in such armour as his; and over the wraith Trojans and goodly Achaians each hewed the others' bucklers on their breasts, their round shields and fluttering targes.

Then to impetuous Ares said Phoebus Apollo: "Ares, Ares, blood-stained bane of mortals, thou stormer of walls, wilt thou not follow after this man and withdraw him from the battle, this Tydeides, who now would fight even with father Zeus? First in close fight he wounded Kypris in her hand hard by the wrist, and then sprang he upon myself like unto a god."

So saying he sate himself upon the height of Pergamos, and baleful Ares entered among the Trojan ranks and aroused them in the likeness of fleet Akamas, captain of the Thracians. On the heaven-nurtured sons of Priam he called saying: "O ye sons of Priam, the heaven-nurtured king, how long will ye yet suffer your host to be slain of the Achaians? Shall it be even until they fight about our well-builded gates? Low lieth the warrior whom we esteemed like unto goodly Hector, even Aineias son of Anchises great of heart. Go to now, let us save from the tumult our valiant comrade."

So saying he aroused the spirit and soul of every man. Thereat Sarpedon sorely chode noble Hector: "Hector, where now is the spirit gone that erst thou hadst? Thou saidst forsooth that without armies or allies thou wouldest hold the city, alone with thy sisters' husbands and thy brothers; but now can I not see any of these neither perceive them, but they are cowering like hounds about a lion; and we are fighting that are but allies among you."

So spake Sarpedon, and his word stung Hector to the heart. Forthwith he leapt from his chariot in his armour to the earth, and brandishing two keen spears went everywhere through the host, urging them to fight, and roused the dread battle-cry. So they were rallied and stood to face the Achaians: and the Argives withstood them in close array and fled not. Even as a wind carrieth the chaff about the sacred threshing-floors when men are winnowing, and the chaff-heaps grow white—so now grew the Achaians white with falling dust which in their midst the horses' hooves beat up into the brazen heaven, as fight was joined again, and the charioteers wheeled round. Thus bare they forward the fury of their hands: and impetuous Ares drew round them a veil of night to aid the Trojans in the battle, ranging everywhere. And Apollo himself sent forth Aineias from his rich sanctuary and put courage in the heart of him, shepherd of the hosts. So Aineias took his place amid his comrades, and they were glad to see him come among them alive and sound and full of valiant spirit. Yet they questioned him not at all, for all the toil forbade them that the god of the silver bow was stirring and Ares bane of men and Strife raging insatiably.

And on the other side the two Aiantes and Odysseus and Diomedes stirred the Danaans to fight; yet these of themselves feared neither the Trojans' violence nor assaults, but stood like mists that Kronos' son setteth in windless air on the mountain tops, at peace, while the might of the north wind sleepeth and of all the violent winds that blow with keen breath and scatter apart the shadowing clouds. Even so the Danaans withstood the Trojans steadfastly and fled not. And Atreides ranged through the throng exhorting instantly: "My friends, quit you like men and take heart of courage, and shun dishonour in one another's eyes amid the stress of battle. Of men that shun dishonour more are saved than slain, but for them that flee is neither glory found nor any safety."

So saying he darted swiftly with his javelin and smote a foremost warrior, even great-hearted Aineias' comrade Deïkoon son of Pergasos, whom the Trojans held in like honour with Priam's sons, because he was swift to do battle amid the foremost. Him lord Agamemnon smote with his dart upon the shield, and it stayed not the spear, but the point passed through, so that he drave it through the belt into his nethermost belly: and he fell with a crash and his armour clanged upon him.

Then did Aineias slay two champions of the Danaans, even the sons of Diokles, Krethon and Orsilochos. Like them, two lions on the mountain tops are nurtured by their dam in the deep forest thickets; and these harry the kine and goodly sheep and make havoc of the farmsteads of men, till in their turn they too are slain at men's hands with the keen bronze; in such wise were these twain vanquished at Aineias' hands and fell like tall pine-trees.

But Menelaos dear to Ares had pity of them in their fall, and strode through the forefront, harnessed in flashing bronze, brandishing his spear; and Ares stirred his courage, with intent that he might fall beneath Aineias' hand. But Antilochos, great-hearted Nestor's son, beheld him, and strode through the forefront; because he feared exceedingly for the shepherd of the host, lest aught befall him and disappoint them utterly of their labour. So those two were now holding forth their hands and sharp spears each against the other, eager to do battle; when Antilochos came and stood hard by the shepherd of the host. But Aineias faced them not, keen warrior though he was, when he beheld two men abiding side by side; so these haled away the corpses to the Achaians' host, and laid the hapless twain in their comrades' arms, and themselves turned back and fought on amid the foremost.

But Hector marked them across the ranks, and sprang on them with a shout, and the battalions of the Trojans followed him in their might: and Ares led them on and dread Enyo, she bringing ruthless turmoil of war, the while Ares wielded in his hands his monstrous spear, and ranged now before Hector's face, and now behind.

Then Diomedes of the loud war-cry shuddered to behold him; and even as a shiftless man crossing a great plain cometh on a swift-streaming river flowing on to the sea, and seeing it boil with foam springeth backwards, even so now Tydeides shrank back and spake to the host: "Friends, how marvel we that noble Hector is a spearman and bold man of war! Yet ever is there beside him some god that wardeth off destruction; even as now Ares is there by him in likeness of a mortal man. But with faces towards the Trojans still give ground backwards, neither be desirous to fight amain with gods."

Now the Argives before the face of Ares and mail-clad Hector neither turned them round about toward their black ships, nor charged forward in battle, but still fell backward, when they heard of Ares amid the Trojans. But when the white-armed goddess Hera marked them making havoc of the Argives in the press of battle, anon she spake winged words to Athene: "Out on it, thou daughter of aegis-bearing Zeus, unwearied maiden! Was it for naught we pledged our word to Menelaos, that he should not depart till he had laid waste well-walled Ilios,—if thus we let baleful Ares rage? Go to now, let us twain also take thought of impetuous valour."

So said she, and the bright-eyed goddess Athene disregarded not. So Hera the goddess queen, daughter of Kronos, went her way to harness the gold-frontleted steeds. And Athene, daughter of aegis-bearing Zeus, cast down at her father's threshold her woven vesture many-coloured, that herself had wrought and her hands had fashioned, and put on her the tunic of Zeus the cloud-gatherer, and arrayed her in her armour for dolorous battle. About her shoulders cast she the tasselled aegis terrible, whereon is Panic as a crown all round about, and Strife is therein and Valour and horrible Onslaught withal, and therein is the dreadful monster's Gorgon head, dreadful and grim, portent of aegis-bearing Zeus. Upon her head set she the two-crested golden helm with fourfold plate, bedecked with men-at-arms of a hundred cities. Upon the flaming chariot set she her foot, and grasped her heavy spear, great and stout, wherewith she vanquisheth the ranks of men, even of heroes with whom she of the awful sire is wroth. Then Hera swiftly smote the horses with the lash; self-moving groaned upon their hinges the gates of heaven whereof the Hours are warders, to whom is committed great heaven and Olympus, whether to throw open the thick cloud or set it to. There through the gates guided they their horses patient of the lash. And they found the son of Kronos sitting apart from all the gods on the topmost peak of many-ridged Olympus. Then the white-armed goddess Hera stayed her horses and questioned the most high Zeus, the son of Kronos, and said: "Father Zeus, hast thou no indignation with Ares for these violent deeds? How great and goodly a company of Achaians hath he destroyed recklessly and in unruly wise, unto my sorrow. But here in peace Kypris and Apollo of the silver bow take their pleasure, having set on this mad one that knoweth not any law. Father Zeus, wilt thou at all be wroth with me if I smite Ares and chase him from the battle in sorry plight?"

And Zeus the cloud-gatherer answered and said to her: "Go to now, set upon him Athene driver of the spoil, who most is wont to bring sore pain upon him."

So spake he, and the white-armed goddess Hera disregarded not, and lashed her horses; they nothing loth flew on between earth and starry heaven. As far as a man seeth with his eyes into the haze of distance as he sitteth on a place of outlook and gazeth over the wine-dark sea, so far leap the loudly neighing horses of the gods. Now when they came to Troy and the two flowing rivers, even to where Simoeis and Skamandros join their streams, there the white-armed goddess Hera stayed her horses and loosed them from the car and poured thick mist round about them, and Simoeis made ambrosia spring up for them to graze. So the goddesses went their way with step like unto turtle-doves, being fain to bring succour to the men of Argos. And when they were now come where the most and most valiant stood, thronging about mighty Diomedes tamer of horses, in the semblance of ravening lions or wild boars whose strength is nowise feeble, then stood the white-armed goddess Hera and shouted in the likeness of great-hearted Stentor with voice of bronze, whose cry was loud as the cry of fifty other men: "Fie upon you, Argives, base things of shame, so brave in semblance! While yet noble Achilles entered continually into battle, then issued not the Trojans even from the Dardanian gate; for they had dread of his terrible spear. But now fight they far from the city at the hollow ships."

So saying she aroused the spirit and soul of every man. And to Tydeides' side sprang the bright-eyed goddess Athene. That lord she found beside his horses and chariot, cooling the wound that Pandaros with his dart had pierced, for his sweat vexed it by reason of the broad baldrick of his round shield, therewith was he vexed and his arm grew weary, so he was lifting up the baldrick and wiping away the dusky blood. Then the goddess laid her hand on his horses' yoke, and said: "Of a truth Tydeus begat a son little after his own likeness. Tydeus was short of stature, but a man of war."

And stalwart Diomedes made answer to her and said: "I know thee, goddess daughter of aegis-bearing Zeus: therefore with my whole heart will I tell thee my thought and hide it not. Neither hath disheartening terror taken hold upon me, nor any faintness, but I am still mindful of thy behest that thou didst lay upon me. Thou forbadest me to fight face to face with all the blessed gods, save only if Zeus' daughter Aphrodite should enter into battle, then to wound her with the keen bronze. Therefore do I now give ground myself and have bidden all the Argives likewise to gather here together; for I discern Ares lording it in the fray."

Then the bright-eyed goddess Athene answered him: "Diomedes son of Tydeus, thou joy of mine heart, fear thou, for that, neither Ares nor any other of the immortals; so great a helper am I to thee. Go to now, at Ares first guide thou thy whole-hooved horses, and smite him hand to hand, nor have any awe of impetuous Ares, raving here, a curse incarnate, the renegade that of late in converse with me and Hera pledged him to fight against the Trojans and give succour to the Argives, but now consorteth with the Trojans and hath forgotten these."

So speaking, with her hand she drew back Sthenelos and thrust him from the chariot to earth, and instantly leapt he down; so the goddess mounted the car by noble Diomedes' side right eagerly. The oaken axle creaked loud with its burden, bearing the dread goddess and the man of might. Then Athene grasped the whip and reins; forthwith against Ares first guided she the whole-hooved horses. Now he was stripping huge Periphas, most valiant far of the Aitolians, Ochesios' glorious son. Him was blood-stained Ares stripping; and Athene donned the helm of Hades, that terrible Ares might not behold her. Now when Ares scourge of mortals beheld noble Diomedes, he left huge Periphas lying there, where at the first he had slain him and taken away his life, and made straight at Diomedes tamer of horses. Now when they were come nigh in onset on one another, first

Ares thrust over the yoke and horse's reins with spear of bronze, eager to take away his life. But the bright-eyed goddess Athene with her hand seized the spear and thrust it up over the car, to spend itself in vain. Next Diomedes of the loud war-cry attacked with spear of bronze; and Athene drave it home against Ares' nethermost belly, where his taslets were girt about him. There smote he him and wounded him, rending through his fair skin, and plucked forth the spear again. Then brazen Ares bellowed loud as nine thousand warriors or ten thousand cry in battle as they join in strife and fray. Thereat trembling gat hold of Achaians and Trojans for fear, so mightily bellowed Ares insatiate of battle.

Even as gloomy mist appeareth from the clouds when after heat a stormy wind ariseth, even so to Tydeus' son Diomedes brazen Ares appeared amid clouds, faring to wide heaven. Swiftly came he to the gods' dwelling, steep Olympus, and sat beside Zeus son of Kronos with grief at heart, and shewed the immortal blood flowing from the wound, and piteously spake to him winged words: "Father Zeus, hast thou no indignation to behold these violent deeds? For ever cruelly suffer we gods by one another's devices, in shewing men grace. With thee are we all at variance, because thou didst beget that reckless maiden and baleful, whose thought is ever of iniquitous deeds. For all the other gods that are in Olympus hearken to thee, and we are subject every one; only her thou chastenest not, neither in deed nor word, but settest her on, because this pestilent one is thine own offspring. Now hath she urged on Tydeus' son, even overweening Diomedes, to rage furiously against the immortal gods. Kypris first he wounded in close fight, in the wrist of her hand, and then assailed he me, even me, with the might of a god. Howbeit my swift feet bare me away; else had I long endured anguish there amid the grisly heaps of dead, or else had lived strengthless from the smitings of the spear."

Then Zeus the cloud-gatherer looked sternly at him and said: "Nay, thou renegade, sit not by me and whine. Most hateful to me art thou of all gods that dwell in Olympus: thou ever lovest strife and wars and battles. Truly thy mother's spirit in intolerable, unyielding, even Hera's; her can I scarce rule with words. Therefore I deem that by her prompting thou art in this plight. Yet will I no longer endure to see thee in anguish; mine offspring art thou, and to me thy mother bare thee."

So spake he and bade Paieon heal him. And Paieon laid assuaging drugs upon the wound. Even as fig juice maketh haste to thicken white milk, that is liquid but curdleth speedily as a man stirreth, even so swiftly healed he impetuous Ares. And Hebe bathed him, and clothed him in gracious raiment, and he sate him down by Zeus son of Kronos, glorying in his might.

Then fared the twain back to the mansion of great Zeus, even Hera and Athene, having stayed Ares scourge of mortals from his man-slaying.

BOOK VI

How Diomedes and Glaukos, being about to fight, were known to each other, and parted in friendliness. And how Hector returning to the city bade farewell to Andromache his wife.

So was the dread fray of Trojans and Achaians left to itself, and the battle swayed oft this way and that across the plain, as they aimed against each other their bronze-shod javelins, between Simoeis and the streams of Xanthos.

Now had the Trojans been chased again by the Achaians, dear to Ares, up into Ilios, in their weakness overcome, but that Priam's son Helenos, far best of augurs, stood by Aineias' side and Hector's, and spake to them: "Aineias and Hector, seeing that on you lieth the task of war in chief of Trojans and Lykians, because for every issue ye are foremost both for fight and counsel, stand ye your ground, and range the host everywhither to rally them before the gates, ere yet they fall fleeing in their women's arms, and be made a rejoicing to the foe. Then when ye have aroused all our battalions we will abide here and fight the Danaans, though in sore weariness; for necessity presseth us hard: but thou, Hector, go into the city, and speak there to thy mother and mine; let her gather the aged wives to bright-eyed Athene's temple in the upper city, and with her key open the doors of the holy house; and let her lay the robe, that seemeth to her the most gracious and greatest in her hall and far dearest unto herself, upon the knees of beauteous-haired Athene; and vow to her to sacrifice in her temple twelve sleek kine, that have not felt the goad, if she will have mercy on the city and the Trojans' wives and little children. So may she perchance hold back Tydeus' son from holy Ilios, the furious spearman, the mighty deviser of rout, whom in good sooth I deem to have proved himself mightiest of the Achaians. Never in this wise feared we Achilles, prince of men, who they say is born of a goddess; nay, but he that we see is beyond measure furious; none can match him for might."

So spake he, and Hector disregarded not his brother's word, but leapt forthwith from his chariot in his armour to earth, and brandishing two sharp spears passed everywhere through the host, rousing them to battle, and stirred the dread war-cry. So they were rallied and stood to face the Achaians, and the Argives gave ground and ceased from slaughter, and deemed that some immortal had descended from starry heaven to bring the Trojans succour, in such wise rallied they. Then Hector called to the Trojans with far-reaching shout: "O high-souled Trojans and ye far-famed allies, quit you like men, my friends, and take thought of impetuous courage, while I depart to Ilios and bid the elders of the council and our wives pray to the gods and vow them hecatombs."

So saying Hector of the glancing helm departed, and the black hide beat on either side against his ankles and his neck, even the rim that ran uttermost about his bossed shield.

Now Glaukos son of Hippolochos and Tydeus' son met in the mid-space of the foes, eager to do battle. Thus when the twain were come nigh in onset on each other, to him first spake Diomedes of the loud war-cry: "Who art thou, noble sir, of mortal men? For never have I beheld thee in glorious battle ere this, yet now hast thou far outstripped all men in thy hardihood, seeing thou abidest my far-shadowing spear. Luckless are the fathers whose children face my might. But if thou art some immortal come down from heaven, then will not I fight with heavenly gods. But if thou art of men that eat the fruit of the field, come nigh, that anon thou mayest enter the toils of destruction."

Then Hippolochos' glorious son made answer to him: "Great-hearted Tydeides, why enquirest thou of my generation? Even as are the generations of leaves such are those likewise of men; the leaves that be the wind scattereth on the earth, and the forest buddeth and putteth forth more again, when the season of spring is at hand; so of the generations of men one putteth forth and another ceaseth. Yet if thou wilt, have thine answer, that thou mayest well know our lineage, whereof many men have knowledge. Hippolochos, son of Bellerophon, begat me, and of him do I declare me to be sprung; he sent me to Troy and bade me very instantly to be ever the best and to excel all other men, nor put to shame the lineage of my fathers that were of noblest blood in Ephyre and in wide Lykia. This is the lineage and blood whereof I avow myself to be."

So said he, and Diomedes of the loud war-cry was glad. He planted his spear in the bounteous earth and with soft words spake to the shepherd of the host: "Surely then thou art to me a guest-friend of old times through my father: for goodly Oineus of yore entertained noble Bellerophon in his halls and kept him twenty days. Moreover they gave each the other goodly gifts of friendship; Oineus gave a belt bright with purple, and Bellerophon a gold two-handled cup. Therefore now am I to thee a dear guest-friend in midmost Argos, and thou in Lykia, whene'er I fare to your land. So let us shun each other's spears, even amid the throng; Trojans are there in multitudes and famous allies for me to slay, whoe'er it be that God vouchsafeth me and my feet overtake; and for thee are there Achaians in multitude, to slay whome'er thou canst. But let us make exchange of arms between us, that these also may know how we avow ourselves to be guest-friends by lineage."

So spake the twain, and leaping from their cars clasped each the other by his hand, and pledged their faith. But now Zeus son of Kronos took from Glaukos his wits, in that he made exchange with Diomedes Tydeus' son of golden armour for bronze, the price of five score oxen for the price of nine.

Now when Hector came to the Skaian gates and to the oak tree, there came running round about him the Trojans' wives and daughters, enquiring of sons and brethren and friends and husbands. But he bade them thereat all in turn pray to the gods; but sorrow hung over many.

But when he came to Priam's beautiful palace, adorned with polished colonnades—and in it were fifty chambers of polished stone, builded hard by one another, wherein Priam's sons slept beside their wedded wives; and for his daughters over against them on the other side within the courtyard were twelve roofed chambers of polished stone builded hard by one another, wherein slept Priam's sons-in-law beside their chaste wives—then came there to meet him his bountiful mother, leading with her Laodike, fairest of her daughters to look on; and she clasped her hand in his, and spake, and called upon his name: "My son, why hast thou left violent battle to come hither. Surely the sons of the Achaians—name of evil!—press thee hard in fight about thy city, and so thy spirit hath brought thee hither, to come and stretch forth thy hands to Zeus from the citadel. But tarry till I bring thee honey-sweet wine, that thou mayest pour libation to Zeus and all the immortals first, and then shalt thou thyself also be refreshed if thou wilt drink. When a man is awearied wine greatly maketh his strength to wax, even as thou art awearied in fighting for thy fellows."

Then great Hector of the glancing helm answered her: "Bring me no honey-hearted wine, my lady mother, lest thou cripple me of my courage and I be forgetful of my might. But go thou to the temple of Athene, driver of the spoil, with offerings, and gather the aged wives together; and the robe that seemeth to thee the most gracious and greatest in thy palace, and dearest unto thyself, that lay thou upon the knees of beauteous-haired Athene, and vow to her to sacrifice in her temple twelve sleek kine, that have not felt the goad, if she will have mercy on the city and the Trojans' wives and little children. So go thou to the temple of Athene, driver of the spoil; and I will go after Paris, to summon him, if perchance he will hearken to my voice. Would that the earth forthwith might swallow him up! The Olympian fostered him to be a sore bane to the Trojans and to great-hearted Priam, and to Priam's sons. If I but saw him going down to the gates of death, then might I deem that my heart had forgotten its sorrows."

So said he, and she went unto the hall, and called to her handmaidens, and they gathered the aged wives throughout the city. Then she herself went down to her fragrant chamber where were her embroidered robes, the work of Sidonian women, whom godlike Alexandros himself brought from Sidon, when he sailed over the wide sea, that journey wherein he brought home high-born Helen. Of these Hekabe took one to bear for an offering to Athene, the one that was fairest for adornment and greatest, and shone like a star, and lay nethermost of all. Then went she her way and the multitude of aged wives hasted after her.

And Hector was come to Alexandros' fair palace, that himself had builded with them that were most excellent carpenters then in deep-soiled Troy-land; these made him his chamber and hall and courtyard hard by to Priam and Hector, in the upper city. There entered in Hector dear to Zeus, and his hand bare his spear, eleven cubits long: before his face glittered the bronze spear-point, and a ring of gold ran round about it. And he found Paris in his chamber busied with his beauteous arms, his shield and breastplate, and handling his curbed bow; and Helen of Argos sate among her serving-women and appointed brave handiwork for her handmaidens. Then when Hector saw him he rebuked him with scornful words: "Good sir, thou dost not well to cherish this rancour in thy heart. The folk are perishing about the city and high wall in battle, and for thy sake the battle-cry is kindled and war around this city; yea thyself wouldest thou fall out with another, didst thou see him shrinking from hateful war. Up then, lest the city soon be scorched with burning fire."

And godlike Alexandros answered him: "Hector, since in measure thou chidest me and not beyond measure, therefore will I tell thee; lay thou it to thine heart and hearken to me. Not by reason so much of the Trojans, for wrath and indignation, sate I me in my chamber, but fain would I yield me to my sorrow. Even now my wife hath persuaded me with soft words, and urged me into battle; and I moreover, even I, deem that it will be better so; for victory shifteth from man to man. Go to then, tarry awhile, let me put on my armour of war; or else fare thou forth, and I will follow; and I think to overtake thee."

So said he, but Hector of the glancing helm answered him not a word. But Helen spake to him with gentle words: "My brother, even mine that am a dog, mischievous and abominable, would that on the day when my mother bare me at the first, an evil storm-wind had caught me away to a mountain or a billow of the loud-sounding sea, where the billow might have swept me away before all these things came to pass. Howbeit, seeing the gods devised all these ills in this wise, would that then I had been mated with a better man, that felt dishonour and the multitude of men's reproachings. But as for him, neither hath he now sound heart, nor ever will have; thereof deem I moreover that he will reap the fruit. But now come, enter in and sit thee here upon this bench, my brother, since thy heart chiefly trouble hath encompassed, for the sake of me, that am a dog, and for Alexandros' sin; on whom Zeus bringeth evil doom, that even in days to come we may be a song in the ears of men that shall be hereafter."

Then great Hector of the glancing helm answered her: "Bid me not sit, Helen, of thy love; thou wilt not persuade me. Already my heart is set to succour the men of Troy, that have great desire for me that am not with them. But rouse thou this fellow, yea let himself make speed, to overtake me yet within the city. For I shall go into mine house to behold my housefolk and my dear wife, and infant boy; for I know not if I shall return home to them again, or if the gods will now overthrow me at the hands of the Achaians."

So spake Hector of the glancing helm and departed; and anon he came to his well-stablished house. But he found not white-armed Andromache in the halls; she with her boy and fair-robed handmaiden had taken her stand upon the tower, weeping and wailing. And when Hector found not his noble wife within, he came and stood upon the threshold and spake amid the serving women: "Come tell me now true, my serving women. Whither went white-armed Andromache forth from the hall? Hath she gone out to my sisters or unto my brothers' fair-robed wives, or to Athene's temple, where all the fair-tressed Trojan women propitiate the awful goddess?"

Then a busy housedame spake in answer to him: "Hector, seeing thou straitly chargest us tell thee true, neither hath she gone out to any of thy sisters or thy brothers' fair-robed wives, neither to Athene's temple, where all the fair-tressed Trojan women are propitiating the awful goddess; but she went to the great tower of Ilios, because she heard the Trojans were hard pressed, and great victory was for the

Achaians. So hath she come in haste to the wall, like unto one frenzied; and the nurse with her beareth the child."

So spake the housedame, and Hector hastened from his house back by the same way down the well-builded streets. When he had passed through the great city and was come to the Skaian gates, whereby he was minded to issue upon the plain, then came his dear-won wife, running to meet him, even Andromache daughter of great-hearted Eëtion. So she met him now, and with her went the handmaid bearing in her bosom the tender boy, the little child, Hector's loved son, like unto a beautiful star. Him Hector called Skamandrios, but all the folk Astyanax; for only Hector guarded Ilios. So now he smiled and gazed at his boy silently, and Andromache stood by his side weeping, and clasped her hand in his, and spake and called upon his name. "Dear my lord, this thy hardihood will undo thee, neither hast thou any pity for thine infant boy, nor for me forlorn that soon shall be thy widow; for soon will the Achaians all set upon thee and slay thee. But it were better for me to go down to the grave if I lose thee; for never more will any comfort be mine, when once thou, even thou, hast met thy fate, but only sorrow. Nay, Hector, thou art to me father and lady mother, yea and brother, even as thou art my goodly husband. Come now, have pity and abide here upon the tower, lest thou make thy child an orphan and thy wife a widow."

Then great Hector of the glancing helm answered her: "Surely I take thought for all these things, my wife; but I have very sore shame of the Trojans and Trojan dames with trailing robes, if like a coward I shrink away from battle. Moreover mine own soul forbiddeth me, seeing I have

learnt ever to be valiant and fight in the forefront of the
Trojans, winning my father's great glory and mine own.
Yea of a surety I know this in heart and soul; the day shall
come for holy Ilios to be laid low, and Priam and the folk of
Priam of the good ashen spear. Yet doth the anguish of the
Trojans here after not so much trouble me, neither Hekabe's own, neither king Priam's, neither my brethren's, the
many and brave that shall fall in the dust before their foemen, as doth thine anguish in the day when some mail-clad
Achaian shall lead thee weeping and rob thee of the light of
freedom. So shalt thou abide in Argos and ply the loom at
another woman's bidding, and bear water from fount Mes-
seis or Hypereia, being grievously entreated, and sore constraint shall be laid upon thee. And then shall one say that
beholdeth thee weep: 'This is the wife of Hector, that was
foremost in battle of the horse-taming Trojans when men
fought about Ilios.' Thus shall one say hereafter, and fresh
grief will be thine for lack of such an husband as thou hadst
to ward off the day of thraldom. But me in death may the
heaped-up earth be covering, ere I hear thy crying and thy
carrying into captivity."

So spake glorious Hector, and stretched out his arm to his
boy. But the child shrunk crying to the bosom of his fair-
girdled nurse, dismayed at his dear father's aspect, and in
dread at the bronze and horse-hair crest that he beheld nod-
ding fiercely from the helmet's top. Then his dear father
laughed aloud, and his lady mother; forthwith glorious
Hector took the helmet from his head, and laid it, all gleaming, upon the earth; then kissed he his dear son and dandled
him in his arms, and spake in prayer to Zeus and all the

gods, "O Zeus and all ye gods, vouchsafe ye that this my son may likewise prove even as I, pre-eminent amid the Trojans, and as valiant in might, and be a great king of Ilios. Then may men say of him, 'Far greater is he than his father' as he returneth home from battle; and may he bring with him blood-stained spoils from the foeman he hath slain, and may his mother's heart be glad."

So spake he, and laid his son in his dear wife's arms; and she took him to her fragrant bosom, smiling tearfully. And her husband had pity to see her, and caressed her with his hand, and spake and called upon her name: "Dear one, I pray thee be not of oversorrowful heart; no man against my fate shall hurl me to Hades; only destiny, I ween, no man hath escaped, be he coward or be he valiant, when once he hath been born. But go thou to thine house and see to thine own tasks, the loom and distaff, and bid thine handmaidens ply their work; but for war shall men provide, and I in chief of all men that dwell in Ilios."

So spake glorious Hector, and took up his horse-hair crested helmet; and his dear wife departed to her home, oft looking back, and letting fall big tears. Anon she came to the well-stablished house of man-slaying Hector, and found therein her many handmaidens, and stirred lamentation in them all. So bewailed they Hector, while yet he lived, within his house: for they deemed that he would no more come back to them from battle, nor escape the fury of the hands of the Achaians.

Neither lingered Paris long in his lofty house, but clothed on him his brave armour, bedight with bronze, and hasted through the city, trusting to his nimble feet. Even as when a stalled horse, full-fed at the manger, breaketh his tether and speedeth at the gallop across the plain, being wont to bathe him in the fair-flowing stream, exultingly; and holdeth his head on high, and his mane floateth about his shoulders, and he trusteth in his glory, and nimbly his limbs bear him to the haunts and pasturages of mares; even so Priam's son Paris, glittering in his armour like the shining sun, strode down from high Pergamos laughingly, and his swift feet bare him. Forthwith he overtook his brother noble Hector, even as he was on the point to turn him away from the spot where he had dallied with his wife. To him first spake god-like Alexandros: "Sir, in good sooth I have delayed thee in thine haste by my tarrying, and came not rightly as thou badest me."

And Hector of the glancing helm answered him and said: "Good brother, no man that is rightminded could make light of thy doings in fight, seeing thou art strong: but thou art wilfully remiss and hast no care; and for this my heart is grieved within me, that I hear shameful words concerning thee in the Trojans' mouths, who for thy sake endure much toil. But let us be going; all this will we make good here-after, if Zeus ever vouchsafe us to set before the heavenly gods that are for everlasting the cup of deliverance in our halls, when we have chased out of Troy-land the well-greaved Achaians."

BOOK VII

Of the single combat between Aias and Hector, and of the burying of the dead, and the building of a wall about the Achaian ships.

So spake glorious Hector and issued from the gates, and with him went his brother Alexandros; and both were eager of soul for fight and battle. Even as God giveth to longing seamen fair wind when they have grown weary of beating the main with polished oars, and their limbs are fordone with toil, even so appeared these to the longing Trojans.

Now when the goddess bright-eyed Athene marked them making havoc of the Argives in the press of battle, she darted down from the crests of Olympus to holy Ilios. But Apollo rose to meet her, for he beheld her from Pergamos, and would have victory for the Trojans. So the twain met each the other by the oak-tree. To her spake first king Apollo son of Zeus: "Why now art thou come thus eagerly from Olympus, thou daughter of great Zeus, and why hath thy high heart sent thee? Surely it is to give the Danaans unequal victory in battle! seeing thou hast no mercy on the Trojans, that perish. But if thou wouldest hearken to me— and it were far better so—let us now stay battle and warring for the day; hereafter shall they fight again, till they reach the goal of Ilios, since thus it seemeth good to your hearts, goddesses immortal, to lay waste this city."

And the goddess bright-eyed Athene made answer to him: "So be it, Far-darter; in this mind I likewise came from Olympus to the midst of Trojans and Achaians. But come, how thinkest thou to stay the battle of the warriors?"

And king Apollo, son of Zeus, made answer to her: "Let us arouse the stalwart spirit of horse-taming Hector, if so be he will challenge some one of the Danaans in single fight man to man to meet him in deadly combat. So shall the bronze-greaved Achaians be jealous and stir up one to fight singly with goodly Hector."

So spake he and the bright-eyed goddess Athene disregarded not. Now Helenos Priam's dear son understood in spirit their resolve that the gods in counsel had approved; and he went to Hector and stood beside him, and spake a word to him: "Hector son of Priam, peer of Zeus in counsel, wouldest thou now hearken at all to me? for I am thy brother. Make the other Trojans sit, and all the Achaians, and thyself challenge him that is best of the Achaians to meet thee man to man in deadly combat. It is not yet thy destiny to die and meet thy doom; for thus heard I the voice of the gods that are form everlasting."

So said he, and Hector rejoiced greatly to hear his saying, and went into the midst and refrained the battalions of the Trojans with his spear grasped by the middle; and they all sate them down: and Agamemnon made the well-greaved Achaians sit. And Athene withal and Apollo of the silver bow, in the likeness of vulture birds, sate them upon a tall oak holy to aegis-bearing father Zeus, rejoicing in their warriors; and the ranks of all of them sate close together, bristling with shields and plumes and spears. Even as there spreadeth across the main the ripple of the west wind newly risen, and the sea grows black beneath it, so sate the ranks of Achaians and Trojans upon the plain. And Hector spake between both hosts: "Hearken to me, Trojans and well-greaved Achaians, that I may speak what my mind within my breast biddeth me. Our oaths of truce Kronos' son, enthroned on high, accomplished not; but evil is his intent and ordinance for both our hosts, until either ye take fair-towered Troy or yourselves be vanquished beside your sea-faring ships. But in the midst of you are the chiefest of all the Achaians; therefore now let the man whose heart bid-deth him fight with me come hither from among you all to be your champion against goodly Hector. And this declare I, and be Zeus our witness thereto; if that man slay me with the long-edged sword, let him spoil me of my armour and bear it to the hollow ships, but give back my body to my home, that Trojans and Trojans' wives may give me my due of burning in my death. But if I slay him and Apollo vouchsafe me glory, I will spoil him of his armour and bear it to holy Ilios and hang it upon the temple of far-darting Apollo, but his corpse will I render back to the well-decked ships, that the flowing-haired Achaians may entomb him, and build him a barrow beside wide Hellespont. So shall one say even of men that be late born, as he saileth in his benched ship over the wine-dark sea: 'This is the barrow of a man that died in days of old, a champion whom glorious Hector slew.' So shall a man say hereafter, and this my glory shall never die."

So spake he and they all were silent and held their peace; to deny him they were ashamed, and feared to meet him. But at the last stood up Menelaos and spake amid them and chiding upbraided them, and groaned deep at heart: "Ah me, vain threateners, ye women of Achaia and no more men, surely all this shall be a shame, evil of evil, if no one of the Danaans now goeth to meet Hector. Nay, turn ye all to earth and water, sitting there each man disheartened, helplessly inglorious; against him will I myself array me; and from on high the threads of victory are guided of the immortal gods."

So spake he and donned his fair armour. And now, O Menelaos, had the end of life appeared for thee at Hector's hands, seeing he was stronger far, but that the princes of the Achaians started up and caught thee. And Atreus' son himself, wide-ruling Agamemnon, took him by his right hand and spake a word and called upon his name: "Thou doest madly, Menelaos fosterling of Zeus; yet is it no time for this thy madness. Draw back, though it be with pain, nor think for contention's sake to fight with one better than thou, with Hector, Priam's son, whom others beside thee abhor. Yea, this man even Achilles dreadeth to meet in battle, wherein is the warrior's glory; and Achilles is better far than thou. Go therefore now and sit amid the company of thy fellows; against him shall the Achaians put forth another champion. Fearless though he be and insatiate of turmoil, I ween that he shall be fain to rest his knees, if he escape from the fury of war and terrible fray."

So spake the hero and persuaded his brother's heart with just counsel; and he obeyed. So his squires thereat with gladness took his armour from his shoulders; and Nestor stood up and spake amid the Argives: "Fie upon it, verily sore lamentation cometh on the land of Achaia. Verily old Peleus driver of chariots would groan sore, that goodly counsellor of the Myrmidons and orator, who erst questioned me in his house, and rejoiced greatly, inquiring of the lineage and birth of all the Argives. If he heard now of those that all were cowering before Hector, then would he lift his hands to the immortals, instantly praying that his soul might depart from his limbs down to the house of Hades. Would to God I were thus young and my strength were sound; then would Hector of the glancing helm soon find his combat. But of those of you that be chieftains of the host of the Achaians, yet desireth no man of good heart to meet Hector face to face."

So the old man upbraided them, and there stood up nine in all. Far first arose Agamemnon king of men, and after him rose Tydeus' son stalwart Diomedes, and after them the Aiantes clothed with impetuous might, and after them Idomeneus and Idomeneus' brother-in-arms Meriones, peer of Enyalios slayer of men, and after them Eurypylos Euaimon's glorious son; and up rose Thoas Andraimon's son and goodly Odysseus. So all these were fain to fight with goodly Hector. And among them spake again knightly Nestor of Gerenia: "Now cast ye the lot from the first unto the last, for him that shall be chosen: for he shall in truth profit the well-greaved Achaians, yea and he shall have profit of his own soul, if he escape from the fury of war and terrible fray."

So said he, and they marked each man his lot and cast

them in the helmet of Agamemnon Atreus' son; and the hosts prayed and lifted up their hands to the gods. And thus would one say, looking up to wide heaven: "O father Zeus, vouchsafe that the lot fall upon Aias or Tydeus' son, or else on the king of Mykene rich in gold."

So spake they, and knightly Nestor of Gerenia shook the helmet, and there leapt forth the lot that themselves desired, even the lot of Aias. And Aias saw and knew the token upon the lot, and rejoiced in heart, and spake: "My friends, verily the lot is mine, yea and myself am glad at heart, because I deem that I shall vanquish goodly Hector. But come now, while I clothe me in my armour of battle, pray ye the while to Kronos' son king Zeus, in silence to yourselves, that the Trojans hear you not—nay rather, openly if ye will, for we have no fear of any man soever. For none by force shall chase me, he willing me unwilling, neither by skill; seeing I hope that not so skill-less, either, was I born in Salamis nor nurtured."

So said he, and they prayed to Kronos' son, king Zeus; and thus would one speak, looking up to wide heaven: "O father Zeus that rulest from Ida, most glorious, most great, vouchsafe to Aias victory and the winning of great glory. But if thou so lovest Hector indeed, and carest for him, grant unto either equal prowess and renown."

So said they, while Aias arrayed him in flashing bronze. And when he had now clothed upon his flesh all his armour, then marched he as huge Ares coming forth, when he goeth to battle amid heroes whom Kronos' son setteth to fight in fury of heart-consuming strife. So rose up huge Aias, bulwark of the Achaians, with a smile on his grim face: and went with long strides of his feet beneath him, shaking his far-shadowing spear. Then moreover the Argives rejoiced to look upon him, but sore trembling came upon the Trojans, on the limbs of every man, and Hector's own heart beat within his breast. But in no wise could he now flee nor shrink back into the throng of the host, seeing he had challenged him to battle. And Aias came near bearing his tower-like shield of bronze, with sevenfold ox-hide, and stood near to Hector, and spake to him threatening: "Hector, now verily shalt thou well know, man to man, what manner of princes the Danaans likewise have among them, even after Achilles, render of men, the lion-hearted. But he amid his beaked seafaring ships lieth in sore wrath with Agamemnon shepherd of the host; yet are we such as to face thee, yea and many of us. But make thou beginning of war and battle."

And great Hector of the glancing helm answered him: "Aias of the seed of Zeus, son of Telamon, chieftain of the host, tempt not thou me like some puny boy or woman that knoweth not deeds of battle. But I well know wars and slaughterings. To right know I, to left know I the wielding of my tough targe; therein I deem is stalwart soldiership. And I know how to charge into the melee of fleet chariots, and how in close battle to join in furious Ares' dance. Howbeit, I have no mind to smite thee, being such an one as thou art, by spying thee unawares; but rather openly, if perchance I may hit thee."

He spake, and poised his far-shadowing spear, and hurled and smote Aias' dread shield of sevenfold hide upon the uttermost bronze, the eighth layer that was thereon.

Through six folds went the stubborn bronze cleaving, but in the seventh hide it stayed. Then heaven-sprung Aias hurled next his far-shadowing spear, and smote upon the circle of the shield of Priam's son. Through the bright shield passed the violent spear, and through the curiously wrought corslet pressed it on; and straight forth beside the flank the spear rent his doublet; but he swerved aside and escaped black death. Then both together with their hands plucked forth their long spears and fell to like ravening lions or wild boars whose might is nowise feeble. Then Priam's son smote the shield's midst with his dart, but the bronze brake not through, for the point turned back; but Aias leapt on him and pierced his buckler, and straight through went the spear and staggered him in his onset, and cleft its way unto his neck, so that the dark blood gushed up. Yet even then did not Hector of the glancing helm cease from fight, but yielded ground and with stout hand seized a stone lying upon the plain, black and rugged and great; therewith hurled he and smote Aias' dread shield of sevenfold ox-hide in the midst upon the boss, and the bronze resounded. Next Aias lifted a far greater stone, and swung and hurled it, putting might immeasurable therein. So smote he the buckler and burst it inwards with the rock like unto a millstone, and beat down his knees; and he was stretched upon his back, pressed into his shield; but Apollo straightway raised him up. And now had they been smiting hand to hand with swords, but that the heralds, messengers of gods and men, came, one from the Trojans, one from the mailclad Achaians, even Talthybios and Idaios, both men discreet. Between the two held they their staves, and herald

Idaios spake a word, being skilled in wise counsel: "Fight ye no more, dear sons, neither do battle; seeing Zeus the cloud-gatherer loveth you both, and both are men of war; that verily know we all. But night already is upon us: it is well withal to obey the hest of night."

Then Telamonian Aias answered and said to him: "Idaios, bid ye Hector to speak those words; of his own self he challenged to combat all our best. Let him be first, and I will surely follow as he saith."

Then great Hector of the glancing helm said to him: "Aias, seeing God gave thee stature and might and wisdom, and with the spear thou art excellent above all the Achaians, let us now cease from combat and battle for the day; but hereafter will we fight until God judge between us, giving to one of us the victory. But come, let us give each the other famous gifts, that men may thus say, Achaians alike and Trojans: 'These, having fought for sake of heart-consuming strife, parted again reconciled in friendship.'"

So said he, and gave him his silver-studded sword, with scabbard and well-cut baldrick; and Aias gave his belt bright with purple. So they parted, and one went to the Achaian host, and one betook him to the throng of Trojans. And these rejoiced to behold him come to them alive and sound, escaped from the fury of Aias and his hands unapproachable; and they brought him to the city saved beyond their hope. And Aias on their side the well-greaved Achaians brought to noble Agamemnon, exulting in his victory.

So when these were come unto the huts of Atreides, then did Agamemnon king of men slay them an ox, a male of five years old, for the most mighty son of Kronos. This they flayed and made ready, and divided it all, and minced it cunningly, and pierced it through with spits, and roasted it carefully, and drew all off again. Then as soon as they had rest from the task and had made ready the meal, they began the feast, nor was their soul aught stinted of the equal banquet. And the hero son of Atreus, wide-ruling Agamemnon, gave to Aias slices of the chine's full length for his honour. And when they had put from them the desire of meat and drink, then first the old man began to weave the web of counsel, even Nestor whose rede of old time was proved most excellent. He made harangue among them and said: "Son of Atreus and ye other princes of the Achaians, seeing that many flowing-haired Achaians are dead, and keen Ares hath spilt their dusky blood about fair-flowing Skamandros, and their souls have gone down to the house of Hades; therefore it behoveth thee to make the battle of the Achaians cease with daybreak; and we will assemble to wheel hither the corpses with oxen and mules; so let us burn them; and let us heap one barrow about the pyre, rearing it from the plain for all alike; and thereto build with speed high towers, a bulwark for our ships and for ourselves. In the midst thereof let us make gates well compact, that through them may be a way for chariot-driving. And without let us dig a deep foss hard by, to be about it and to hinder horses and footmen, lest the battle of the lordly Trojans be heavy on us hereafter."

So spake he and all the chiefs gave assent. But meanwhile there was in the high town of Ilios an assembly of the Trojans, fierce, confused, beside Priam's gate. To them discreet

Antenor began to make harangue: "Hearken to me, Trojans and Dardanians and allies, that I may tell you that my soul within my breast commandeth me. Lo, go to now, let us give Helen of Argos and the wealth with her for the sons of Atreus to take away. Now fight we in guilt against the oaths of faith; therefore is there no profit for us that I hope to see fulfilled, unless we do thus."

So spake he and sate him down; and there stood up among them noble Alexandros, lord of Helen beautiful-haired; he made him answer and spake winged words: "Antenor, these words from thee are no longer to my pleasure; yet thou hast it in thee to devise other sayings more excellent than this. But if indeed thou sayest this in earnest, then verily the gods themselves have destroyed thy wit. But I will speak forth amid the horse-taming Trojans, and declare outright; my wife will I not give back; but the wealth I brought from Argos to our home, all that I have a mind to give, and add more of mine own substance."

So spake he and sate him down, and there stood up among them Priam of the seed of Dardanos, the peer of gods in counsel; he made harangue to them, and said: "Hearken to me, Trojans and Dardanians and allies, that I may tell you that my soul within my breast commandeth me. Now eat your supper throughout the city as of old, and take thought to keep watch, and be wakeful every man. And at dawn let Idaios fare to the hollow ships to tell to Atreus' sons Agamemnon and Menelaos the saying of Alexandros, for whose sake strife is come about: and likewise to ask them this wise word, whether they are minded to refrain from noisy war till we have burned our dead; afterwards will we fight again, till heaven part us and give one or other victory."

So spake he, and they hearkened diligently to him and obeyed: and at dawn Idaios fared to the hollow ships. He found the Danaans in assembly, the men of Ares' company, beside the stern of Agamemnon's ship; and so the loud-voiced herald stood in their midst and said unto them: "Atreides and ye other princes of the Achaians, Priam and all the noble Trojans bade me tell you—if perchance it might find favour and acceptance with you—the saying of Alexandros, for whose sake strife hath come about. The wealth that Alexandros brought in his hollow ships to Troy —would he had perished first!—all that he hath a mind to give, and to add more thereto of his substance. But the wedded wife of glorious Menelaos he saith he will not give; yet verily the Trojans bid him do it. Moreover they bade me ask this thing of you; whether ye are minded to refrain from noisy war until we have burned our dead; afterwards will we fight again, till heaven part us and give one or other victory."

So said he and they all kept silence and were still. But at the last spake Diomedes of the loud war-cry in their midst: "Let no man now accept Alexandros' substance, neither Helen's self; known is it, even to him that hath no wit at all, how that the issues of destruction hang already over the Trojans."

So spake he, and all the sons of the Achaians shouted, applauding the saying of horse-taming Diomedes. And then lord Agamemnon spake to Idaios: "Idaios, thyself thou hearest the saying of the Achaians, how they answer thee; and the like seemeth good to me. But as concerning the dead, I grudge you not to burn them; for dead corpses is there no stinting, when they once are dead, of the swift propitiation of fire. And for the oaths let Zeus be witness, the loud-thundering lord of Hera."

So saying he lifted up his sceptre in the sight of all the gods, and Idaios departed back to holy Ilios. Now Trojans and Dardanians sate in assembly, gathered all together to wait till Idaios should come; and he came and stood in their midst and declared his message. Then they made them ready very swiftly for either task, some to bring the dead, and some to seek for wood. And on their part the Argives hasted from their well-decked ships, some to bring the dead and some to seek for wood.

Now the sun was newly beating on the fields as he climbed heaven from the deep stream of gently-flowing Ocean, when both sides met together. Then was it a hard matter to know each man again; but they washed them with water clean of clotted gore, and with shedding of hot tears lifted them upon the wains. But great Priam bade them not wail aloud; so in silence heaped they the corpses on the pyre, stricken at heart; and when they had burned them with fire departed to holy Ilios. And in like manner on their side the well-greaved Achaians heaped the corpses on the pyre, stricken at heart, and when they had burned them with fire departed to the hollow ships.

And when day was not yet, but still twilight of night, then was the chosen folk of the Achaians gathered together around the pyre, and made one barrow about it, rearing it from the plain for all alike; and thereto built they a wall and lofty towers, a bulwark for their ships and for themselves. In the midst thereof made they gates well-compacted, that through them might be a way for chariot-driving. And without they dug a deep foss beside it, broad and great, and planted a palisade therein.

Thus toiled the flowing-haired Achaians: and the gods sate by Zeus, the lord of lightning, and marvelled at the great work of the mail-clad Achaians. And Poseidon shaker of earth spake first to them: "O father Zeus, is there any man throughout the boundless earth that will any more declare to the immortals his mind and counsel? Seest thou not how the flowing-haired Achaians have now again built them a wall before their ships, and drawn a foss around it, but gave not excellent hecatombs to the gods? Verily the fame thereof shall reach as far as the dawn spreadeth, and men will forget the wall that I and Phoebus Apollo built with travail for the hero Laomedon."

And Zeus the cloud-gatherer said to him, sore troubled: "Out on it, far-swaying Shaker of earth, for this thing thou sayest. Well might some other god fear this device, one that were far feebler than thou in the might of his hands: but thine shall be the fame as far as the dawn spreadeth. Go to now, hereafter when the flowing-haired Achaians be departed upon their ships to their dear native land, then burst thou this wall asunder and scatter it all into the sea, and cover the great sea-beach over with sand again, that the great wall of the Achaians be brought to naught."

BOOK VIII

How Zeus bethought him of his promise to avenge Achilles'
wrong on Agamemnon: and therefore bade the gods refrain
from war, and gave victory to the Trojans.

Now Dawn the saffron-robed was spreading over all
the earth, and Zeus whose joy is in the thunder let
call an assembly of the gods upon the topmost peak of
many-ridged Olympus, and himself made harangue to them
and all the gods gave ear: "Hearken to me, all gods and
all ye goddesses, that I may tell you what my heart within
my breast commandeth me. One thing let none essay, be
it goddess or be it god, to wit, to thwart my saying; approve ye it all together, that with all speed I may accomplish
these things. Whomsoever I shall perceive minded to go,
apart from the gods, to succour Trojans or Danaans,
chastened in no seemly wise shall he return to Olympus, or
I will take and cast him into misty Tartaros, right far away,
where is the deepest gulf beneath the earth; there are the
gate of iron and threshold of bronze, as far beneath Hades
as heaven is high above the earth: then shall he know how
far I am mightiest of all gods. Go to now, ye gods, make
trial that ye all may know. Fasten ye a rope of gold from
heaven, and all ye gods lay hold thereof and all goddesses;
yet could ye not drag from heaven to earth Zeus, counsellor
supreme, not though ye toiled sore. But once I likewise were

minded to draw with all my heart, then should I draw you up with very earth and sea withal. Thereafter would I bind the rope about a pinnacle of Olympus, and so should all those things be hung in air. By so much am I beyond gods and beyond men."

So saying he let harness to his chariot his bronze-shod horses, fleet of foot, with flowing manes of gold; and himself clad him with gold upon his flesh, and grasped the whip of gold, well wrought, and mounted upon his car, and lashed the horses to start them; they nothing loth sped on between earth and starry heaven. So fared he to many-fountained Ida, mother of wild beasts, even unto Gargaros, where is his demesne and fragrant altar. There did the father of men and gods stay his horses, and unloose them from the car, and cast thick mist about them; and himself sate on the mountain-tops rejoicing in his glory, to behold the city of the Trojans and ships of the Achaians.

Now the flowing-haired Achaians took meat hastily among the huts and thereafter arrayed themselves. Likewise the Trojans on their side armed them throughout the town— a smaller host, yet for all that were they eager to fight in battle, of forceful need, for their children's sake and their wives'. And the gates were opened wide and the host issued forth, footmen and horsemen; and mighty din arose.

So when they were met together and come unto one spot, then clashed they targe and spear and fury of bronze-clad warrior; the bossed shields pressed each on each, and mighty din arose. Then were heard the voice of groaning and the voice of triumph together of the slayers and the slain, and the earth streamed with blood.

Now while it yet was morn and the divine day waxed, so long from either side lighted the darts amain and the people fell. But when the sun bestrode mid-heaven, then did the Father balance his golden scales, and put therein two fates of death that layeth men at their length, one for horse-taming Trojans one for mail-clad Achaians; and he took the scale-yard by the midst and lifted it, and the Achaians' day of destiny sank down. So lay the Achaians' fates on the bounteous earth, and the Trojans' fates were lifted up to-wards wide heaven. And the god thundered aloud from Ida, and sent his blazing flash amid the host of the Achaians; and they saw and were astonished, and pale fear gat hold upon all.

Then had Idomeneus no heart to stand, neither Agamem-non, neither stood the twain Aiantes, men of Ares' com-pany. Only Nestor of Gerenia stood his ground, he the Warden of the Achaians; neither he of purpose, but his horse was fordone, which noble Alexandros, beauteous-haired Helen's lord, had smitten with an arrow upon the top of the crest where the foremost hairs of horses grow upon the skull; and there is the most deadly spot. So the horse leapt up in anguish and the arrow sank into his brain, and he brought confusion on the steeds as he writhed upon the dart. While the old man leapt forth and with his sword began to hew the traces, came Hector's fleet horses through the tumult, bearing a bold charioteer, even Hector. And now had the old man lost his life, but that Diomedes of the loud war-cry was swift to mark. Terribly shouted he, sum-moning Odysseus: "Heaven-born son of Laertes, Odysseus of many wiles, whither fleest thou with thy back turned, like a coward in the throng? Beware lest as thou fleest one plant a spear between thy shoulders. Nay, stand thy ground, till we thrust back from the old man his furious foe."

So spake he, but much-enduring noble Odysseus heard him not, but hastened by to the hollow ships of the Achaians. Yet Tydeides, though but one, mingled amid the fighters in the forefront, and took his stand before the steeds of the old man, Neleus' son, and spake to him winged words, and said: "Old man, of a truth young warriors beset thee hard; and thy force is abated, and old age is sore upon thee, and thy squire is but a weakling, and thy steeds are slow. Come then, mount upon my car, that thou mayest see of what sort are the steeds of Tros, well skilled for following or fleeing hither or thither very fleetly across the plain, even those that erst I took from Aineias inspirer of fear. Thine let our squires tend, and these let us guide straight against the horse-taming Trojans, that even Hector may know whether my spear also rageth in my hands."

So said he, and knightly Nestor of Gerenia disregarded not. Then the two squires tended Nestor's horses, even Sthenelos the valiant and kindly Eurymedon: and the other twain both mounted upon Diomedes' car. And Nestor took into his hands the shining reins, and lashed the horses; and soon they drew nigh Hector. Then Tydeus' son hurled at him as he charged straight upon them: him missed he, but his squire that drave his chariot, Eniopeus, high-hearted Thebaios' son, even him as he held the reins, he smote upon the breast beside the nipple. So he fell from out the car, and his fleet-footed horses swerved aside; and there his soul and spirit were unstrung. Then sore grief encompassed Hector's soul for sake of his charioteer. Yet left he him there lying, though he sorrowed for his comrade, and drave in quest of a bold charioteer; and his horses lacked not long a master, for anon he found Iphitos' son, bold Archeptolemos, and him he made mount behind his fleet horses, and gave the reins into his hands.

Then had destruction come and deeds beyond remedy been wrought, and so had they been penned in Ilios like lambs, had not the father of gods and men been swift to mark. So he thundered terribly and darted his white lightning and hurled it before Diomedes' steeds to earth; and there arose a terrible flame of sulphur burning, and the two horses were affrighted and cowered beneath the car. And the shining reins dropped from Nestor's hands, and he was afraid at heart and spake to Diomedes: "Come now Tydeides, turn back thy whole-hooved horses to flight: seest thou not that victory from Zeus attendeth not on thee? Now doth Kronos' son vouchsafe glory to this Hector, for the day; hereafter shall he grant it us likewise, if he will. A man may not at all ward off the will of Zeus, not though one be very valiant; he verily is mightier far."

Then Diomedes of the loud war-cry answered him: "Yea verily, old man, all this thou sayest is according unto right. But this is the sore grief that entereth my heart and soul Hector some day shall say as he maketh harangue amid the Trojans: 'Tydeides betook him to the ships in flight before my face.' So shall he boast—in that day let the wide earth yawn for me."

So spake he and turned the whole-hooved horses to flight, back through the tumult; and the Trojans and Hector with wondrous uproar poured upon them their dolorous darts. And over him shouted loudly great Hector of the glancing helm: "Tydeides, the fleet-horsed Danaans were wont to honour thee with the highest place, and meats, and cups brimful, but now will they disdain thee; thou art after all no better than a woman. Begone, poor puppet; not for my flinching shalt thou climb on our towers, neither carry our wives away upon thy ships; ere that will I deal thee thy fate."

So said he, and Tydeides was of divided mind, whether to wheel his horses and fight him face to face. Thrice doubted he in heart and soul, and thrice from Ida's mountains thundered Zeus the lord of counsel, and gave to the Trojans a sign, the turning of the course of battle. And Hector with loud shout called to the Trojans: "Trojans and Lykians and Dardanians that love close fight, be men, my friends, and bethink you of impetuous valour. I perceive that of good will Kronion vouchsafest me victory and great glory, and to the Danaans destruction. Fools, that devised these walls weak and of none account; they shall not withhold our fury, and lightly shall our steeds overleap the delved foss. But when I be once come amid the hollow ships, then be thought taken of consuming fire, that with fire I may burn the ships and slay the men."

So spake he and shouted to his steeds, and said: "Xanthos, and thou Podargos, and Aithon and goodly Lampos, now pay me back your tending, even the abundance that Andromache, great-hearted Eëtion's daughter, set before you of honey-hearted wheat, and mingled wine to drink at the heart's bidding. Pursue ye now and haste, that we may seize Nestor's shield, the fame whereof now reacheth unto heaven, how that it is of gold throughout, armrods and all; and may seize moreover from horse-taming Diomedes' shoulders his richly dight breastplate that Hephaistos wrought cunningly. Could we but take these, then might I hope this very night to make the Achaians to embark on their fleet ships."

And now had he burned the trim ships with blazing fire, but that queen Hera put it in Agamemnon's heart himself to bestir him and swiftly arouse the Achaians. So he went his way along the huts and ships of the Achaians, holding a great cloak of purple in his stalwart hand, and stood by Odysseus' black ship of mighty burden, that was in the midst, so that a voice could be heard to either end. Then shouted he in a piercing voice, and called to the Danaans aloud: "Fie upon you, Argives, ye sorry things of shame, so brave in semblance! Whither are gone our boastings when we said that we were bravest, the boasts ye uttered vaingloriously when in Lemnos, as ye ate your fill of flesh of tall-horned oxen and drank goblets crowned with wine, and said that every man should stand in war to face fivescore yea tenscore Trojans? yet now can we not match one, even this Hector that anon will burn our ships with flame of fire. O Father Zeus, didst ever thou blind with such a blindness any mighty king, and rob him of great glory? Nay, Zeus, this hope fulfil thou me; suffer that we ourselves at least flee and escape, neither suffer that the Achaians be thus vanquished of the Trojans."

So spake he, and the Father had pity on him as he wept, and vouchsafed him that his folk should be saved and perish not. Forthwith sent he an eagle—surest sign among winged fowl—holding in his claws a fawn, the young of a fleet hind; beside the beautiful altar of Zeus he let fall the fawn, where the Achaians did sacrifice unto Zeus lord of all oracles. So when they saw that the bird was come from Zeus, they sprang the more upon the Trojans and bethought them of the joy of battle.

Now could no man of the Danaans, for all they were very many, boast that he before Tydeus' son had guided his fleet horses forth, and driven them across the trench and fought man to man; first by far was Tydeides to slay a warrior of the Trojans in full array, even Agelaos son of Phradmon. Now he had turned his steeds to flee; but as he wheeled the other plunged the spear into his back between his shoulders, and drave it through his breast. So fell he from his chariot, and his armour clanged upon him.

And after him came Atreus' sons, even Agamemnon and Menelaos, and after them the Aiantes clothed upon with impetuous valour, and after them Idomeneus and Idomeneus' brother in arms Meriones, peer of Enyalios slayer of men, and after them Eurypylos, Euaimon's glorious son. And ninth came Teukros, stretching his back-bent bow, and took his stand beneath the shield of Aias son of Telamon. And so Aias would stealthily withdraw the shield, and Teukros would spy his chance; and when he had shot and smitten one in the throng, then fell such an one and gave up the ghost, and Teukros would return, and as a child beneath his mother, so gat he him to Aias; who hid him with the shining shield.

And Agamemnon king of men rejoiced to behold him

making havoc with his stalwart bow of the battalions of the Trojans, and he came and stood by his side and spake to him, saying: "Teukros, dear heart, thou son of Telamon, prince of the host, shoot on in this wise, if perchance thou mayest be found the salvation of the Danaans and glory of thy father Telamon.

And noble Teukros made answer and said to him: "Most noble son of Atreus, why urgest thou me that myself am eager? Verily with such strength as is in me forbear I not, but ever since we drave them towards Ilios I watch with my bow to slay the foemen. Eight long-barbed arrows have I now sped, and all are buried in the flesh of young men swift in battle; only this mad dog can I not smite."

He said, and shot another arrow from the string right against Hector; and his heart was fain to smite him. Yet missed he once again, for Apollo turned the dart away; but Archeptolemos, Hector's bold charioteer, he smote on the breast beside the nipple as he hasted into battle: so he fell from his car and his fleet-footed horses swerved aside; and there his soul and spirit were unstrung. Then sore grief encompassed Hector's soul for his charioteer's sake; yet left he him, though he sorrowed for his comrade, and bade Kebriones his own brother, being hard by, take the chariot reins; and he heard and disregarded not. And himself he leapt to earth from the resplendent car, with a terrible shout; and in his hand he caught a stone, and made right at Teukros, and his heart bade him smite him. Now Teukros had plucked forth from his quiver a keen arrow, and laid it on the string; but even as he drew it back, Hector of the glancing helm smote him with the jagged stone, as he aimed

eagerly against him, even beside his shoulder, where the col-
larbone fenceth off neck and breast, and where is the most
deadly spot; and he brake the bowstring, and his hand from
the wrist grew numb, and he stayed fallen upon his knee,
and his bow dropped from his hand. But Aias disregarded
not his brother's fall, but ran and strode across him and hid
him with his shield. Then two trusty comrades bent down to
him, even Mekisteus son of Echios and goodly Alastor, and
bare him, groaning sorely, to the hollow ships. And once
again the Olympian aroused the spirit of the Trojans. So
they drove the Achaians straight toward the deep foss, and
amid the foremost went Hector exulting in his strength.
And even as when a hound behind wild boar or lion, with
swift feet pursuing snatcheth at him, at flank or buttock,
and watcheth for him as he wheeleth, so Hector pressed
hard on the flowing-haired Achaians, slaying ever the
hindmost, and they fled on. But when they were passed in
flight through palisade and foss, and many were fallen beneath the Trojans' hands, then halted they and tarried beside the ships, calling one upon another, and lifting up their
hands to all the gods prayed each one instantly. But Hector
wheeled round his beauteous-maned steeds this way and
that, and his eyes were as the eyes of Gorgon or Ares bane
of mortals.

Now at the sight of them the white-armed goddess Hera
had compassion, and anon spake winged words to Athene:
"Out on it, thou child of aegis-bearing Zeus, shall not we
twain any more take thought for the Danaans that perish, if
only for this last time? Now will they fill up the measure of
evil destiny and perish by one man's onslaught; seeing that

he is furious now beyond endurance, this Hector son of Priam, and verily hath wrought many a deed of ill."

And the bright-eyed goddess Athene made answer to her, "Yea in good sooth, may this fellow yield up strength and life, and perish at the Argives' hands in his native land; only mine own sire is furious, with no good intent, headstrong, ever sinful, the foiler of my purposes. But now make thou ready our whole-hooved horses, while I enter into the palace of aegis-bearing Zeus and gird me in my armour for battle, that I may see if Priam's son, Hector of the glancing helm, shall be glad at the appearing of us twain amid the highways of the battle. Surely shall many a Trojan likewise glut dogs and birds with fat and flesh, fallen dead at the ships of the Achaians."

So said she, and the white-armed goddess Hera disregarded not. But when father Zeus beheld from Ida, he was sore wroth, and sped Iris golden-winged to bear a message: "Go thy way, fleet Iris, turn them back, neither suffer them to face me; for in no happy wise shall we join in combat. For thus will I declare, and even so shall the fulfilment be; I will maim their fleet horses in the chariot, and them will I hurl out from the car, and will break in pieces the chariot; neither within the courses of ten years shall they heal them of the wounds the thunderbolt shall tear; that the bright-eyed one may know the end when she striveth against her father. But with Hera have I not so great indignation nor wrath: seeing it ever is her wont to thwart me, whate'er I have decreed."

So said he, and whirlwind-footed Iris arose to bear the message, and departed from the mountains of Ida unto high

Olympus. And even at the entrance of the gates of Olympus many-folded she met them and stayed them, and told them the saying of Zeus.

And father Zeus drave from Ida his fair-wheeled chariot and horses unto Olympus, and came unto the session of the gods. For him also the noble Shaker of Earth unyoked the steeds, and set the car upon the stand, and spread a cloth thereover; and far-seeing Zeus himself sate upon his golden throne, and beneath his feet great Olympus quaked. Only Athene and Hera sate apart from Zeus, and spake no word to him neither questioned him. But he was ware thereof in his heart, and said, "Why are ye thus vexed, Athene and Hera? Surely ye are not wearied of making havoc in glorious battle of the Trojans, for whom ye cherish bitter hate! Howsoever, seeing that my might is so great and my hands invincible, all the gods that are in Olympus could not turn me: and for you twain, trembling erst gat hold upon your bright limbs ere that ye beheld war and war's fell deeds. For thus will I declare, and even so had the fulfilment been— never had ye, once smitten with the thunderbolt, fared on your chariots back unto Olympus where is the habitation of the immortals."

So spake he, and Athene and Hera murmured, that were sitting by him and devising ills for the Trojans. Now Athene held her peace, and said not anything, for wrath at father Zeus, and fierce anger gat hold upon her; but Hera's heart contained not her anger, and she spake: "Most dread son of Kronos, what word is this thou hast said? Well know we, even we, that thy might is no wise puny; yet still have we pity for the Danaan spearmen, that now shall perish and fill up the measure of grievous fate."

And Zeus the cloud-gatherer answered and said: "At morn shalt thou behold most mighty Kronion, if thou wilt have it so, O Hera, ox-eyed queen, making yet more havoc of the vast army of Argive spearmen; for headlong Hector shall not refrain from battle till that Peleus' son fleet of foot have arisen beside the ships, that day when these shall fight amid the sterns in most grievous stress, around Patroklos fallen. Such is the doom of heaven. And for thine anger reck I not, not even though thou go to the nethermost bounds of earth and sea, where sit Iapetos and Kronos and have no joy in the beams of Hyperion the Sun-god, neither in any breeze, but deep Tartaros is round about them. Though thou shouldest wander till thou come even thither, yet reck I not of thy vexation, seeing there is no thing more unabashed than thou."

So said he, but white-armed Hera spake him no word. And the sun's bright light dropped into Ocean, drawing black night across Earth the grain-giver. Against the Tro- jans' will daylight departed, but welcome, thrice prayed for, to the Achaians came down the murky night.

Now glorious Hector made an assembly of the Trojans, taking them apart from the ships, beside the eddying river, in an open space where was found a spot clear of dead. And they came down from their chariots to the ground to hear the word that Hector, dear unto Zeus, proclaimed. He in his hand held his spear eleven cubits long; before his face gleamed the spearhead of bronze, and a ring of gold ran

round about it. Thereon he leaned and spake to the Trojans, saying: "Hearken to me, Trojans and Dardanians and
allies. I thought but now to make havoc of the ships and all
the Achaians and depart back again to windy Ilios; but
dusk came too soon, and that in chief hath now saved the
Argives and the ships beside the beach of the sea. So let us
now yield to black night, and make our supper ready; unyoke ye from the chariots your fair-maned horses, and set
fodder beside them. And from the city bring kine and
goodly sheep with speed; and provide you with honey-
hearted wine, and corn from your houses, and gather much
wood withal, that all night long until early-springing dawn
we may burn many fires, and the gleam may reach to
heaven; lest perchance even by night the flowing-haired
Achaians strive to take flight over the broad back of the sea.
Verily must they not embark upon their ships unvexed, at
ease: but see ye that many a one of them have a wound to
nurse even at home, being stricken with arrow or keen-
pointed spear as he leapeth upon his ship; that so many
another man may dread to wage dolorous war on the horse-
taming men of Troy. And let the heralds dear to Zeus proclaim throughout the city that young maidens and old men
of hoary heads camp round the city on the battlements
builded of the gods; and let the women folk burn a great fire
each in her hall; and let there be a sure watch set, lest an
ambush enter the city when the host is absent. Howbeit for
the night will we guard our own selves, and at morn by daybreak, arrayed in our armour, let us awake keen battle at
the hollow ships. I will know whether Tydeus' son stalwart
Diomedes shall thrust me from the ships back to the wall, or

I shall lay him low with my spear and bear away his gory spoils. To-morrow shall he prove his valour, whether he can abide the onslaught of my spear. Would that I were immortal and ageless all my days and honoured like as Athene is honoured and Apollo, so surely as this day bringeth the Argives ill."

So Hector made harangue, and the Trojans clamoured applause. And they loosed their sweating steeds from the yoke, and tethered them with thongs, each man beside his chariot; and from the city they brought kine and goodly sheep with speed, and provided them with honey-hearted wine and corn from their houses, and gathered much wood withal. And from the plain the winds bare into heaven the sweet savour. But these with high hopes sate them all night along the highways of the battle, and their watchfires burned in multitude. Even as when in heaven the stars about the bright moon shine clear to see, when the air is windless, and all the peaks appear and the tall headlands and glades, and from heaven breaketh open the infinite air, and all stars are seen, and the shepherd's heart is glad; even in like multitude between the ships and the streams of Xanthos appeared the watchfires that the Trojans kindled in front of Ilios. A thousand fires burned in the plain and by the side of each sate fifty in the gleam of blazing fire. And the horses champed white barley and spelt, and standing by their chariots waited for the throned Dawn.

BOOK IX

How Agamemnon sent an embassage to Achilles, beseeching him to be appeased; and how Achilles denied him.

T HUS kept the Trojans watch; but the Achaians were holden of heaven-sent panic, handmaid of palsying fear, and all their best were stricken to the heart with grief intolerable. Like as two winds stir up the main, the home of fishes, even the north wind and the west wind that blow from Thrace, coming suddenly; and the dark billow straightway lifteth up its crest and casteth much tangle out along the sea; even so was the Achaians' spirit troubled in their breast.

But Atreides was stricken to the heart with sore grief, and went about bidding the clear-voiced heralds summon every man by name to the assembly, but not to shout aloud; and himself he toiled amid the foremost. So they sat sorrowful in assembly, and Agamemnon stood up weeping like unto a fountain of dark water that from a beetling cliff poureth down its black stream; even so with deep groaning he spake amid the Argives and said: "My friends, leaders and captains of the Argives, Zeus son of Kronos hath bound me with might in grievous blindness of soul; hard of heart is he, for that erewhile he promised and gave his pledge that not till I had laid waste well-walled Ilios should I depart, but now hath planned a cruel wile, and biddeth me return in

124

dishonour to Argos with the loss of many of my folk. Such meseemeth is the good pleasure of most mighty Zeus, that hath laid low the heads of many cities, yea and shall lay low; for his is highest power. So come, even as I shall bid let us all obey; let us flee with our ships to our dear native land, for now shall we never take wide-wayed Troy."

So said he, and they all held their peace and kept silence. Long time were the sons of the Achaians voiceless for grief, but at the last Diomedes of the loud war-cry spake amid them and said: "Atreides, with thee first in thy folly will I contend, where it is just, O king, even in the assembly; be not thou wroth therefor. My valour didst thou blame in chief amid the Danaans, and saidst that I was no man of war but a coward; and all this know the Argives both young and old. But the son of crooked-counselling Kronos hath endowed thee but by halves; he granted thee to have the honour of the sceptre above all men, but valour he gave thee not, wherein is highest power. Sir, deemest thou that the sons of the Achaians are thus indeed cowards and weaklings as thou sayest? If thine own heart be set on departing, go thy way; the way is before thee, and thy ships stand beside the sea, even the great multitude that followed thee from Mykene. But all the other flowing-haired Achaians will tarry here until we lay waste Troy. Nay, let them too flee on their ships to their dear native land; yet will we twain, even I and Sthenelos, fight till we attain the goal of Ilios; for in God's name are we come."

So said he, and all the sons of the Achaians shouted aloud, applauding the saying of horse-taming Diomedes. Then knightly Nestor arose and said amid them: "Tydeides, in battle art thou passing mighty, and in council art thou best among thine equals in years; none of all the Achaians will make light of thy word nor gainsay it. Now let us yield to black night and make ready our meal; and let the sentinels bestow them severally along the deep-delved foss without the wall. This charge give I to the young men; and thou, Atreides, lead then the way, for thou art the most royal. Spread thou a feast for the councillors; that is thy place and seemly for thee. Thy huts are full of wine that the ships of the Achaians bring thee by day from Thrace across the wide sea; all entertainment is for thee, being king over many. In the gathering of many shalt thou listen to him that deviseth the most excellent counsel; sore need have all the Achaians of such as is good and prudent, because hard by the ships our foemen are burning their watch-fires in multitude; what man can rejoice thereat? This night shall either destroy or save the host."

So said he, and they gladly hearkened to him and obeyed. Forth sallied the sentinels in their harness. Seven were the captains of the sentinels, and with each went fivescore young men bearing their long spears in their hands; and they took post midway betwixt foss and wall, and kindled a fire and made ready each man his meal.

Then Atreides gathered the councillors of the Achaians, and led them to his hut, and spread before them an abundant feast. So they put forth their hands to the good cheer that lay before them. And when they had put away from them the desire of meat and drink, then the old man first began to weave his counsel, even Nestor, whose rede of old time was approved the best. He spake to them and said:

"Most noble son of Atreus, Agamemnon king of men, in thy name will I end and with thy name begin, because thou art king over many hosts, and to thy hand Zeus hath entrusted sceptre and law, that thou mayest take counsel for thy folk. Thee therefore more than any it behoveth both to speak and hearken, and to accomplish what another than thou may say. No other man shall have a more excellent thought than this that I bear in mind from old time even until now, since the day when thou, O heaven-sprung king, didst go and take the damsel Briseis from angry Achilles' hut by no consent of ours. Nay, I right heartily dissuaded thee; but thou yieldedst to thy proud spirit, and dishonouredst a man of valour whom even the immortals honoured; for thou didst take and keepest from him his meed of valour. Still let us even now take thought how we may appease him and persuade him with gifts of friendship and kindly words."

And Agamemnon king of men answered and said to him: "Old sir, in no false wise hast thou accused my folly. Fool was I, I myself deny it not. Worth many hosts is he whom Zeus loveth in his heart, even as now he honoureth this man and destroyeth the host of the Achaians. But seeing I was a fool in that I yielded to my sorry passion, I will make amends and give a recompense beyond telling. In the midst of you all I will name the excellent gifts; seven tripods untouched of fire, and ten talents of gold and twenty gleaming caldrons, and twelve stalwart horses, winners in the race, that have taken prizes by their speed. No lackwealth were that man whose substance were as great as the prizes my whole-hooved steeds have borne me off. And seven women will I give, skilled in excellent handiwork, Lesbians whom I

chose me from the spoils the day that he himself took stablished Lesbos, surpassing womankind in beauty. These will
I give him, and with them shall be she whom erst I took
from him, even the daughter of Briseus. All these things
shall be set straightway before him; and if hereafter the
gods grant us to lay waste the great city of Priam, then let
him enter in when we Achaians be dividing the spoil, and
lade his ship full of gold and bronze, and himself choose
twenty Trojan women, the fairest that there be after Helen
of Argos. And if we win to the richest of lands, even Achaian Argos, he shall be my son and I will hold him in like
honour with Orestes, my stripling boy that is nurtured in all
abundance. Three daughters are mine in my well-builded
hall, Chrysothemis and Laodike and Iphianassa; let him
take of them which he will, without gifts of wooing, to
Peleus' house; and I will add a great dower such as no man
ever yet gave with his daughter. And seven well-peopled
cities will I give him, Kardamyle and Enope and grassy Hire
and holy Pherai and Antheia deep in meads, and fair Aipeia
and Pedasos land of vines. And all are nigh to the salt sea,
on the uttermost border of sandy Pylos; therein dwell men
abounding in flocks and kine, men that shall worship him
like a god with gifts, and beneath his sway fulfil his prosper-
ous ordinances. All this will I accomplish so he but cease
from wrath. Let him yield; Hades I ween is not to be
softened neither overcome, and therefore is he hatefullest of
all gods to mortals. Yea, let him be ruled by me, inasmuch
as I am more royal and avow me to be the elder in years."

Then knightly Nestor of Gerenia answered and said:
"Most noble son of Atreus, Agamemnon king of men, now

are these gifts not lightly to be esteemed that thou offerest king Achilles. Come therefore, let us speed forth picked men to go with all haste to the hut of Peleus' son Achilles. Lo now, whomsoever I appoint let them consent. First let Phoinix dear to Zeus lead the way, and after him great Aias and noble Odysseus; and for heralds let Odios and Eurybates be their companions. And now bring water for our hands, and bid keep holy silence, that we may pray unto Zeus the son of Kronos, if perchance he will have mercy upon us."

So said he, and spake words that were well-pleasing unto all. Forthwith the heralds poured water on their hands, and the young men crowned the bowls with drink and gave each man his portion after they had poured the libation in the cups. And when they had made libation and drunk as their heart desired, they issued forth from the hut of Agamemnon son of Atreus. And knightly Nestor of Gerenia gave them full charge, with many a glance to each, and chiefest to Odysseus, how they should essay to prevail on Peleus' noble son.

So the twain went along the shore of the loud-sounding sea, making instant prayer to the earth-embracer, the Shaker of the Earth, that they might with ease prevail on Aiakides' great heart. So they came to the huts and ships of the Myrmidons, and found their king taking his pleasure of a loud lyre, fair, of curious work, with a silver cross-bar upon it. Therein he was delighting his soul, and singing the glories of heroes. And over against him sate Patroklos alone in silence, watching till Aiakides should cease from singing. So the twain came forward, and noble Odysseus led the way, and they stood before his face; and Achilles sprang up amazed with the lyre in his hand, and left the seat where he was sitting, and in like manner Patroklos when he beheld the men arose. Then Achilles fleet of foot greeted them and said: "Welcome; verily ye are friends that are come—sore indeed is the need—even ye that are dearest of the Achaians to me even in my wrath."

So spake noble Achilles and led them forward, and made them sit on settles and carpets of purple; and anon he spake to Patroklos being near: "Bring forth a greater bowl, thou son of Menoitios; mingle stronger drink, and prepare each man a cup, for dearest of men are these that are under my roof."

Then put they forth their hands to the good cheer lying before them. And when they had put from them the desire of meat and drink, Aias nodded to Phoinix. But noble Odysseus marked it, and filled a cup with wine and pledged Achilles: "Hail, O Achilles! The fair feast lack we not either in the hut of Agamemnon son of Atreus neither now in thine; for feasting is there abundance to our heart's desire, but our thought is not for matters of the delicious feast; nay, we behold very sore destruction, thou fosterling of Zeus, and are afraid. Now is it in doubt whether we save the benched ships or behold them perish, if thou put not on thy might. Nigh unto ships and wall have the high-hearted Trojans and famed allies pitched their camp, and kindled many fires throughout their host, and ween that they shall no more be withheld but will fall on our black ships. And Zeus son of Kronos sheweth them signs upon the right by lightning, and Hector greatly exulteth in his might and rageth furiously, trusting in Zeus, and recketh not of god nor man, for mighty madness hath possessed him. He prayeth bright Dawn to shine forth with all speed, for he hath passed his word to smite off from the ships the ensigns' tops, and to fire the hulls with devouring flame, and hard thereby to make havoc of the Achaians confounded by the smoke. Therefore am I sore afraid in my heart lest the gods fulfil his boastings, and it be fated for us to perish here in Troy-land, far from Argos pasture-land of horses. Up then! if thou art minded even at the last to save the failing sons of the Achaians from the war-din of the Trojans. Eschew thy grievous wrath; Agamemnon offereth thee worthy gifts, so thou wilt cease from anger. Lo now, hearken thou to me, and I will tell thee all the gifts that in his hut Agamemnon promised thee. But if Agamemnon be too hateful to thy heart, both he and his gifts, yet have thou pity on all the Achaians that faint throughout the host; these shall honour thee as a god, for verily thou wilt earn exceeding great glory at their hands. Yea now mightest thou slay Hector, for he would come very near thee in his deadly madness, because he deemeth that there is no man like unto him among the Danaans that the ships brought hither."

And Achilles fleet of foot answered and said unto him: "Heaven-sprung son of Laertes, Odysseus of many wiles, in openness must I now declare unto you my saying, even as I am minded and as the fulfilment thereof shall be, that ye may not sit before me and coax this way and that. For hateful to me even as the gates of hell is he that hideth one thing in his heart and uttereth another: but I will speak what meseemeth best. Not me, I ween, shall Agamemnon son of

Atreus persuade, nor the other Danaans, seeing we were to have no thank for battling with the foemen ever without respite. He that abideth at home hath equal share with him that fighteth his best, and in like honour are held both the coward and the brave; death cometh alike to the untoiling and to him that hath toiled long. Neither have I any profit for that I endured tribulation of soul, ever staking my life in fight. Even as a hen bringeth her unfledged chickens each morsel as she winneth it, and with herself it goeth hard, even so I was wont to watch out many a sleepless night and pass through many bloody days of battle, warring with folk for their women's sake. Twelve cities of men have I laid waste from ship-board, and from land eleven, throughout deep-soil Troy-land; out of all these took I many goodly treasures and would bring and give them all to Agamemnon son of Atreus, and he staying behind amid the fleet ships would take them and portion out some few but keep the most. Now some he gave to be meeds of honour to the princes and the kings, and theirs are left untouched; only from me of all the Achaians took he my darling lady and keepeth her. But why must the Argives make war on the Trojans? why hath Atreides gathered his host and led them hither? is it not for lovely-haired Helen's sake? Do then the sons of Atreus alone of mortal men love their wives? surely whatsoever man is good and sound of mind loveth his own and cherisheth her, even as I too loved mine with all my heart, though but the captive of my spear. But now that he hath taken my meed of honour from mine arms and hath deceived me, let him not tempt me that know him full well; he shall not prevail. Nay, Odysseus, let him take counsel with thee and all the princes to ward from the ships the consuming fire. Verily without mine aid he hath wrought many things, and built a wall and dug a foss about it wide and deep, and set a palisade therein; yet even so can he not stay murderous Hector's might. But so long as I was fighting amid the Achaians, Hector had no mind to array his battle far from the wall, but scarce came unto the Skaian gates and to the oak-tree; there once he awaited me alone and scarce escaped my onset. But now, seeing I have no mind to fight with noble Hector, I will to-morrow do sacrifice to Zeus and all the gods, and store well my ships when I have launched them on the salt sea—then shalt thou see, if thou wilt and hast any care therefor, my ships sailing at break of day over Hellespont, the fishes' home, and my men right eager at the oar; and if the great Shaker of the Earth grant me good journey, on the third day should I reach deep-soiled Phthia. There are my great possessions that I left when I came hither to my hurt; and yet more gold and ruddy bronze shall I bring from hence, and fair-girdled women and grey iron, all at least that were mine by lot; only my meed of honour hath he that gave it me taken back in his despitefulness, even lord Agamemnon son of Atreus. To him declare ye everything even as I charge you, openly, that all the Achaians likewise may have indignation, if haply he hopeth to beguile yet some other Danaan, for that he is ever clothed in shamelessness. Verily not in my face would he dare to look, though he have the front of a dog. Neither will I devise counsel with him nor any enterprise, for utterly he hath deceived me and done wickedly; but never again shall he beguile me with fair speech—let this suffice him. Let him

begone in peace; Zeus the lord of counsel hath taken away
his wits. Hateful to me are his gifts, and I hold him at a
straw's worth. Not even if he gave me ten times, yea twenty,
all that now is his, and all that may come to him other-
whence, even all the revenue of Orchomenos or Egyptian
Thebes where the treasure-houses are stored fullest—Thebes
of the hundred gates, whence sally forth two hundred warriors through each with horses and chariots—nay, nor gifts
in number as sand or dust; not even so shall Agamemnon
persuade my soul till he have paid me back all the bitter
despite. And the daughter of Agamemnon son of Atreus
will I not wed, not were she rival of golden Aphrodite for
fairness and for handiwork matched bright-eyed Athene—
not even then will I wed her; let him choose him of the
Achaians another that is his peer and is more royal than I.
For if the gods indeed preserve me and I come unto my
home, then will Peleus himself seek me a wife. Many
Achaian maidens are there throughout Hellas and Phthia,
daughters of princes that ward their cities; whomsoever of
these I wish will I make my dear lady. Very often was my
high soul moved to take me there a wedded wife, a help
meet for me, and have joy of the possessions that the old
man Peleus possesseth. For not of like worth with life hold
I even all the wealth that men say was possessed of the
well-peopled city of Ilios in days of peace gone by, before
the sons of the Achaians came; neither all the treasure
that the stone threshold of the archer Phoebus Apollo
encompasseth in rocky Pytho. For kine and goodly flocks
are to be had for the harrying, and tripods and chestnut
horses for the purchasing; but to bring back man's life

neither harrying nor earning availeth when once it hath passed the barrier of his lips. For thus my goddess mother telleth me, Thetis the silver-footed, that twain fates are bearing me to the issue of death. If I abide here and besiege the Trojans' city, then my returning home is taken from me, but my fame shall be imperishable; but if I go home to my dear native land, my high fame is taken from me, but my life shall endure long while, neither shall the issue of death soon reach me. Moreover I would counsel you all to set sail homeward, seeing ye shall never reach your goal of steep Ilios; of a surety far-seeing Zeus holdeth his hand over her and her folk are of good courage. So go your way and tell my answer to the princes of the Achaians, even as is the office of elders, that they may devise in their hearts some other better counsel, such as shall save them their ships and the host of the Achaians amid the hollow ships: since this counsel availeth them naught that they have now devised, by reason of my fierce wrath. But let Phoinix now abide with us and lay him to rest, that he may follow with me on my ships to our dear native land to-morrow, if he will; for I will not take him perforce."

So spake he, and they all held their peace and were still, and marvelled at his saying; for he denied them very vehemently. But at the last spake to them the old knight Phoinix, bursting into tears, because he was sore afraid for the ships of the Achaians: "If indeed thou ponderest departure in thy heart, glorious Achilles, and hast no mind at all to save the fleet ships from consuming fire, because that wrath hath entered into thy heart; how can I be left of thee, dear son, alone thereafter? To thee did the old knight

Peleus send me the day he sent thee to Agamemnon forth from Phthia, a stripling yet unskilled in equal war and in debate wherein men wax pre-eminent. Therefore sent he me to teach thee all these things, to be both a speaker of words and a doer of deeds. Yea, I reared thee to this greatness, thou godlike Achilles, with my heart's love; for with none other wouldest thou go unto the feast, neither take meat in the hall, till that I had set thee upon my knees and stayed thee with the savoury morsel cut first for thee, and put the wine-cup to thy lips. Oft hast thou stained the doublet on my breast with sputtering of wine in thy sorry helplessness. Thus I suffered much with thee, and much I toiled, being mindful that the gods in nowise created any issue of my body; but I made thee my son, thou godlike Achilles, that thou mayest yet save me from grievous destruction. Therefore, Achilles, rule thy high spirit; neither beseemeth it thee to have a ruthless heart. Nay, even the very gods can bend, and theirs withal is loftier majesty and honour and might. Nay, come for the gifts; the Achaians shall honour thee even as a god. But if without gifts thou enter into battle the bane of men, thou wilt not be held in like honour, even though thou avert the fray."

And Achilles fleet of foot made answer and said to him: "Phoinix my father, thou old man fosterling of Zeus, such honour need I in no wise; for I deem that I have been honoured by the judgment of Zeus, which shall abide upon me amid my beaked ships as long as breath tarrieth in my body and my limbs are strong. Moreover I will say this thing to thee and lay thou it to thine heart; trouble not my

soul by weeping and lamentation, to do the pleasure of warrior Atreides; neither beseemeth it thee to cherish him, lest
thou be hated of me that cherish thee. It were good that
thou with me shouldest vex him that vexeth me. Be thou
king even as I, and share my sway by halves, but these shall
bear my message. So tarry thou here and lay thee to rest in a
soft bed, and with break of day will we consider whether to
depart unto our own, or to abide."

He spake, and nodded his brow in silence unto Patroklos
to spread for Phoinix a thick couch, that the others might
bethink them to depart from the hut with speed. Then spake
to them Aias, Telamon's godlike son, and said: "Heaven-
sprung son of Laertes, Odysseus of many wiles, let us go
hence; for methinks the purpose of our charge will not by
this journey be accomplished; and we must tell the news,
though it be no wise good, with all speed unto the Danaans,
that now sit awaiting. But Achilles hath wrought his proud
soul to fury within him—stubborn man, that recketh naught
of his comrades' love, wherein we worshipped him beyond
all men amid the ships—unmerciful! Yet doth a man accept
recompense of his brother's murderer or for his dead son;
and so the man-slayer for a great price abideth in his own
land, and the kinsman's heart is appeased, and his proud
soul, when he hath taken the recompense. But for thee, the
gods have put within thy breast a spirit implacable and evil,
by reason of one single damsel. And now we offer thee
seven damsels, far best of all, and many other gifts besides;
entertain thou then a kindly spirit, and have respect unto
thine home; because we are guests of thy roof, sent of the

multitude of Danaans, and we would fain be nearest to thee and dearest beyond all other Achaians, as many as there be."

And Achilles fleet of foot made answer and said to him: "Aias sprung of Zeus, thou son of Telamon, prince of the folk, thou seemest to speak all this almost after mine own mind; but my heart swelleth with wrath as oft as I bethink me of those things, how Atreides entreated me arrogantly among the Argives, as though I were some worthless sojourner. But go ye and declare my message; I will not take thought of bloody war until that wise Priam's son, noble Hector, come to the Myrmidons' huts and ships, slaying the Argives, and smirch the ships with fire. But about mine hut and black ship I ween that Hector, though he be very eager for battle, shall be refrained."

So said he, and they took each man a two-handled cup, and made libation and went back along the line of ships; and Odysseus led the way. And Patroklos bade his fellows and handmaidens spread with all speed a thick couch for Phoinix; and they obeyed and spread a couch as he ordained, fleeces and rugs and fine flock of linen. Then the old man laid him down and tarried for bright Dawn.

Now when those were come unto Atreides' huts, the sons of the Achaians stood up on this side and on that, and pledged them in cups of gold, and questioned them; and Agamemnon king of men asked them first: "Come now, tell me, Odysseus full of praise, thou great glory of the Achaians; will he save the ships from consuming fire, or said he nay, and hath wrath yet hold of his proud spirit?"

And steadfast goodly Odysseus answered him: "Most

noble son of Atreus, Agamemnon king of men, he yonder hath no mind to quench his wrath, but is yet more filled of fury, and spurneth thee and thy gifts. He biddeth thee take counsel for thyself amid the Argives, how to save the ships and folk of the Achaians. And for himself he threateneth that at break of day he will launch upon the sea his trim well-benched ships. Moreover he said that he would counsel all to sail for home, because ye now shall never reach your goal of steep Ilios; surely far-seeing Zeus holdeth his hand over her and her folk are of good courage. Even so said he, and here are also these to tell the tale that were my companions, Aias and the two heralds, both men discreet. But the old man Phoinix laid him there to rest, even as Achilles bade him, that he may follow with him on his ships to his dear native land to-morrow, if he will; for he will not take him perforce."

So said he, and they all held their peace and were still, marvelling at his saying, for he harangued very vehemently. Long were the sons of the Achaians voiceless for grief, but at the last Diomedes of the loud war-cry spake amid them: "Most noble son of Atreus, Agamemnon king of men, would thou hadst never besought Peleus' glorious son with offer of gifts innumerable; proud is he at any time, but now hast thou yet far more encouraged him in his haughtiness. Howbeit we will let him bide, whether he go or tarry; here-after he shall fight, whenever his heart within him biddeth and god arouseth him. Come now, even as I shall say let us all obey. Go ye now to rest, full to your hearts' desire of meat and wine, wherein courage is and strength; but when fair rosy-fingered Dawn appeareth, array thou with all speed before the ships thy folk and horsemen, and urge them on; and fight thyself amid the foremost."

So said he, and all the princes gave assent, applauding the saying of Diomedes tamer of horses. And then they made libation and went every man to his hut, and there laid them to rest and took the boon of sleep.

BOOK X

How Diomedes and Odysseus slew Dolon, a spy of the Trojans,
and themselves spied on the Trojan camp, and took the horses
of Rhesos, the Thracian king.

Now beside the ships the other leaders of the whole
Achaian host were sleeping all night long, by soft
Sleep overcome, but Agamemnon son of Atreus, shepherd
of the host, sweet Sleep held not, so many things he debated
in his mind. And even as when the lord of fair-tressed Hera
lighteneth, fashioning either a mighty rain unspeakable, or
hail, or snow, when the flakes sprinkle all the ploughed
lands, or fashioning perchance the wide mouth of bitter
war, even so oft in his breast groaned Agamemnon, from
the very deep of his heart, and his spirits trembled within
him. And whensoever he looked toward that Trojan plain,
he marvelled at the many fires that blazed in front of Ilios,
and at the sound of flutes and pipes, and the noise of men;
but whensoever to the ships he glanced and the host of the
Achaians, then rent he many a lock clean forth from his
head, to Zeus that is above, and greatly groaned his noble
heart.

And this in his soul seemed to him the best counsel, to go
first of all to Nestor son of Neleus, if perchance he might
contrive with him some right device that should be for the
warding off of evil from all the Danaans.

Then he rose, and did on his doublet about his breast, and

beneath his shining feet he bound on fair sandals, and thereafter clad him in the tawny skin of a lion fiery and great, a skin that reached to the feet, and he grasped his spear.

And even in like wise did trembling fear take hold on Menelaos, (for neither on his eyelids did Sleep settle down,) lest somewhat should befall the Argives, who verily for his sake over wide waters were come to Troy-land, with fierce war in their thoughts.

With a dappled pard's skin first he covered his broad shoulders, and he raised and set on his head a casque of bronze, and took a spear in his strong hand. Then went he on his way to rouse his brother, that mightily ruled over all the Argives, and as a god was honoured by the people. Him found he harnessing his goodly gear about his shoulders, by the stern of the ship, and glad to his brother was his coming. Then Menelaos of the loud war-cry first accosted him: "Wherefore thus, dear brother, art thou arming? Wilt thou speed forth any of thy comrades to spy on the Trojans? Nay, terribly I fear lest none should undertake for thee this deed, even to go and spy out the foeman alone through the ambrosial night; needs must he be a man right hardy of heart."

The the lord Agamemnon answered him and spake: "Need of good counsel have I and thou, Menelaos fosterling of Zeus, of counsel that will help and save the Argives and the ships, since the heart of Zeus hath turned again. Surely on the sacrifices of Hector hath he set his heart rather than on ours. For never did I see, nor heard any tell, that one man devised so many terrible deeds in one day, as Hector, dear to Zeus, hath wrought on the sons of the Achaians, unaided; though no dear son of a goddess is he, nor of a god. He hath done deeds that methinks will be a sorrow to the Argives, lasting and long, such evils hath he devised against the Achaians. But go now, run swiftly by the ships, and summon Aias and Idomeneus, but I will betake me to noble Nestor, and bid him arise, if perchance he will be fain to go to the sacred company of the sentinels and lay on them his command. For to him above others would they listen, for his own son is chief among the sentinels, he and the brother in arms of Idomeneus, even Meriones, for to them above all we entrusted this charge."

Then Menelaos of the loud war-cry answered him: "How meanest thou this word wherewith thou dost command and exhort me? Am I to abide there with them, waiting till thou comest, or run back again to thee when I have well delivered to them thy commandment?"

Then the king of men, Agamemnon, answered him again: "There do thou abide lest we miss each other as we go, for many are the paths through the camp. But call aloud, wheresoever thou goest, and bid men awake, naming each man by his lineage, and his father's name, and giving all their dues of honour, nor be thou proud of heart. Nay rather let us ourselves be labouring, for even thus did Zeus from our very birth dispense to us the heaviness of toil."

So he spake, and sent his brother away, having clearly laid on him his commandment. Then went he himself after Nestor, the shepherd of the host, whom he found by his hut and black ship, in his soft bed: beside him lay his arms, a shield, and two spears, and a shining helmet. Beside him lay his glittering girdle wherewith the old man was wont to gird himself when he harnessed him for war, the bane of men, and led on the host, for he yielded not to grievous old age. Then he raised him on his elbow, lifting his head, and spake to the son of Atreus, inquiring of him with this word: "Who are thou that farest alone by the ships, through the camp in the dark night, when other mortals are sleeping? Seekest thou one of thy mules, or of thy comrades? speak, and come not silently upon me. What need hast thou?"

Then the king of men, Agamemnon, answered him: "O Nestor, son of Neleus, great glory of the Achaians, thou shalt know Agamemnon, son of Atreus, whom above all men Zeus hath planted for ever among labours, while my breath abides within my breast, and my knees move. I wander thus, for that sweet sleep rests not on mine eyes, but war is my care, and the troubles of the Achaians. Yea, greatly I fear for the sake of the Danaans, nor is my heart firm, but I am tossed to and fro, and my heart is leaping from my breast, and my good knees tremble beneath me. But if thou wilt do aught, since neither on thee cometh sleep, let us go thither to the sentinels, that we may see them, lest they be fordone with toil, and so are slumbering, and have quite forgotten to keep watch. And hostile men camp hard by, nor know we at all but that they are keen to do battle in the night."

Then knightly Nestor of Gerenia answered him: "Verily will I follow after thee, but let us also rouse others again, both the son of Tydeus, spearman renowned, and Odysseus, and swift Aias, and the strong son of Phyleus. But well it would be if one were to go and call those also, the godlike Aias, and Idomeneus the prince; for their ships are furthest of all, and nowise close at hand. But Menelaos will I blame, dear as he is and worshipful, yea, even if thou be angry with me, nor will I hide my thought, for that he slumbereth, and to thee alone hath left the toil; now should he be toiling among all the chiefs and beseeching them, for need no longer tolerable is coming upon us."

And the king of men, Agamemnon, answered him again: "Old man, another day I even bid thee blame him, for often is he slack, and willeth not to labour, yielding neither to unreadiness nor heedlessness of heart, but looking toward me, and expecting mine instance. But now he awoke far before me, and came to me, and him I sent forward to call those concerning whom thou inquirest. But let us be gone, and them shall we find before the gates, among the sentinels, for there I bade them gather."

Then knightly Nestor of Gerenia answered him: "So will none of the Argives be wroth with him or disobey him, when soever he doth urge any one, and give him his commands."

So spake he, and did on his doublet about his breast, and beneath his bright feet he bound goodly shoon, and all around him buckled a purple cloak, with double folds and wide, and thick down all over it.

And he took a strong spear, pointed with sharp bronze, and he went among the ships of the mail-clad Achaians. Then Odysseus first, the peer of Zeus in counsel, did knightly Gerenian Nestor arouse out of sleep, with his voice, and quickly the cry came all about his heart, and he came forth from the hut and spake to them saying: "Wherefore thus among the ships and through the camp do ye wander alone, in the ambrosial night; what so great need cometh upon you?"

Then knightly Nestor of Gerenia answered him: "Laertes' son, be not wroth, for great trouble besetteth the Achaians. Nay follow, that we may arouse others too, even all that it behoveth to take counsel, whether we should fly, or fight."

So spake he, and Odysseus of the many counsels came to the hut, and cast a shield about his shoulders, and went after them.

And they went to seek Diomedes, son of Tydeus, and him they found outside his hut, with his arms, and around him his comrades were sleeping with their shields beneath their heads, but their spears were driven into the ground erect on the spikes of the butts, and afar shone the bronze, like the lightning of father Zeus. Now that hero was asleep, and under him was strewn the hide of an ox of the field, but beneath his head was stretched a shining carpet. Beside him went and stood knightly Nestor of Gerenia and stirred him with a touch of his foot, and aroused him, chiding him to his face, saying: "Wake, son of Tydeus, why all night long dost thou sleep? Knowest thou not that the Trojans on the high place of the plain are camped near the ships, and but a little space holdeth them apart?"

So spake he, and Diomedes sprang swiftly up out of sleep, and spake to him winged words: "Hard art thou, old man, and from toil thou never ceasest. Now are there not other younger sons of the Achaians, who might rouse when there is need each of the kings, going all around the host? but thou, old man, art indomitable."

And him knightly Nestor of Gerenia answered again,

"Nay verily, my son, all this that thou sayest is according unto right. Noble sons have I, and there be many of the host, of whom each man might go and call the others. But a right great need hath assailed the Achaians. For now to all of us it standeth on a razor's edge, either pitiful ruin for the Achaians, or life. But come now, if indeed thou dost pity me, rouse swift Aias, and the son of Phyleus, for thou art younger than I."

So spake he, and Diomedes cast round his shoulders the skin of a great fiery lion, that reached to his feet, and he grasped his spear, and started on his way, and roused the others from their place and led them on.

Now when they had come among the assembled sentinels, they found not the leaders of the sentinels asleep, but they all sat wide awake with their arms. And even as hounds keep difficult guard round the sheep in a fold, having heard a hardy wild beast that cometh through the wood among the hills, and much clamour riseth round him of hounds and men, and sleep perisheth from them, even so sweet sleep did perish from their eyes, as they watched through the wicked night, for ever were they turning toward the plains, when they heard the Trojans moving.

And that old man was glad when he saw them, and heartened them with his saying, and calling out to them he spake winged words: "Even so now, dear children, do ye keep watch, nor let sleep take any man, lest we become a cause of rejoicing to them that hate us."

So saying he sped through the moat, and they followed with him, the kings of the Argives, who had been called to the council. And with them went Meriones, and the glorious son of Nestor, for they called them to share their counsel. So they went clean out of the delved foss, and sat down in the open, where the mid-space was clear of dead men fallen, where fierce Hector had turned again from destroying the Argives, when night covered all. There sat they down, and declared their saying each to the other, and to them knightly Nestor of Gerenia began discourse: "O friends, is there then no man that would trust to his own daring spirit, to go among the great-hearted Trojans, if perchance he might take some straggler of the enemy, yea, or hear perchance some rumour among the Trojans, and what things they devise among themselves, whether they are fain to abide there by the ships, away from the city, or will retreat again to the city, now that they have conquered the Achaians? All this might such an one learn, and back to us come scatheless: great would be his fame under heaven among all men, and a goodly gift will be given him. For all the best men that bear sway by the ships, each and all of them will give him a black ewe, with her lamb at her foot, and ever will he be present at feasts and clan-drinkings."

So spake he, and thereon were they all silent, holding their peace, but to them spake Diomedes of the loud war-cry: "Nestor, my heart and manful spirit urge me to enter the camp of the foemen hard by, even of the Trojans: and if some other man will follow with me, more comfort and more courage will there be. If two go together, one before another perceiveth a matter, how there may be gain therein; but if one alone perceive aught, even so his wit is shorter, and weak his device."

So spake he, and many were they that wished to follow

Diomedes. The two Aiantes were willing, men of Ares' company, and Meriones was willing, and right willing the son of Nestor, and the son of Atreus, Menelaos, spearman renowned, yea and the hardy Odysseus was willing to steal into the throng of Trojans, for always daring was his heart within him. But among them spake the king of men, Agamemnon: "Diomedes son of Tydeus, joy of mine heart, thy comrade verily shalt thou choose, whomsoever thou wilt, the best of them that be here, for many are eager. But do not thou, out of reverent heart, leave the better man behind, and give thyself the worse companion, yielding to regard for any, and looking to their lineage, even if one be more kingly born."

So spake he, but was in fear for the sake of fair-haired Menelaos. But to them again answered Diomedes of the loud war-cry: "If indeed ye bid me choose myself a comrade, how then could I be unmindful of godlike Odysseus, whose heart is passing eager, and his spirit so manful in all manner of toils; and Athene loveth him. But while he cometh with me, even out of burning fire might we both return, for he excelleth in understanding."

Then him again answered the steadfast noble Odysseus: "Son of Tydeus, praise me not overmuch, neither blame me aught, for thou speakest thus among the Argives that themselves know all. But let us be going, for truly the night is waning, and near is the dawn, and the stars have gone onward, and the night has advanced more than two watches, but the third watch is yet left."

So spake they, and harnessed them in their dread armour. To the son of Tydeus did Thrasymedes steadfast in war give a two-edged sword (for his own was left by his ship) and a shield, and about his head set a helm of bull's hide, without cone or crest, that is called a skull-cap, and keeps the heads of stalwart youths. And Meriones gave Odysseus a bow and a quiver, and a sword, and on his head set a helm made of leather, and with many a thong was it stiffly wrought within, while without the white teeth of a boar of flashing tusks were arrayed thick set on either side, well and cunningly, and in the midst was fixed a cap of felt.

So when these twain had harnessed them in their dread armour, they set forth to go, and left there all the best of the host. And to them did Pallas Athene send forth an omen on the right, a heron hard by the way, and they beheld it not with their eyes, through the dark night, but they heard its shrill cry. And Odysseus was glad in the omen of the bird, and prayed to Athene: "Listen to me, thou child of aegis-bearing Zeus, that ever in all toils dost stand by me, nor doth any motion of mine escape thee: but now again above all be thou friendly to me, Athene, and grant that we come back with renown to the ships, having wrought a great work, that shall be sorrow to the Trojans."

Next again prayed Diomedes of the loud war-cry: "Listen now likewise to me, thou child of Zeus, unwearied maiden, and follow with me as when with my father thou didst follow, even noble Tydeus, into Thebes, when he went forth as a messenger from the Achaians. Even so now stand thou by me willingly, and protect me. And to thee will I sacrifice a yearling heifer, broad of brow, unbroken, that never yet hath man led below the yoke. Her will I sacrifice to thee, and gild her horns with gold."

So spake they in their prayer, and Pallas Athene heard them. And when they had prayed to the daughter of mighty Zeus, they went forth on their way, like two lions, through the dark night, amid the slaughter, amid the slain men, through the arms and the black blood.

Nay, nor the stout-hearted Trojans did Hector suffer to sleep, but he called together all the best of them, all that were chiefs and leaders of the Trojans, them did he call together, and contrived a crafty counsel: "Who is there that would promise and perform for me this deed, for a great gift? yea his reward shall be sufficient. For I will give him a chariot, and two horses of arching neck, the best that be at the swift ships of the Achaians, to whosoever shall dare the deed, and for himself shall win glory. And the deed is this; to go near the swift-faring ships, and seek out whether the swift ships are guarded, as of old, or whether already, being subdued beneath our hands, the foes are devising of flight among themselves, and have no care to watch through the night, being fordone with dread weariness."

So spake he, but they were all silent and held their peace. Now there was among the Trojans one Dolon, the son of Eumedes the godlike herald, and he was rich in gold, and rich in bronze: and verily he was ill favoured to look upon, but swift of foot. So he spake then a word to the Trojans and to Hector: "Hector, my heart and manful spirit urge me to go near the swift-faring ships, and spy out all. But come, I pray thee, hold up the staff, and swear to me, that verily thou wilt give me the horses and the chariots bedight with bronze that bear the noble son of Peleus. But to thee I will prove no vain spy, nor disappoint thy hope. For I will go straight to the camp, until I may come to the ship of Agamemnon, where surely the chiefs are like to hold council, whether to fight or flee."

So spake he, and Hector took the staff in his hand, and sware to him: "Now let Zeus himself be witness, the loud-thundering lord of Hera, that no other man of the Trojans shall mount those horses, but thou, I declare, shalt rejoice in them for ever."

So spake he, and sware a bootless oath thereto, and aroused Dolon to go. And straightway he cast on his shoulders his crooked bow, and did on thereover the skin of a grey wolf, and on his head a helm of ferret-skin, and took a sharp javelin, and went on his way to the ships from the host. But he was not like to come back from the ships and bring word to Hector.

But when he had left the throng of men and horses, he went forth eagerly on the way, and Odysseus of the seed of Zeus was ware of him as he approached, and said unto Diomedes: "Lo, here is some man, Diomedes, coming from the camp, I know not whether as a spy to our ships, or to strip certain of the dead men fallen. But let us suffer him to pass by us a little way on the plain, and thereafter may we rush on him and take him speedily, and if it chance that he outrun us by speed of foot, ever do thou hem him in towards the ships and away from the camp, rushing on him with thy spear, lest in any wise he escape towards the city."

So they spake, and turning out of the path they lay down among the bodies of the dead; and swiftly Dolon ran past them in his witlessness. But when he was as far off as is the length of the furrow made by mules, these twain ran after him, and he stood still when he heard the sound, supposing in his heart that they were friends come from among the Trojans to turn him back, at the countermand of Hector. But when they were about a spear-cast off, or even less, he knew them for foemen, and stirred his swift limbs to fly, and speedily they started in pursuit.

And as when two sharp-toothed hounds, well skilled in the chase, press ever hard on a doe or a hare through a wooded land, and it runs screaming before them, even so Tydeus' son and Odysseus the sacker of cities cut Dolon off from the host, and ever pursued hard after him. But when he was just about to come among the sentinels, in his flight towards the ships, then Athene poured strength into the son of Tydeus, that none of the mail-clad Achaians might boast himself the first to smite, and he come second. And strong Diomedes leaped upon him with the spear, and said: "Stand, or I shall overtake thee with the spear, and methinks that thou shalt not long avoid sheer destruction at my hand."

So spake he, and threw his spear, but of his own will he missed the man, and passing over his right shoulder the point of the polished spear stuck fast in the ground: and Dolon stood still in great dread and trembling, and the teeth chattered in his mouth, and he was green with fear. Then the twain came up with him, panting, and gripped his hands, and weeping he spake: "Take me alive, and I will ransom myself, for within our house there is bronze, and gold, and smithied iron, wherefrom my father would do you grace with ransom untold, if he should learn that I am alive among the ships of the Achaians."

Then Odysseus of the many counsels answered him and said: "Take courage, let not death be in thy mind, but come speak and tell me truly all the tale, why thus from the host dost thou come all alone among the ships, through the black night, when other mortals are sleeping? Comest thou to strip certain of the dead men fallen, or did Hector send thee forth to spy out everything at the hollow ships, or did thine own spirit urge thee on?"

Then Dolon answered him, his limbs trembling beneath him: "With many a blind hope did Hector lead my wits astray, who vowed to give me the whole-hooved horses of the proud son of Peleus, and his car bedight with bronze: and he bade me fare through the swift black night, and draw nigh the foemen, and seek out whether the swift ships are guarded, as of old, or whether, already, being subdued beneath our hands, they are devising of flight among themselves, and have no care to watch through the night, being fordone with dread weariness."

And smiling thereat did Odysseus of the many counsels make him answer: "Verily now thy soul was set on great rewards, even the horses of the wise son of Aiakos, but hard are they for mortal men to master, and hard to drive, for any but Achilles only, whom a deathless mother bare. But come, tell me all this truly, all the tale: where when thou camest hither didst thou leave Hector, shepherd of the host, and where lie his war-like gear, and where his horses? And how are disposed the watches, and the beds of the other Trojans? And what counsel take they among themselves; are they fain to abide there nigh the ships afar from the city, or will they return to the city again, seeing that they have subdued unto them the Achaians?"

Then Dolon son of Eumedes made him answer again: "Lo, now all these things will I recount to thee most truly. Hector with them that are counsellors holdeth council by the barrow of godlike Ilos, apart from the din, but as for the guards whereof thou askest, oh hero, no chosen watch nor guard keepeth the host. As for all the watch fires of the Trojans—on them is necessity, so that they watch and encourage each other to keep guard; but, for the allies called from many lands, they are sleeping and to the Trojans they leave it to keep watch, for no wise near dwell the children and wives of the allies."

Then Odysseus of the many counsels answered him and said: "How stands it now, do they sleep amidst the horse-taming Trojans, or apart? tell me clearly, that I may know."

Then answered him Dolon son of Eumedes: "Verily all this likewise will I recount to thee truly. Towards the sea lie the Karians, and Paionians of the bended bow, and the Leleges and Kaukones, and noble Pelasgoi. And towards Thymbre the Lykians have their place, and the haughty Mysians, and the Phrygians that fight from chariots, and Maionians lords of chariots. But wherefore do ye inquire of me throughly concerning all these things? for if ye desire to steal into the throng of Trojans, lo, there be those Thracians, new comers, at the furthest point apart from the rest, and among them their king Rhesos, son of Eïoneus. His be the fairest horses that ever I beheld, and the greatest, whiter than snow, and for speed like the winds. And his chariot is fashioned well with gold and silver, and golden is his armour that he brought with him, marvellous, a wonder to behold; such as it is in no wise fit for mortal men to bear, but for the deathless gods. But bring me now to the swift ships, or leave me here, when ye have bound me with a ruthless bond, that ye may go and make trial of me whether I have spoken to you truth, or lies."

Then strong Diomedes, looking grimly on him, said: "Put no thought of escape, Dolon, in thy heart, for all the good tidings thou hast brought, since once thou hast come into our hands. For if now we release thee or let thee go, on some later day wilt thou come to the swift ships of the Achaians, either to play the spy, or to fight in open war, but if subdued beneath my hands thou lose thy life, never again wilt thou prove a bane to the Argives."

He spake, and that other with strong hand was about to touch his chin, and implore his mercy, but Diomedes smote him on the midst of the neck, rushing on him with the sword, and cut through both the sinews, and the head of him still speaking was mingled with the dust. And they stripped him of the casque of ferret's skin from off his head, and of his wolfskin, and his bended bow, and his long spear, and these to Athene the Giver of Spoil did noble Odysseus hold aloft in his hand, and he prayed and spake a word: "Rejoice, O goddess, in these, for to thee first of all the immortals in Olympus will we call for aid; nay, but yet again send us on against the horses and the sleeping places of the Thracian men."

So spake he aloud, and lifted from him the spoils on high, and set them on a tamarisk bush, and raised thereon a mark right plain to see, gathering together reeds, and luxuriant shoots of tamarisk, lest they should miss the place as they returned again through the swift dark night.

So the twain went forward through the arms, and the black blood, and quickly they came to the company of Thracian men. Now they were slumbering, fordone with toil, but their goodly weapons lay by them on the ground, all orderly, in three rows, and by each man his pair of steeds. And Rhesos slept in the midst, and beside him his swift horses were bound with thongs to the topmost rim of the chariot. Him Odysseus spied from afar, and showed him unto Diomedes: "Lo, Diomedes, this is the man, and these are the horses whereof Dolon that we slew did give us tidings. But come now, put forth thy great strength; it doth not behove thee to stand idle with thy weapons: nay, loose the horses; or do thou slay the men, and of the horses will I take heed."

So spake he, and into that other bright-eyed Athene breathed might, and he began slaying on this side and on that, and hideously went up their groaning, as they were smitten with the sword, and the earth was reddened with blood. And like as a lion cometh on flocks without a herds-man, on goats or sheep, and leaps upon them with evil will, so set the son of Tydeus on the men of Thrace, till he had slain twelve. But whomsoever the son of Tydeus drew near and smote with the sword, him did Odysseus of the many counsels seize by the foot from behind, and drag him out of the way, with this design in his heart, that the fair-maned horses might lightly issue forth, and not tremble in spirit, when they trod over the dead; for they were not yet used to dead men. But when the son of Tydeus came upon the king, he was the thirteenth from whom he took sweet life away, as he was breathing hard, for an evil dream stood above his head that night through the device of Athene. Meanwhile the hardy Odysseus loosed the whole-hooved horses, and bound them together with thongs, and drave them out of the press, smiting them with his bow, since he had not taken thought to lift the shining whip with his hands from the chariot: then he whistled for a sign to noble Diomedes.

But Diomedes stood and pondered what most daring deed he might do, whether he should take the chariot, where lay the armour, and drag it out by the pole, or lift it upon high, and so bear it forth, or whether he should take the life away from yet more of the Thracians. And while he was pondering this in his heart, then Athene drew near, and stood, and spake to noble Diomedes: "Bethink thee of returning, O son of great-hearted Tydeus, to the hollow ships, lest perchance thou come thither in flight, and perchance another god rouse up the Trojans likewise."

So spake she, and he observed the voice of the utterance of the goddess, and swiftly he sprang upon the steeds, and Odysseus smote them with his bow, and they sped to the swift ships of the Achaians.

Nay, nor a vain watch kept Apollo of the silver bow, when he beheld Athene caring for the son of Tydeus; in wrath against her he stole among the crowded press of Trojans, and aroused a counsellor of the Thracians, Hippokoon, the noble kinsman of Rhesos. And he started out of sleep, when he beheld the place desolate where the swift horses had stood, and beheld the men gasping in the death struggle; then he groaned aloud, and called out by name to his comrade dear. And a clamour arose and din unspeakable of the Trojans hasting together, and they marvelled at the terrible deeds, even all that the heroes had wrought, and had gone thereafter to the hollow ships.

But when those others came to the place where they had slain the spy of Hector, there Odysseus, dear to Zeus, checked the swift horses, and Tydeus' son, leaping to the ground, set the bloody spoil in the hands of Odysseus, and again mounted, and lashed the horses, and they sped onward nothing loth. But Nestor first heard the sound, and said: "O friends, leaders and counsellors of the Argives, shall I be wrong to speak sooth? for my heart bids me speak. The sound of swift-footed horses strikes upon mine ears. Would to god that Odysseus and that strong Diomedes may even instantly be driving the whole-hooved horses from among the Trojans; but terribly I fear in mine heart lest the bravest of the Argives suffer aught through the Trojans' battle din."

Not yet was his whole word spoken, when they came themselves, and leaped down to earth, but gladly the others welcomed them with hand-clasping, and with honeyed words. And first did knightly Nestor of Gerenia make question: "Come, tell me now, renowned Odysseus, great glory of the Achaians, how ye twain took those horses? Was it by stealing into the press of Trojans? Or did some god meet you, and give you them? Wondrous like are they to rays of the sun. Ever with the Trojans do I mix in fight, nor methinks do I tarry by the ships, old warrior as I am. But never yet saw I such horses, nor deemed of such. Nay, methinks some god must have encountered you and given you these. For both of you doth Zeus the cloud-gatherer love, and the maiden of aegis-bearing Zeus, bright-eyed Athene."

And him answered Odysseus of the many counsels: "O Nestor, son of Neleus, great glory of the Achaians, lightly could a god, if so he would, give even better steeds than these, for the gods are far stronger than we. But as for these new-come horses, whereof, old man, thou askest me, they are Thracian, but their lord did brave Diomedes slay, and beside him all the twelve best men of his company. The thirteenth man was a spy we took near the ships, one that Hector and the other haughty Trojans sent forth to pry upon our camp."

So spake he, and drave the whole-hooved horses through the foss, laughing; and the other Achaians went with him joyfully. But when they had come to the well-built hut of the son of Tydeus, they bound the horses with well-cut thongs, at the mangers where the swift horses of Diomedes stood eating honey-sweet barley.

And Odysseus placed the bloody spoils of Dolon in the stern of the ship, that they might make ready a sacred offering to Athene. But for themselves, they went into the sea, and washed off the thick sweat from shins, and neck, and thighs. But when the wave of the sea had washed the thick sweat from their skin, and their hearts revived again, they went into polished baths, and were cleansed.

And when they had washed, and anointed them with olive oil, they sat down at supper, and from the full mixing bowl they drew off the honey-sweet wine, and poured it forth to Athene.

BOOK XI

Despite the glorious deeds of Agamemnon, the Trojans press
hard on the Achaians, and the beginning of evil comes on
Patroklos.

Now Dawn arose from her couch beside proud Titho-
nos, to bring light to the immortals and to mortal
men. But Zeus sent forth fierce Discord unto the fleet ships
of the Achaians, and in her hands she held the signal of
war. And she stood upon the huge black ship of Odysseus,
that was in the midst, to make her voice heard on either
side, both to the huts of Aias, son of Telamon, and to the
huts of Achilles, for these twain, trusting in their valour
and the might of their hands, had drawn up their trim ships
at the two ends of the line. There stood the goddess and
cried shrilly in a great voice and terrible, and mighty
strength she set in the heart of each of the Achaians, to war
and fight unceasingly. And straightway to them war grew
sweeter than to depart in the hollow ships to their dear native land.

Then each man gave in charge his horses to his charioteer, to hold them in by the foss, well and orderly, and
themselves as heavy men at arms were hasting about, being
harnessed in their gear, and unquenchable the cry arose into
the Dawn. And long before the charioteers were they arrayed at the foss, but after them a little way came up the

drivers. And among them the son of Kronos aroused an evil din, and from above rained down dew danked with blood out of the upper air, for that he was about to send many strong men down to Hades.

But the Trojans on the other side, on the high ground of the plain, gathered them around great Hector, and noble Polydamus, and Aineias that as a god was honoured by the people of the Trojans, and the three sons of Antenor, Polybos, and noble Agenor, and young Akamas like unto the immortals. And Hector in the foremost rank bare the circle of his shield. And as from amid the clouds appeareth glittering a baneful star, and then again sinketh within the shadowy clouds, even so Hector would now appear among the foremost ranks, and again would be giving command in the rear, and all in bronze he shone, like the lightning of aegis-bearing father Zeus.

And even as when reapers over against each other drive their swaths through a rich man's field of wheat or barley, and thick fall the handfuls, even so the Trojans and Achaians leaped upon each other, destroying, and neither side took thought of ruinous flight; and equal heads had the battle, and they rushed on like wolves. And woful Discord was glad at the sight, for she alone of the gods was with them in the war; for the other gods were not beside them, but in peace they sat within their halls, where the goodly mansion of each was builded in the folds of Olympus. And they all were blaming the son of Kronos, lord of the storm-cloud, for that he willed to give glory to the Trojans. But of them took the father no heed, but aloof from the others he sat apart, glad in his glory, looking toward the city of the

Trojans, and the ships of the Achaians, and the glitter of bronze, and the slayers and the slain.

So long as morning was, and the sacred day still waxed, so long did the shafts of both hosts strike, and the folk fell, but about the hour when a woodman maketh ready his meal, in the dells of a mountain, when he hath tired his hands with felling tall trees, and weariness cometh on his soul, and desire of sweet food taketh his heart, even then the Danaans by their valour brake the battalions, and called on their comrades through the lines. And in rushed Agamemnon first of all, where thickest clashed the battalions, there he set on, and with him all the well-greaved Achaians. Footmen kept slaying footmen as they were driven in flight, and horsemen slaying horsemen with the sword, and from beneath them rose up the dust from the plain, stirred by the thundering hooves of horses. And the lord Agamemnon, ever slaying, followed after, calling on the Argives. And as when ruinous fire falleth on dense woodland, and the whirling wind beareth it everywhere, and the thickets fall utterly before it, being smitten by the onset of the fire, even so beneath Agamemnon son of Atreus fell the heads of the Trojans as they fled; and many strongnecked horses rattled empty cars along the highways of the battle, lacking their noble charioteers; but they on the earth were lying, far more dear to the vultures than to their wives.

But Hector did Zeus draw forth from the darts and the dust, from the man-slaying, and the blood, and the din, and the son of Atreus followed on, crying eagerly to the Danaans. And past the tomb of ancient Ilos, son of Dardanos, across the mid plain, past the place of the wild fig-tree they

sped, making for the city, and ever the son of Atreus followed shouting, and his invincible hands were defiled with
gore. But when they were come to the Skaian gates, and the
oak-tree, there then they halted, and awaited each other.
But some were still in full flight through the mid plain, like
kine that a lion hath scattered, coming on them in the dead
of night; all hath he scattered, but to one sheer death appeareth instantly, and he breaketh her neck first, seizing her
with strong teeth, and thereafter swalloweth greedily the
blood and all the guts; even so lord Agamemnon son of
Atreus followed hard on the Trojans, ever slaying the hindmost man, and they were scattered in flight, and on face or
back many of them fell from their chariots beneath the
hands of Agamemnon, for mightily he raged with the spear.
But when he was nowabout coming below the city, and the
steep wall, then did the father of men and gods sit him down
on the crests of many-fountained Ida, from heaven descend-
ing, with the thunderbolt in his hands.

Then sent he forth Iris of the golden wings, to bear his
word: "Up and go, swift Iris, and tell this word unto Hector: So long as he sees Agamemnon, shepherd of the host,
raging among the foremost fighters, and ruining the ranks
of men, so long let him hold back, but bid the rest of the
host war with the foe in strong battle. But when, or smitten
with the spear or wounded with arrow shot, Agamemnon
leapeth into his chariot, then will I give Hector strength to
slay till he come even to the well-timbered ships, and the sun
go down, and sacred darkness draw on."

So swift-footed Iris spake to Hector the words of Zeus

and departed, but Hector with his harness leaped from the chariot to the ground, and, shaking his sharp spears went through all the host, stirring up his men to fight, and he roused the dread din of battle. And they wheeled round, and stood and faced the Achaians, while the Argives on the other side strengthened their battalions. And battle was made ready, and they stood over against each other, and Agamemnon first rushed in, being eager to fight far in front of all.

Tell me now, ye Muses that inhabit mansions in Olympus, who was he that first encountered Agamemnon, whether of the Trojans themselves, or of their allies renowned? It was Iphidamas, son of Antenor, great and mighty, who was nurtured in Thrace rich of soil, the mother of sheep; he it was that then encountered Agamemnon son of Atreus. And when they were come near in onset against each other, Atreus' son missed, and his spear was turned aside, but Iphidamas smote him on the girdle, below the corslet, and himself pressed on, trusting to his heavy hand, but pierced not the gleaming girdle, for long ere that the point struck on the silver, and was bent like lead. Then wide-ruling Agamemnon caught the spear with his hand and drew it toward him furiously, like a lion, and snatched it out of the hand of Iphidamas, and smote his neck with the sword, and unstrung his limbs. So even there he fell, and slept a sleep of bronze most piteously. Then did Agamemnon son of Atreus strip him, and went bearing his goodly harness into the throng of the Achaians.

Now when Koön beheld him, Koön Antenor's eldest son,

illustrious among men, strong sorrow came on him, covering his eyes, for his brother's fall: and he stood on one side with his spear, and unmarked of noble Agamemnon smote him on the mid-arm, beneath the elbow, and clean through went the point of the shining spear. Then Agamemnon king of men shuddered, yet not even so did he cease from battle and war, but rushed against Koön, grasping his wind-nurtured spear. Verily then Koön seized right lustily by the foot Iphidamas, his brother, and his father's son, and called to all the best of his men; but him, as he dragged the dead through the press, beneath his bossy shield Agamemnon wounded with a bronze-shod spear, and unstrung his limbs, and drew near and cut off his head over Iphidamas. There the sons of Antenor, at the hands of Agamemnon the king, filled up the measure of their fate, and went down within the house of Hades.

But Agamemnon ranged among the ranks of men, with spear, and sword, and great stones for throwing, while yet the blood welled warm from his wound. But when the wound waxed dry, and the blood ceased to flow, then keen pangs came on the might of the son of Atreus. Then leaped he into his chariot, and bade his charioteer drive to the hollow ships, for he was sore vexed at heart. And he called in a piercing voice, and shouted to the Danaans: "O friends, leaders and counsellors of the Argives, do ye now ward from the seafaring ships the harsh din of battle, for Zeus the counsellor suffers me not all day to war with the Trojans."

So spake he, and his charioteer lashed the fair-maned steeds toward the hollow ships, and they flew onward nothing loth, and their breasts were covered with foam, and their bellies were stained with dust, as they bore the wounded king away from the war.

But Hector, when he beheld Agamemnon departed, cried to the Trojans and Lykians with a loud shout: "Ye Trojans and Lykians, and Dardanians that war in close fight, be men, my friends, and be mindful of your impetuous valour. The best man of them hath departed and to me hath Zeus, the son of Kronos, given great renown. But straightway drive ye the whole-hooved horses against the mighty Danaans, that ye may be the masters and bear away the higher glory."

So spake he, and aroused the might and spirit of every man. Himself with high thoughts he fared among the foremost, and fell upon the fight, like a roaring blast, that leapeth down and stirreth the violet-coloured deep. There whom first, whom last did he slay, even Hector, son of Priam, when Zeus vouchsafed him renown?

Asaios first, and Autonoos, and Opites, and Dolops, son of Klytios, and Opheltios, and Agelaos, and Aisymnos, and Oros, and Hipponoos steadfast in the fight; these leaders of the Danaans he slew, and thereafter smote the multitude, even as when the West Wind driveth the clouds of the white South Wind, smiting with deep storm, and the wave swelleth huge, rolling onward, and the spray is scattered on high beneath the rush of the wandering wind; even so many heads of the host were smitten by Hector.

There had ruin begun, and deeds remediless been wrought, and now would all the Achaians have fled and fallen among the ships, if Odysseus had not called to Diomedes, son of Tydeus: "Tydeus' son, what ails us that we forget our impetuous valour? Nay, come hither, friend, and take thy stand by me, for verily it will be shame if Hector of the glancing helm take the ships."

And to him strong Diomedes spake in answer: "Verily will I abide and endure, but short will be all our profit, for Zeus, the cloud-gatherer, clearly desireth to give victory to the Trojans rather than to us."

He spake, and drave Thymbraios from his chariot to the ground, smiting him with the spear in the left breast, and Odysseus smote Molion the godlike squire of that prince. These then they let be, when they had made them cease from war, and then the twain fared through the crowd with a din, as when two boars full of valour fall on the hunting hounds; so rushed they on again, and slew the Trojans, while gladly the Achaians took breath again in their flight from noble Hector.

But Hector quickly spied them among the ranks, and rushed upon them shouting, and with him followed the battalions of the Trojans. And beholding him, Diomedes of the loud war-cry shuddered, and straightway spake to Odysseus that was hard by: "Lo, on us this ruin, even mighty Hector, is rolling: let us stand, and await him, and ward off his onset."

So spake he, and swayed and sent forth his far-shadowing spear, and smote him nor missed, for he aimed at the head, on the summit of the crest, and bronze by bronze was turned, nor reached his fair flesh, for it was stopped by the threefold helm with its socket, that Phoebus Apollo to Hector gave. But Hector sprang back a wondrous way, and mingled with the throng, and he rested, fallen on his knee, and leaned on the ground with his stout hand, and dark night veiled his eyes.

But while Tydeus' son was following after his spear-cast, far through the foremost fighters, where he saw it sink into the earth, Hector gat breath again, and leaping back into his chariot drave out into the throng, and avoided black Fate. Then rushing on with his spear mighty Diomedes spake to him: "Dog, thou art now again escaped from death; yet came ill very nigh thee: but now hath Phoebus Apollo saved thee, to whom thou must surely pray when thou goest amid the clash of spears. Verily I will slay thee yet when I meet thee hereafter, if any god is helper of me too. Now will I make after the rest, whomsoever I may seize."

So spake he, and stripped the son of Paeon, spearman renowned. But Alexandros, the lord of fair-tressed Helen, aimed with his arrows at Tydeides, shepherd of the host; leaning as he aimed against a pillar on the barrow, by men fashioned, of Ilos, son of Dardanos, an elder of the people in time gone by. Now Diomedes was stripping the shining corslet of strong Agastrophos from about his breast, and the shield from his shoulders, and his strong helmet, when Paris drew the centre of his bow; nor vainly did the shaft fly from his hand, for he smote the flat of the right foot of Diomedes, and the arrow went clean through, and stood fixed in the earth; and right sweetly laughing Paris leaped up from his lair, and boasted, and said: "Thou art smitten, nor vainly hath the dart flown forth; would that I had smitten thee in the nether belly, and taken thy life away. So should the Trojans have breathed again from their trouble, they that shudder at thee, as bleating goats at a lion."

But him answered strong Diomedes, no wise dismayed: "Bowman, reviler, proud in thy bow of horn, thou gaper after girls, verily if thou madest trial in full harness, man to man, thy bow and showers of shafts would nothing avail thee, but now thou boastest vainly, for that thou hast grazed the sole of my foot. I care not, more than if a woman had struck me or a senseless boy, for feeble is the dart of a craven man and a worthless. In other wise from my hand, yea, if it do but touch the sharp shaft flieth, and straightway layeth low its man, and torn are the cheeks of his wife, and fatherless his children, and he, reddening the earth with his blood, doth rot away, more birds than women round him."

So spake he, and Odysseus, spearman renowned, drew near, and stood in front of him, and Diomedes sat down behind him, and drew the sharp arrow from his foot, and a sore pang passed through his flesh. Then sprang he into his car, and bade his charioteer drive back to the hollow ships, for he was hurt at heart. Then Odysseus, spearman renowned, was left alone, nor did one of the Argives abide by him, for fear had fallen on them all. Then in heaviness he spoke to his own great-hearted spirit: "Ah me, what thing shall befall me! A great evil it is if I flee, in dread of the throng; yet worse is this, if I be taken all alone, for the other Danaans hath Kronion scattered in flight. But wherefore doth my heart thus converse with herself? for I know that they are cowards, who flee the fight, but whosoever is a hero in war, him it mainly behoves to stand stubbornly, whether he be smitten, or whether he smite another."

While he pondered thus in heart and spirit, the ranks came on of the Trojans under shield, and hemmed him in the midst, setting among them their own bane. And even as when hounds and young men in their bloom press round a boar, and he cometh forth from his deep lair, whetting his white tusk between crooked jaws, and round him they rush, and the sound of the gnashing of tusks ariseth, and straightway they await his assault, so dread as he is, even so then round Odysseus, dear to Zeus, rushed the Trojans. And first he wounded noble Deïopites, from above, in the shoulder, leaping on him with sharp spear, and next he slew Thoon and Ennomos, and next Chersidamas, being leapt down from his chariot, he smote with the spear on the navel beneath the bossy shield, and he fell in the dust and clutched the ground with the hollow of his hand. These left he, and wounded Charops, son of Hippasos, with the spear, the brother of high-born Sokos. And to help him came Sokos, a godlike man, and stood hard by him, and spake saying: "O renowned Odysseus, insatiable of craft and toil, to-day shalt thou either boast over two sons of Hippasos, as having slain two such men of might, and stripped their harness, or smitten by my spear shalt lose thy life."

So spake he, and smote him on the circle of his shield; through the shining shield passed the strong spear, and through the fair-dight corslet it was thrust, and tore clean off the flesh of the flanks, but Pallas Athene did not suffer it to mingle with the bowels of the hero, and Odysseus knew that the dart had in nowise lighted on a deadly spot, and drawing backward, he spake unto Sokos: "Ah, wretched one, verily sheer destruction is come upon thee. Surely thou hast made me to cease from warring among the Trojans, but here to thee I declare that slaying and black Fate will be upon thee this day, and beneath my spear overthrown shalt thou give glory to me, and thy soul to Hades of the noble steeds."

He spake, and the other turned, and started to flee, and in his back as he turned he fixed the spear, between the shoulders, and drave it through the breast. Then he fell with a crash, and noble Odysseus boasted over him: "Ah, Sokos, son of wise-hearted Hippasos the tamer of horses, the end of death hath come upon and caught thee, nor hast thou avoided. Ah, wretch, thy father and lady mother shall not close thine eyes in death, but birds that eat flesh raw shall tear thee, shrouding thee in the multitude of their wings. But to me, if I die, the noble Achaians will yet give due burial."

So spake he, and drew the mighty spear of wise-hearted Sokos forth from his flesh, and from his bossy shield, and his blood flowed forth when the spear was drawn away, and afflicted his spirit. And the great-hearted Trojans when they beheld the blood of Odysseus, with clamour through the throng came all together against him. But he gave ground, and shouted unto his comrades: thrice he shouted then, as loud as man's mouth might cry, and thrice did Menelaos dear to Zeus hear his call, and quickly he spake to Aias that was hard by him: "Aias, of the seed of Zeus, child of Telamon, lord of the hosts, the shout of Odysseus of the hardy heart rings round me, like as though the Trojans were oppressing him alone among them, and had cut him off in the strong battle. Nay, let us speed into the throng, for better it is to rescue him. I fear lest he suffer some evil, being alone among the Trojans, so brave as he is, and lest great sorrow for his loss come upon the Danaans."

So spake he, and led the way, and the other followed him, a godlike man. Then found they Odysseus dear to Zeus, and the Trojans beset him like tawny jackals from the hills round a wounded horned stag, that a man hath smitten with an arrow from the bow-string, and the stag hath fled from him by speed of foot, as long as the blood is warm and his limbs are strong, but when the swift arrow hath overcome him, then do the ravening jackals rend him in the hills, in a dark wood, and then god leadeth a murderous lion thither, and the jackals flee before him, but he rendeth them, so then, round wise-hearted Odysseus of the crafty counsels, did the Trojans gather, many and mighty, but that hero thrusting on with the spear held off the pitiless day. Then Aias drew near, bearing his shield like a tower, and stood thereby, and the Trojans fled from him, where each man might. Then warlike Menelaos led Odysseus out of the press, holding him by the hand, till the squire drave up the horses.

Then Aias leaped on the Trojans, and slew Doyrklos, bastard son of Priam, and thereafter wounded he Pandokos, and he wounded Lysandros, and Pyrasos, and Pylartes. And as when a brimming river cometh down upon the plain, in winter flood from the hills, swollen by the rain of Zeus, and many dry oaks and many pines it sucketh in, and much soil it casteth into the sea, even so renowned Aias charged them, pursuing through the plain, slaying horses and men. Nor wist Hector thereof at all, for he was fighting on the left of all the battle, by the banks of the river Skamandros, whereby chiefly fell the heads of men and an unquenchable cry arose, around great Nestor and warlike Idomeneus. And Hector with them was warring, and terrible things did he, with the spear and in horsemanship, and he ravaged the battalions of the young men. Nor would the noble Achaians have yet given ground from the path, if Alexandros, the lord of fair-tressed Helen, had not stayed Machaon shepherd of the host in his valorous deeds, and smitten him on the right shoulder with a three-barbed arrow. Therefore were the Achaians, breathing valour, in great fear, lest men should seize Machaon in the turning of the fight.

Then Idomeneus spake to noble Nestor: "O Nestor, son of Neleus, great glory of the Achaians, arise, get thee up into thy chariot, and with thee let Machaon go, and swiftly drive to the ships the whole-hooved horses. For a leech is worth many other men, to cut out arrows, and spread soothing medicaments."

So spake he, nor did knightly Nestor of Gerenia disobey him, but straightway gat up into his chariot, and with him went Machaon, son of Asklepios the good leech, and he lashed the horses, and willingly flew they forward to the hollow ships, where they desired to be.

But Kebriones, the charioteer of Hector, beheld the Trojans driven in flight, and spake to him, and said: "Hector, here do we contend with the Danaans, at the limit of the wailful war, but, lo, the other Trojans are driven in flight confusedly, men and horses. And Aias son of Telamon is driving them; well I know him, for wide is the shield round his shoulders. Nay, let us too urge thither the horses and chariot, there where horsemen and footmen thickest in the forefront of evil strife are slaying each other, and the cry goes up unquenchable."

So spake he, and smote the fair-maned horses with the shrill-sounding whip, and they felt the lash, and fleetly bore the swift chariot among the Trojans and Achaians, treading on the dead, and the shields, and with blood was sprinkled all the axle-tree beneath, and the rims round the car with the drops from the hooves of the horses, and with drops from the tires about the wheels. And Hector was eager to enter the press of men, and to leap in and break through, and evil din of battle he brought among the Danaans, and brief space rested he from smiting with the spear. Nay, but he ranged among the ranks of other men, with spear, and sword, and with great stones, but he avoided the battle of Aias son of Telamon.

Now father Zeus, throned in the highest, roused dread in Aias, and he stood in amaze, and cast behind him his seven-fold shield of bull's hide, and gazed round in fear upon the throng, like a wild beast, turning this way and that, and slowly retreating step by step. And as when hounds and country folk drive a tawny lion from the mid-fold of the kine, and suffer him not to carry away the fattest of the herd; all night they watch, and he in great desire for the flesh maketh his onset, but takes nothing thereby, for thick the darts fly from strong hands against him, and the burning brands, and these he dreads for all his fury, and in the dawn he departeth with vexed heart; even so at that time departed Aias, vexed at heart, from among the Trojans, right unwillingly, for he feared sore for the ships of the Achaians. And as when a lazy ass going past a field hath the better of the boys with him, an ass that hath had many a cudgel broken about his sides, and he fareth into the deep crop, and wasteth it, while the boys smite him with cudgels, and feeble is the force of them, but yet with might and main they drive him forth, when he hath had his fill of fodder, even so did the high-hearted Trojans and allies, called from many lands, smite great Aias, son of Telamon, with darts on the centre of his shield, and ever followed after him. And Aias would now be mindful of his impetuous valour, and turn again, and hold at bay the battalions of the horse-taming Trojans, and once more he would turn him again to flee. Yet he hindered them all from making their way to the fleet ships, and himself stood and smote between the Trojans and the Achaians, and the spears from strong hands stuck some of them in his great shield, fain to win further, and many or ever they reached his white body stood fast halfway in the earth, right eager to sate themselves with his flesh.

So they fought like unto burning fire.

But the mares of Neleus all sweating bare Nestor out of the battle, and also carried they Machaon, shepherd of the host. Then the noble Achilles, swift of foot, beheld and was ware of him, for Achilles was standing by the stern of his great ship, watching the dire toil, and the woful rout of battle. And straightway he spake to his own comrade, Patroklos, calling to him from beside the ship, and he heard, and from the hut he came, like unto Ares; and this to

him was the beginning of evil. Then the strong son of
Menoitios spake first to Achilles: "Why dost thou call me,
Achilles, what need hast thou of me?"

Then swift-footed Achilles answered him and spake:
"Noble son of Menoitios, dear to my heart, now methinks
that the Achaians will stand in prayer about my knees, for
need no longer tolerable cometh upon them. But go now,
Patroklos dear to Zeus, and ask Nestor who is this that he
bringeth wounded from the war. Verily from behind he is
most like Machaon, that child of Asklepios, but I beheld
not the eyes of the man, for the horses sped past me, straining forward eagerly."

So spake he and Patroklos obeyed his dear comrade, and
started and ran past the ships, and the huts of the Achaians.

Now when they came to the hut of the son of Neleus, they
lighted down on the bounteous earth, and the squire,
Eurymedon, loosed the horses of that old man from the car,
and they dried the sweat from their doublets, standing before the breeze, by the shore of the sea, and thereafter came
they to the hut, and sat them down on chairs. And fair-
tressed Hekamede mixed for them a mess, Hekamede that
the old man won from Tenedos, when Achilles sacked it,
and she was the daughter of great-hearted Arsinoos, and
her the Achaians chose out for him, because always in
counsel he excelled them all. First she drew before them a
fair table, polished well, with feet of cyanus, and thereon a
vessel of bronze, with onion, for relish to the drink, and pale
honey, and the grain of sacred barley, and beside it a right
goodly cup, that the old man brought from home, embossed
with studs of gold, and four handles there were to it, and

round each two golden doves were feeding, and to the cup were two feet below. Another man could scarce have lifted the cup from the table, when it was full, but Nestor the Old raised it easily. In this cup the woman, like unto the goddesses, mixed a mess for them, with Pramnian wine, and therein grated cheese of goats' milk, with a grater of bronze, and scattered white barley thereover, and bade them drink, whenas she had made ready the mess.

So when the twain had drunk, and driven away parching thirst, they took their pleasure in discourse, speaking each to the other. Now Patroklos stood at the doors, a godlike man, and when the old man beheld him, he arose from his shining chair, and took him by the hand, and led him in, and bade him be seated. But Patroklos, from over against him, was for refusing, and spake and said: "No time to sit have I, old man, fosterling of Zeus, nor wilt thou persuade me. Revered and dreaded is he that sent me forth to ask thee who this man is that thou bringest home wounded. Nay, but I know myself, for I see Machaon, shepherd of the host. And now will I go back again, a messenger, to speak a word to Achilles. And well dost thou know, old man, fosterling of Zeus, how terrible a man he is; lightly would he blame even one that is blameless."

Then knightly Nestor of Gerenia answered him again: "Wherefore is Achilles thus sorry for the sons of the Achaians, for as many as are wounded with darts? He knoweth not at all what grief hath arisen in the camp: for the best men lie in the ships, wounded by shaft or smitten by spear. Wounded with the shaft is strong Diomedes, son of Tydeus, and smitten is Odysseus, spearman renowned, and

Agamemnon, and this other have I but newly carried out of battle, wounded with an arrow from the bowstring. But Achilles, for all his valiance, careth not for the Danaans, nor pities them at all. Doth he wait till the fleet ships hard by the shore shall burn in the consuming fire, and till we be slain one upon another? Nay, but even now speak thou thus and thus to wise-hearted Achilles, if perchance he will obey thee. Who knows but that, God helping, thou mightst stir his spirit with thy persuading? and good is the persuasion of a friend. But if in his heart he be shunning some oracle of God, and his lady mother hath told him somewhat from Zeus, natheless let him send forth thee, and let the rest of the host of the Myrmidons follow with thee, if perchance any light shall arise from thee to the Danaans; and let him give thee his fair harness, to bear into the war, if perchance the Trojans may take thee for him, and withhold them from the strife, and the warlike sons of the Achaians might take breath, being wearied; for brief is the breathing time in battle. And lightly might ye, being unwearied, drive men wearied in the war unto the city, away from the ships and the huts."

So spake he, and roused his heart within his breast, and he started and ran by the ships to Achilles of the seed of Aiakos.

BOOK XII

How the Trojans and allies broke within the wall of the Achaians.

STILL they fought confusedly, the Argives and Trojans. Nor were the foss of the Danaans and their wide wall above long to protect them, the wall they had builded for defence of the ships, and the foss they had drawn round about; for neither had they given goodly hecatombs to the gods, that it might guard with its bounds their swift ships and rich spoil.

Then war and the din of war sounded about the well-builded wall, and the beams of the towers rang beneath the strokes; while the Argives, subdued by the scourge of Zeus, were penned and driven in by the hollow ships, in dread of Hector, the mighty maker of flight, but he, as aforetime, fought like a whirlwind. And as when, among hounds and hunting men, a boar or lion wheeleth him about, raging in his strength, and these array themselves in fashion like a tower, and stand up against him, casting many javelins from their hands; but never is his stout heart confused nor afraid, and his courage is his bane, and often he wheeleth him about, and maketh trial of the ranks of men, and where-soever he maketh onset there the ranks of men give way, even so Hector went and besought his comrades through the press, and spurred them on to cross the dyke. But his swift-footed horses dared not, but loud they neighed, standing by the sheer edge, for the wide foss affrighted them, neither easy to leap from hard by, nor to cross, for overhanging banks stood round about it all on either hand, and above it was furnished with sharp stakes that the sons of the Achaians had planted there, thick set and great, a bulwark against hostile men. Thereby not lightly might a horse enter, drawing a well-wheeled chariot; but the footmen were eager, if they might accomplish it. Then Polydamas drew near valiant Hector, and spake to him: "Hector and ye other leaders of the Trojans and allies, foolishly do we drive our fleet horses through the dyke; nay right hard it is to cross, for sharp stakes stand in it, and over against them the wall of the Achaians. Thereby none may go down and fight in chariots, for strait is the place wherein, methinks, we might come by a mischief. For if Zeus that thunders on high is utterly to destroy them in his evil will, and is minded to help the Trojans, verily then I too would desire that even instantly this might be, that the Achaians should perish here nameless far from Argos: but and if they turn again, and we flee back from among the ships, and rush into the delved ditch, then methinks that not even one from among us to bear the tidings will win back to the city before the force of the Achaians when they rally. But come as I declare, let us all obey. Let our squires hold the horses by the dyke, while we being harnessed in our gear as foot soldiers follow all together with Hector, and the Achaians will not withstand us, if indeed the bands of death be made fast upon them."

So spake Polydamas, and his wise word pleased Hector well, and straightway in his harness he leaped from his chariot to the ground. Nor were the other Trojans gathered upon the chariots, but they all leaped forth, when they beheld goodly Hector. There each gave it into the charge of his own charioteer, to keep the horses orderly there by the foss. And they divided, and arrayed themselves, and ordered in five companies they followed with the leaders.

Now they that went with Hector and noble Polydamas, these were most, and bravest, and most were eager to break the wall, and fight by the hollow ships; and with them followed Kebriones for the third, for Hector had left another man with his chariot, a weaker warrior than Kebriones. The second company Paris led, and Alkathoos, and Agenor: and the third company Helenos led, and godlike Deiphobos, —two sons of Priam,—the third was the warrior Asios, Asios Hyrtakos' son, whom his tall sorrel steeds brought out of Arisbe, from the river Selleëis. And of the fourth company was the brave son of Anchises leader, even Aineias; and with him were two sons of Antenor, Archelochos and Akamas, both well skilled in all warfare.

And Sarpedon led the glorious allies, and to be with him he chose Glaukos and warlike Asteropaios, for they seemed to him to be manifestly the bravest of all after himself, but he was excellent, yea, above all the host. And these when they had arrayed one another with well-fashioned shields of bulls' hide, went straight and eager against the Danaans, nor deemed that they could longer resist them, but that themselves should fall on the black ships.

Then the rest of the Trojans and the far-famed allies obeyed the counsel of blameless Polydamas, but Asios, son of Hyrtakos, leader of men, willed not to leave his horses there, and his squire the charioteer, but with them he drew

near the swift ships, fond man! for never was he, avoiding
evil Fates, to return, rejoicing in his horses and chariot,
back from the ships to windy Ilios. Nay, ere that the Fate of
ill name overshadowed him, by the spear of Idomeneus, the
haughty son of Deukalion. For Asios went against the left
flank of the ships, whereby the Achaians returned out of the
plain with chariots and horses: there he drave through his
horses and his car, nor found he the doors shut on the gates,
and the long bar, but men were holding them open if perchance they might save any of their comrades fleeing out of
the battle towards the ships. Straight thereby held he his
horses with unswerving aim, and his men followed him,
crying shrilly, for they deemed that the Achaians could no
longer hold them off, but that themselves would fall on the
black ships: fools, for in the gates they found two men of
the bravest, the high-hearted sons of the warrior Lapithae,
one the son of Peirithoos, strong Polypoites, and one Leon-
teus, peer of Ares the bane of men. These twain stood in
front of the lofty gates, like high-crested oak trees in the
hills, that for ever abide the wind and rain, firm fixed with
roots great and long; even so these twain, trusting to the
mightiness of their hands, abode the coming of great Asios,
and fled not. But straight came the Trojans against the
well-builded wall, holding their shields of dry bulls' hide on
high, with mighty clamour, round the prince Asios, and
Iamenos, and Orestes, and Adamas, son of Asios, and
Thoon, and Oinomaos. But the other twain for a while,
being within the wall, urged the well-greaved Achaians to
fight for the ships; but when they saw the Trojans assailing
the wall, while the Danaans cried and turned in flight, then

forth rushed the twain, and fought in front of the gates like wild boars that in the mountains abide the assailing crew of men and dogs, and charging on either flank they crush the wood around them, cutting it at the root, and the clatter of their tusks waxes loud, till one smite them and take their life away: so clattered the bright bronze on the breasts of the twain, as they were smitten in close fight, for right hardily they fought, trusting to the host above them, and to their own strength.

For the men above were casting with stones from the well-builded towers in defence of themselves and of the huts, and of the swift-faring ships. And like snowflakes the stones fell earthward, flakes that a tempestuous wind, as it driveth the dark clouds, rains thickly down on the bounteous earth: so thick fell the missiles from the hands of Achaians and Trojans alike, and their helms rang harsh and their bossy shields, being smitten with mighty stones. Verily then Asios, son of Hyrtakos, groaned and smote both his thighs, and indignantly he spake: "Father Zeus, verily thou too dost greatly love a lie, for I deemed not that the Achaian heroes could withstand our might and our hands invincible. But they like wasps of nimble body, or bees that have made their dwellings in a rugged path, and leave not their hollow hold, but abide and keep the hunters at bay for the sake of their little ones, even so these men have no will to give ground from the gates, though they are but two, ere they slay or be slain."

So spake he, nor with his speech did he persuade the mind of Zeus, for his will was to give renown to Hector.

The young men who followed with Polydamas and

Hector, they that were most in number and bravest, and most were eager to break the wall and set the ships on fire, these still stood doubtful by the foss, for as they were eager to pass over a bird had appeared to them, an eagle of lofty flight, skirting the host on the left hand. In its talons it bore a blood-red monstrous snake, alive, and struggling still; yea, not yet had it forgotten the joy of battle, but writhed backward and smote the bird that held it on the breast, beside the neck, and the bird cast it from him down to the earth, in sore pain, and dropped it in the midst of the throng; then with a cry sped away down the gusts of the wind. And the Trojans shuddered when they saw the gleaming snake lying in the midst of them; an omen of aegis-bearing Zeus.

Then verily Polydamas stood by brave Hector, and spake: "Hector, ever dost thou rebuke me in the assemblies, though I counsel wisely; since it by no means beseemeth one of the people to speak contrary to thee, in council or in war, but always to increase thy power; but now again will I say all that seemeth to me to be best. Let us not advance and fight with the Danaans for the ships. For even thus, methinks, the end will be, if indeed this bird hath come for the Trojans when they were eager to cross the dyke, this eagle of lofty flight, skirting the host on the left hand, bearing in his talons a blood-red monstrous snake, yet living; then straightway left he hold of him, before he reached his own nest, nor brought him home in the end to give to his nestlings. Even so shall we, though we burst with mighty force the gates and wall of the Achaians, and the Achaians give ground, even so we shall return in disarray from the ships by the way we came; for many of the Trojans shall we leave behind, whom the Achaians will slay with the sword, in defence of the ships. Even so would a soothsayer interpret that in his heart had clear knowledge of omens, and whom the people obeyed."

Then Hector of the glancing helm lowered on him and said: "Polydamas, that thou speakest is no longer pleasing to me; yea, thou knowest how to conceive another counsel better than this. But if thou verily speakest thus in earnest, then the gods themselves have utterly destroyed thy wits; thou that bidst us forget the counsels of loud-thundering Zeus, that himself promised me, and confirmed with a nod of his head! But thou bidst us be obedient to birds long of wing, whereto I give no heed, nor take any care thereof, whether they fare to the right, to the dawn and to the sun, or to the left, to mist and darkness. Nay, for us, let us trust to the counsel of mighty Zeus, who is king over all mortals and immortals. One omen is best, to fight for our own country. And wherefore dost thou fear war and battle? For if all the rest of us be slain by the ships of the Argives, yet needst thou not fear to perish, for thy heart is not warlike, nor enduring in battle. But if thou dost hold aloof from the fight, or winnest any other with thy words to turn him from war, straightway by my spear shalt thou be smitten, and lose thy life."

So spake he, and led on, and they followed with a wondrous din; and Zeus that joyeth in the thunder roused from the hills of Ida a blast of wind, which bare the dust straight against the ships; and he made weak the heart of the Achaians, but gave renown to the Trojans and to Hector. Trusting then in his omens, and their might, they strove to break the great wall of the Achaians. They dragged down the machicolations of the towers, and overthrew the battlements, and heaved up the projecting buttresses, that the Achaians set first in the earth, to be the props of the towers. These they overthrew, and hoped to break the wall of the Achaians. Nor even now did the Danaans give ground from the path, but closed up the battlements with shields of bulls' hides, and cast from them at the foemen as they went below the walls.

Now the two Aiantes went everywhere on the towers, ever urging, and arousing the courage of the Achaians. One they would accost with honeyed words, another with hard words they would rebuke, whomsoever they saw utterly giving ground from the fight: "O friends, whosoever is eminent, or whosoever is of middle station among the Argives, ay, or lower yet, for in no wise are all men equal in war, now is there work for all, and this yourselves well know. Let none turn back to the ships, for that he hath heard one threatening aloud; nay, get ye forward, and cheer another on, if perchance Olympian Zeus, the lord of lightning, will grant us to drive back the assault, and push the foe to the city."

So these twain shouted in the front, and aroused the battle of the Achaians. But as flakes of snow fall thick on a winter day, when Zeus the Counsellor hath begun to snow, showing forth these arrows of his to men, and he hath lulled the winds, and he snoweth continually, till he hath covered the crests of the high hills, and the uttermost headlands, and the grassy plains, and rich tillage of men; and the snow is scattered over the havens and shores of the grey sea, and only the wave as it rolleth in keeps off the snow, but all other things are swathed over, when the shower of Zeus cometh heavily, so from both sides their stones flew thick, some towards the Trojans, and some from the Trojans against the Achaians, while both sides were smitten, and over all the wall the din arose.

Yet never would the Trojans, then, and renowned Hector have broken the gates of the wall, and the long bar, if Zeus the Counsellor had not roused his son Sarpedon against the Argives, like a lion against the kine of crooked horn. Straightway he held forth his fair round shield, of hammered bronze, that the bronze-smith had hammered out, and within had stitched many bulls' hides with rivets of gold, all round the circle, this held he forth, and shook two spears; and sped on his way, like a mountain-nurtured lion, that long lacketh meat, and his brave spirit urgeth him to make assail on the sheep, and come even against a well-builded homestead. Nay, even if he find herdsmen thereby, guarding the sheep with hounds and spears, yet hath he no mind to be driven without an effort from the steading, but he either leapeth on a sheep, and seizeth it, or himself is smitten in the foremost place with a dart from a strong hand. So did his heart then urge on the godlike Sarpedon to rush against the wall, and break through the battlements. And instantly he spake to Glaukos, son of Hippolochos: "Glaukos, wherefore have we twain the chiefest honour, —seats of honour, and messes, and full cups in Lykia, and all men look on us as gods? And wherefore hold we a great demesne by the banks of Xanthos, a fair demesne of orchardland, and wheat-bearing tilth? Therefore now it

behoveth us to take our stand in the first rank of the Lykians, and encounter fiery battle, that certain of the well-
corsleted Lykians may say, 'Verily our kings that rule Lykia
be no inglorious men, they that eat fat sheep, and drink the
choice wine honey-sweet: nay, but they are also of excellent
might, for they war in the foremost ranks of the Lykians.'
Ah, friend, if once escaped from this battle we were for ever
to be ageless and immortal, neither would I fight myself in
the foremost ranks, nor would I send thee into the war that
giveth men renown, but now—for assuredly ten thousand
fates of death do every way beset us, and these no mortal
may escape nor avoid—now let us go forward, whether we
shall give glory to other men, or others to us."

So spake he, and Glaukos turned not apart, nor disobeyed him, and they twain went straight forward, leading
the great host of the Lykians.

Then Menestheus son of Peteos shuddered when he beheld them, for against his tower they went, bringing with
them ruin; and he looked along the tower of the Achaians if
perchance he might see any of the leaders, that would ward
off destruction from his comrades, and he beheld the two
Aiantes, insatiate of war, standing there, and Teukros hard
by, newly come from his hut; but he could not cry to be
heard of them, so great was the din, and the noise went up
unto heaven of smitten shields and helms with horse-hair
crests, and of the gates, for they had all been shut, and the
Trojans stood beside them, and strove by force to break
them, and enter in. Swiftly then to Aias he sent the herald
Thoötes: "Go, noble Thoötes, and run, and call Aias: or
rather the twain, for that will be far the best of all, since

quickly here will there be wrought utter ruin. For hereby press the leaders of the Lykians, who of old are fierce in strong battle. But if beside them too war and toil arise, yet at least let the strong Telamonian Aias come alone and let Teukros the skilled bowman follow with him."

So spake he, and the herald listened and disobeyed him not, but started and ran by the wall of the mail-clad Achaians, and came, and stood by the Aiantes.

Nor did the strong Telamonian Aias disobey, but instantly spake winged words to the son of Oileus: "Aias, do ye twain stand here, thyself and strong Lykomedes, and urge the Danaans to war with all their might; but I go thither, to take my part in battle, and quickly will I come again, when I have well aided them."

So spake Telamonian Aias and departed, and Teukros went with him, his brother by the same father, and with them Pandion bare the bended bow of Teukros.

Now when they came to the tower of great-hearted Menestheus, passing within the wall,—and to men sore pressed they came,—the foe were climbing upon the battlements, like a dark whirlwind, even the strong leaders and counsellors of the Lykians; and they hurled together into the war and the battle-cry arose. Now first did Aias Telamon's son slay a man, Epikles great of heart, the comrade of Sarpedon. With a jagged stone he smote him, a great stone that lay uppermost within the wall, by the battlements. Not lightly could a man hold it in both hands, however strong in his youth, of such mortals as now are, but Aias lifted it, and cast it from above, and shattered the helm of fourfold crest, and broke the bones of the head, and he fell like a diver from the lofty tower, and his life left his bones. And Teukros smote Glaukos, the strong son of Hippolochos, as he came on, with an arrow from the lofty wall; even where he saw his shoulder bare he smote him, and made him cease from delight in battle. Back from the wall he leapt secretly, lest any of the Achaians should see him smitten, and speak boastfully. But sorrow came on Sarpedon when Glaukos departed, so soon as he was aware thereof, but he forgot not the joy of battle. He aimed at Alkmaon, son of Thestor, with the spear, and smote him, and drew out the spear. And Alkmaon following the spear fell prone, and his bronze arms rang round him. Then Sarpedon seized with strong hands the battlement, and dragged, and it all gave way together, while above the wall was stripped bare, and made a path for many.

Then Aias and Teukros did encounter him: Teukros smote him with an arrow, on the bright baldric of his covering shield, about the breast, but Zeus warded off the Fates from his son, that he should not be overcome beside the ships' sterns. Then Aias leaped on and smote his shield, nor did the spear pass clean through, yet shook he Sarpedon in his eagerness. He gave ground a little way from the battlement, yet retreated not wholly, since his heart hoped to win renown. Then he turned and cried to the godlike Lykians: "O Lykians, wherefore thus are ye slack in impetuous valour. Hard it is for me, stalwart as I am, alone to break through, and make a path to the ships, nay, follow hard after me, for the more men, the better work."

So spake he, and they, dreading the rebuke of their king, pressed on the harder around the counsellor and king. And the Argives on the other side made strong their battalions within the wall, and mighty toil began for them. For neither could the strong Lykians burst through the wall of the Danaans, and make a way to the ships, nor could the warlike Danaans drive back the Lykians from the wall, when once they had drawn near thereto. But as two men contend about the marches of their land, with measuring rods in their hands, in a common field, when in narrow space they strive for equal shares, even so the battlements divided them, and over those they smote the round shields of ox hide about the breasts of either side, and the fluttering bucklers. And many were wounded in the flesh with the ruthless bronze, whensoever the back of any of the warriors was laid bare as he turned, ay, and many clean through the very shield. Yea, everywhere the towers and battlements swam with the blood of men shed on either side, by Trojans and Achaians. But even so they could not put the Argives to rout, but they held their ground, as an honest woman that laboureth with her hands holds the balance, and raises the weight and the wool together, balancing them, that she may win scant wages for her children; so evenly was strained their war and battle, till the moment when Zeus gave the greater renown to Hector, son of Priam, who was the first to leap within the wall of the Achaians. In a piercing voice he cried aloud to the Trojans: "Rise, ye horse-taming Trojans, break the wall of the Argives, and cast among the ships fierce blazing fire."

So spake he, spurring them on, and they all heard him with their ears, and in one mass rushed straight against the wall, and with sharp spears in their hands climbed upon the machicolations of the towers. And Hector seized and carried a stone that lay in front of the gates, thick in the hinder part, but sharp at point: a stone that not the two best men of the people, such as mortals now are, could lightly lift from the ground on to a wain, but easily he wielded it alone, for the son of crooked-counselling Kronos made it light for him. And as when a shepherd lightly beareth the fleece of a ram, taking it in one hand, and little doth it burden him, so Hector lifted the stone, and bare it straight against the doors that closely guarded the stubborn-set portals, double gates and tall, and two cross bars held them within, and one bolt fastened them. And he came, and stood hard by, and firmly planted himself, and smote them in the midst, setting his legs well apart, that his cast might lack no strength. And he brake both the hinges, and the stone fell within by reason of its weight, and the gates rang loud around, and the bars held not, and the doors burst this way and that beneath the rush of the stone. Then glorious Hector leaped in, with face like the sudden night, shining in wondrous mail that was clad about his body, and with two spears in his hands. No man that met him could have held him back when once he leaped within the gates: none but the gods, and his eyes shone with fire. Turning towards the throng he cried to the Trojans to overleap the wall, and they obeyed his summons, and speedily some overleaped the wall, and some poured into the fair-wrought gateways, and the Danaans fled in fear among the hollow ships, and a ceaseless clamour arose.

BOOK XIII

Poseidon stirreth up the Achaians to defend the ships. The valour of Idomeneus.

Now Zeus, after that he had brought the Trojans and Hector to the ships, left them to their toil and endless labour there. To Troy no more at all he turned his shining eyes, for he deemed in his heart that not one of the Immortals would draw near, to help either Trojans or Danaans.

But the mighty Earth-shaker held no blind watch, who sat and marvelled on the war and strife, high on the topmost crest of wooded Samothrace, for thence all Ida was plain to see; and plain to see were the city of Priam, and the ships of the Achaians. Thither did he go from the sea and sate him down, and he had pity on the Achaians, that they were subdued to the Trojans, and strong was his anger against Zeus.

Then forthwith he went down from the rugged hill, faring with swift steps, and the high hills trembled, and the woodland, beneath the immortal footsteps of Poseidon as he moved. Three strides he made, and with the fourth he reached his goal, even Aigae, and there was his famous palace in the deeps of the mere, his glistering golden mansions builded, imperishable for ever. Thither went he, and let harness to the car his bronze-hooved horses, swift of flight, clothed with their golden manes. He girt his own golden array about his body, and seized the well-wrought lash of gold, and mounted his chariot, and forth he drove across the waves. And the sea beasts frolicked beneath him, on all sides out of the deeps, for well they knew their lord, and with gladness the sea stood asunder, and swiftly they sped, and the axle of bronze was not wetted beneath, and the bounding steeds bare him on to the ships of the Achaians.

Now there is a spacious cave in the depths of the deep mere, between Tenedos and rugged Imbros; there did Poseidon, the Shaker of the earth, stay his horses, and loosed them out of the chariot, and cast before them ambrosial food to graze withal, and golden tethers he bound about their hooves, tethers neither to be broken nor loosed, that there the horses might continually await their lord's return. And he went to the host of the Achaians.

Now the Trojans like flame or storm-wind were following in close array, with fierce intent, after Hector, son of Priam. With shouts and cries they came, and thought to take the ships of the Achaians, and to slay thereby all the bravest of the host. But Poseidon, that girdleth the world, the Shaker of the earth, was urging on the Argives, and forth he came from the deep salt sea, in form and untiring voice like unto Kalchas. First he spake to the two Aiantes, that themselves were eager for battle: "Ye Aiantes twain, ye shall save the people of the Achaians, if ye are mindful of your might, and reckless of chill fear. For verily I do not otherwhere dread the invincible hands of the Trojans, that have climbed the great wall in their multitude, nay, the well-greaved Achaians will hold them all at bay; but hereby verily do I greatly dread lest some evil befall us, even here where that furious one is leading like a flame of fire, Hector, who boasts him to be son of mighty Zeus. Nay, but here may some god put it into the hearts of you twain, to stand sturdily yourselves, and urge others to do the like; thereby might ye drive him from the fleet-faring ships, despite his eagerness, yea, even if the Olympian himself is rousing him to war."

Therewith the Shaker of the world, the girdler of the earth, struck the twain with his staff, and filled them with strong courage, and their limbs he made light, and their feet, and their hands withal. Then, even as a swift-winged hawk speeds forth to fly, poised high above a tall sheer rock, and swoops to chase some other bird across the plain, even so Poseidon sped from them, the Shaker of the world. And of the twain Oileus' son, the swift-footed Aias, was the first to know the god, and instantly he spake to Aias, son of Telamon: "Aias, since it is one of the gods who hold Olympus, that in the semblance of a seer commands us now to fight beside the ships—not Kalchas is he, the prophet and soothsayer, for easily I knew the tokens of his feet and knees as he turned away, and the gods are easy to discern—lo, then mine own heart within my breast is more eagerly set on war and battle and my feet beneath and my hands above are lusting for the fight."

Then Aias, son of Telamon, answered him saying: "Even so, too, my hands invincible now rage about the spear-shaft, and wrath has risen within me, and both my feet are swift beneath me; yea, I am keen to meet, even in single fight, the ceaseless rage of Hector son of Priam."

So they spake to each other, rejoicing in the delight of

battle, which the god put in their heart. Then the girdler of
the earth stirred up the Achaians that were in the rear and
were renewing their strength beside the swift ships. Their
limbs were loosened by their grievous toil, yea, and their
souls filled with sorrow at the sight of the Trojans, that had
climbed over the great wall in their multitude. And they
looked on them, and shed tears beneath their brows, thinking that never would they escape destruction. But the
Shaker of the earth right easily came among them, and
urged on the strong battalions of warriors. Teukros first he
came and summoned, and Leïtos, and the hero Peneleos,
and Thoas, and Deïpyros, and Meriones, and Antilochos,
lords of the war-cry, all these he spurred on with winged
words: "Shame on you, Argives, shame, ye striplings, in
your battle had I trusted for the salvation of our ships. But
if you are to withdraw from grievous war, now indeed the
day doth shine that shall see us conquered by the Trojans.
Lo, the mighty Hector of the loud war-cry is fighting at the
ships, and the gates and the long bar he hath burst in
sunder."

On this wise did the Earth-enfolder call to and spur on
the Achaians. And straightway they made a stand around
the two Aiantes, strong bands that Ares himself could not
enter and make light of, nor Athene that marshals the host.
Yea, they were the chosen best that abode the Trojans and
goodly Hector, and spear on spear made close-set fence,
and shield on serried shield, buckler pressed on buckler, and
helm on helm, and man on man. The horse-hair crests on
the bright helmet-ridges touched each other as they nodded,
so close they stood each by other, and spears brandished in

bold hands were interlaced; and their hearts were steadfast and lusted for battle.

Then the Trojans drave forward in close array, and Hector led them, pressing straight onwards, like a rolling rock from a cliff, that the winter-swollen water thrusteth from the crest of a hill, having broken the foundations of the stubborn rock with its wondrous flood; leaping aloft it flies, and the wood echoes under it, and unstayed it runs its course, till it reaches the level plain, and then it rolls no more for all its eagerness,—even so Hector for a while threatened lightly to win to the sea through the huts and the ships of the Achaians, slaying as he came, but when he encountered the serried battalions, he was stayed when he drew near against them. But they of the other part, the sons of the Achaians, thrust with their swords and double-pointed spears, and drave him forth from them, that he gave ground and reeled backward. Then he cried with a piercing voice, calling on the Trojans: "Trojans, and Lykians, and close-fighting Dardanians, hold your ground, for the Achaians will not long ward me off, nay, though they have arrayed themselves in fashion like a tower. Rather, methinks, they will flee back before the spear, if verily the chief of gods has set me on, the loud-thundering lord of Hera."

Therewith he spurred on the heart and spirit of each man; and Deïphobos, the son of Priam, strode among them with high thoughts, and held in front of him the circle of his shield, and lightly he stepped with his feet, advancing beneath the cover of his shield. Then Meriones aimed at him with a shining spear, and struck, and missed not, but smote the circle of the bulls'-hide shield, yet no whit did he pierce it; nay, well ere that might be, the long spear-shaft snapped in the socket. Now Deïphobos was holding off from him the bulls'-hide shield, and his heart feared the lance of wise Meriones, but that hero shrunk back among the throng of his comrades, greatly in wrath both for the loss of victory, and of his spear, that he had shivered. So he set forth to go to the huts and the ships of the Achaians, to bring a long spear, that he had left in his hut.

Meanwhile the others were fighting on, and there arose an inextinguishable cry. First Teukros, son of Telamon, slew a man, the spearman Imbrios, the son of Mentor rich in horses. Then Teukros rushed forth, most eager to strip his armour, and Hector cast at him as he came with his shining spear. But Teukros, steadily regarding him, avoided by a little the spear of bronze; so Hector struck Amphimachos, son of Kteatos, son of Aktor, in the breast with the spear, as he was returning to the battle. With a crash he fell, and his armour rang upon him.

Then verily was Poseidon wroth at heart, when his son's son fell in the terrible fray. So he set forth to go by the huts and the ships of the Achaians, to spur on the Danaans, and sorrows he was contriving for the Trojans. Then Idomeneus, spearman renowned, met him on his way from his comrade that had but newly returned to him out of the battle, wounded on the knee with the sharp bronze. Then the mighty Shaker of the earth addressed him, in the voice of Thoas, son of Andraimon, that ruled over the Aitolians in all Pleuron, and mountainous Kalydon, and was honoured like a god by the people: "Come, take thy weapons and away: herein we must play the man together, if any avail there may be, though we are no more than two. Ay, and very cowards get courage from company, but we twain know well how to battle even with the brave."

Therewith the god went back again into the strife of men, but Idomeneus, so soon as he came to his well-builded hut, did on his fair armour about his body, and grasped two spears, and set forth like the lightning that Kronion seizes in his hand and brandishes from radiant Olympus, showing forth a sign to mortal men, and far seen are the flames thereof. Even so shone the bronze about the breast of Idomeneus as he ran, and Meriones, his good squire, met him, while he was still near his hut,—he was going to bring his spear of bronze,—and mighty Idomeneus spake to him: "Meriones son of Molos, fleet of foot, dearest of my company, wherefore hast thou come hither and left the war and strife? Art thou wounded at all, and vexed by a dart's point, or dost thou come with a message for me concerning aught? Verily I myself have no desire to sit in the huts, but to fight."

Then wise Meriones answered him again, saying: "I have come to fetch a spear, if perchance thou hast one left in the huts, for that which before I carried I have shivered in casting at the shield of proud Deïphobos."

Then Idomeneus, leader of the Cretans, answered him again: "Spears, if thou wilt, thou shalt find, one, ay, and twenty, standing in the hut, against the shining side walls, spears of the Trojans whereof I have spoiled their slain. Yea, it is not my mood to stand and fight with foemen from afar, wherefore I have spears, and bossy shields, and helms, and corslets of splendid sheen."

Thus he spake, and Meriones, the peer of swift Ares, quickly bare the spear of bronze from the hut, and went after Idomeneus, with high thoughts of battle. And even as Ares, the bane of men, goes forth into the war, and with him follows his dear son Panic, stark and fearless, that terrifies even the hardy warrior; and these twain leave Thrace, and harness them for fight with the Ephyri, or the great-hearted Phlegyans, yet hearken not to both peoples, but give honour to one only; like these gods did Meriones and Idomeneus, leaders of men, set forth into the fight, harnessed in gleaming bronze. And Meriones spake first to Idomeneus saying: "Child of Deukalion, whither art thou eager to enter into the throng: on the right of all the host, or in the centre, or on the left? Ay, and no other where, methinks, are the flowing-haired Achaians so like to fail in fight."

Then Idomeneus, the leader of the Cretans, answered him again: "In the centre of the ships there are others to bear the brunt, the two Aiantes, and Teukros, the best bowmen of the Achaians, ay, and a good man in close fight; these will give Hector Priam's son toil enough, howsoever keen he be for battle; yea, though he be exceeding stalwart. But guide us twain, as thou sayest, to the left hand of the host, that speedily we may learn whether we are to win glory from others, or other men from us."

So he spake, and Meriones, the peer of swift Ares, led the way, till they came to the host, in that place whither he bade him go.

And when the Trojans saw Idomeneus, strong as flame, and his squire with him, and their glorious armour, they all shouted and made for him through the press. Then their melee began, by the sterns of the ships. And as the gusts speed on, when shrill winds blow, on a day when dust lies thickest on the roads, and the winds raise together a great cloud of dust, even so their battle clashed together, and all were fain of heart to slay each other in the press with the keen bronze. And the battle, the bane of men, bristled with the long spears, the piercing spears they grasped, and the glitter of bronze from gleaming helmets dazzled the eyes, and the sheen of new-burnished corslets, and shining shields, as the men thronged all together. Right hardy of heart would he have been that joyed and sorrowed not at the sight of this labour of battle.

Thus the two mighty sons of Kronos, with contending will, were contriving sorrow and anguish for the heroes. Zeus desired victory for the Trojans and Hector, giving glory to swift-footed Achilles; yet he did not wish the Achaian host to perish utterly before Ilios, but only to give renown to Thetis and her strong-hearted son. But Poseidon went among the Argives and stirred them to war, stealing secretly forth from the grey salt sea: for he was sore vexed that they were overcome by the Trojans, and was greatly in wrath against Zeus. Verily both were of the same lineage and the same place of birth, but Zeus was the elder and the wiser. Therefore also Poseidon avoided to give open aid, but secretly ever he spurred them on, throughout the host, in the likeness of a man.

Even then Idomeneus, though his hair was flecked with grey, called on the Danaans, and leaping among the Trojans, roused their terror. For he slew Othryoneus of

Kabesos and dragged him by the foot across the fierce melee. But Asios came to his aid, on foot before his horses that the charioteer guided so that still their breath touched the shoulders of Asios. And the desire of his heart was to cast at Idomeneus, who was beforehand with him, and smote him with the spear in the throat, below the chin, and drove the point straight through. And he fell as an oak falls, or a poplar, or tall pine tree, that craftsmen have felled on the hills with new whetted axes, to be a ship's timber; even so he lay stretched out before the horses and the chariot, groaning, and clutching the bloody dust. And the charioteer was amazed, and kept not his wits, as of old, and dared not turn his horses and avoid out of the hands of foemen; and Antilochos the steadfast in war smote him, and pierced the middle of his body with a spear. Nothing availed the corslet of bronze he was wont to wear, but he planted the spear fast in the midst of his belly. Therewith he fell gasping from the well-wrought chariot, and Antilochos, the son of great-hearted Nestor, drave the horses out from the Trojans, among the well-greaved Achaians. Then Deïphobos, in sorrow for Asios, drew very nigh Idomeneus, and cast at him with his shining spear. But Idomeneus steadily watching him, avoided the spear of bronze, being hidden beneath the circle of his shield, and the spear of bronze flew over. And his shield rang sharply, as the spear grazed thereon. Yet it flew not vainly from the heavy hand of Deïphobos, but smote Hypsenor, son of Hippasos, the shepherd of the hosts, in the liver, beneath the midriff, and instantly unstrung his knees. And Deïphobos boasted over him terribly, crying aloud: "Ah, verily, not unavenged lies Asios, nay, methinks, that even on his road to Hades, strong Warden of the gate, he will rejoice at heart, since, lo, I have sent him escort for the way!"

So spake he, but grief came on the Argives by reason of his boast, and stirred above all the soul of the wise-hearted Antilochos, yet, despite his sorrow, he was not heedless of his dear comrade, but ran and stood over him, and covered him with his buckler. Then two trusty companions, Mekisteus, son of Echios, and goodly Alastor, stooped down and lifted him, and with heavy groaning bare him to the hollow ships.

And Idomeneus relaxed not his mighty force, but ever was striving, either to cover some one of the Trojans with black night, or himself to fall in warding off death from the Achaians. There the dear son of Aisyetes, fosterling of Zeus, even the hero Alkathoos, was slain. This Alkathoos did Poseidon subdue to Idomeneus, throwing a spell over his shining eyes, and snaring his glorious limbs; so that he might neither flee backwards, nor avoid the stroke, but stood steady as a pillar, or a tree with lofty crown of leaves, when the hero Idomeneus smote him in the midst of the breast with the spear, and rent the coat of bronze about him, that aforetime warded death from his body, but now rang harsh as it was rent by the spear. And he fell with a crash, and the lance fixed in his heart, that, still beating, shook the butt-end of the spear. And Idomeneus boasted terribly, and cried aloud: "Deïphobos, are we to deem it fair acquittal that we have slain three men for one, since thou boastest thus? Nay, sir, but stand thou up also thyself against me, that thou mayst know what manner of son of Zeus am I that have come hither!"

Thus he spake, but the thoughts of Deïphobos were divided, whether he should retreat, and call to his aid some one of the great-hearted Trojans, or should try the adventure alone. And on this wise to his mind it seemed the better, to go after Aineias, whom he found standing the last in the press, for Aineias was ever wroth against goodly Priam, for that Priam gave him no honour, despite his valour among men. So Deïphobos stood by him, and spake winged words to him: "Aineias, thou counsellor of the Trojans, now verily there is great need that thou shouldst succour thy sister's husband, if any care for kin doth touch thee. Nay follow, let us succour Alkathoos, thy sister's husband, who of old did cherish thee in his hall, while thou wert but a little one, and now, lo, spearfamed Idomeneus hath stripped him of his arms!"

So he spake, and roused the spirit in the breast of Aineias, who went to seek Idomeneus, with high thoughts of war. But fear took not hold upon Idomeneus, as though he had been some tender boy, but he stood at bay, like a boar on the hills that trusteth to his strength, and abides the great assailing throng of men in a lonely place. Even so stood spear-famed Idomeneus at bay against Aineias, that came to the rescue, and gave ground no whit, but called on his comrades, glancing to Askalaphos, and Aphareus, and Deïpyros, and Meriones, and Antilochos, all masters of the war-cry; them he spurred up to battle, and spake winged words: "Hither, friends, and rescue me, all alone as I am, and terribly I dread the onslaught of swift-footed Aineias, that is assailing me; for he is right strong to destroy men in battle, and he hath the flower of youth, the greatest avail that may be."

So he spake, and they all, being of one spirit in their hearts, stood hard by each other, with buckler laid on shoulder. But Aineias, on the other side, cried to his comrades, glancing to Deïphobos, and Paris, and noble Agenor, that with him were leaders of the Trojans; and then the hosts followed them, as sheep follow their leader to the water from the pasture.

Then they rushed in close fight around Alkathoos with their long spears, and round their breasts the bronze rang terribly, as they aimed at each other in the press, while two men of war beyond the rest, Aineias and Idomeneus, the peers of Ares, were each striving to hew the flesh of the other with the pitiless bronze. Now Aineias first cast at Idomeneus, who steadily watching him avoided the spear of bronze, and the point of Aineias went quivering in the earth, since vainly it had flown from his stalwart hand. But Idomeneus smote Oinomaos in the midst of the belly, and brake the plate of his corslet, and the bronze let forth the bowels through the corslet, and he fell in the dust and clutched the earth in his palms. And Idomeneus drew forth the far-shadowing spear from the dead, but could not avail to strip the rest of the fair armour from his shoulders, for the darts pressed hard on him. Nay, and his feet no longer served him firmly in a charge, nor could he rush after his own spear, nor avoid the foe. Wherefore in close fight he still held off the pitiless day of destiny, but in retreat his feet no longer bore him swiftly from the battle. And as he was slowly departing, Deïphobos aimed at him with his shining spear, for verily he ever cherished a steadfast hatred against Idomeneus. But this time, too, he missed him, and smote Askalaphos, the son of Enyalios, with his dart, and the strong spear passed through his shoulder, and he fell in the dust, and clutched the earth in his outstretched hand.

Now the people rushed in close fight around Askalaphos, and Deïphobos tore from Askalaphos his shining helm, but Meriones, the peer of swift Ares, leaped forward and smote the arm of Deïphobos with his spear, and from his hand the vizored casque fell clanging to the ground. And Meriones sprang forth instantly, like a vulture, and drew the strong spear from the shoulder of Deïphobos, and fell back among the throng of his comrades. But the own brother of Deïphobos, Polites, stretched his hands round his waist, and led him forth from the evil din of war, even till he came to the swift horses, that waited for him behind the battle and the fight. These bore him heavily groaning to the city, worn with his hurt, and the blood ran down from his newly wounded arm.

So they fought like flaming fire, but Hector, beloved of Zeus had not heard nor knew at all that, on the left of the ships, his host was being subdued by the Argives, and soon would the Achaians have won renown, so mighty was the Holder and Shaker of the earth that urged on the Argives; yea, and himself mightily defended them. But Hector kept where at first he had leaped within the walls and the gate, and broken the serried ranks of shield-bearing Danaans, even where were the ships of Aias and Protesilaos, drawn up on the beach of the hoary sea, while above the wall was builded lowest, and thereby chiefly the heroes and their horses were raging in battle.

Now never at all did Aias, the swift son of Oileus, depart from the side of Aias, son of Telamon, nay, not for an instant, but even as in fallow land two wine-dark oxen with equal heart strain at the shapen plough, and round the roots of their horns springeth up abundant sweat, and nought sunders them but the polished yoke, as they labour through the furrow, till the end of the furrow brings them up, so stood the two Aiantes close by each other. Now verily did many and noble hosts of his comrades follow with the son of Telamon, and bore his shield when labour and sweat came upon his limbs. But the Lokrians followed not with the high-hearted son of Oileus, for their hearts were not steadfast in close brunt of battle, seeing that they had no helmets of bronze, shadowy with horse-hair plumes, nor round shields, nor ashen spears, but trusting in bows and well-twisted slings of sheep's wool, they followed with him to Ilios. Therewith, in the war, they shot thick and fast, and brake the ranks of the Trojans. So the one party in front contended with the Trojans, and with Hector arrayed in bronze, while the others from behind kept shooting from their ambush, and the Trojans lost all memory of the joy of battle, for the arrows confounded them.

There then right ruefully from the ships and the huts would the Trojans have withdrawn to windy Ilios, had not Polydamas come near valiant Hector and said: "Behold all about thee the circle of war is blazing, but the great-hearted

Trojans, now that they have got down the wall, are some with their arms standing aloof and some are fighting, few men against a host, being scattered among the ships. Nay, withdraw thee, and call hither all the best of the warriors. Thereafter shall we take all counsel carefully, whether we should fall on the ships of many benches, if indeed god willeth to give us victory, or after counsel held, should return unharmed from the ships. For verily I fear lest the Achaians repay their debt of yesterday, since by the ships there tarrieth a man insatiate of war, and never, methinks, will he wholly stand aloof from battle."

So spake Polydamas, and his safe counsel pleased Hector well, who spake to him winged words and said: "Polydamas, do thou stay here all the best of the host, but I will go thither to face the war, and swiftly will return again, when I have straitly laid on them my commands."

So he spake, and set forth, in semblance like a snowy mountain, and shouting aloud he flew through the Trojans and allies. And they all sped to Polydamas, the kindly son of Panthoos, when they heard the voice of Hector. But he went seeking Deïphobos, and the strong prince Helenos, and Adamas son of Asios, and Asios son of Hyrtakos, among the warriors in the foremost line, if anywhere he might find them. But them he found not at all unharmed, nor free of bane, but, lo, some among the sterns of the ships of the Achaians lay lifeless, slain by the hands of the Argives, and some were within the wall wounded by thrust or cast. But one he readily found, on the left of the dolorous battle, goodly Alexandros, the lord of fair-tressed Helen, heartening his comrades and speeding them to war. And he drew near to him, and addressed him with words of shame: "Thou evil Paris, fairest of face, thou that lustest for women, thou seducer, where, prithee, are Deïphobos, and the strong prince Helenos, and Adamas son of Asios, and Asios son of Hyrtakos, and where is Othryoneus? Now hath all high Ilios perished utterly. Now, too, thou seest, is sheer destruction sure."

Then godlike Alexandros answered him again saying: "Hector, since thy mind is to blame one that is blameless, some other day might I rather withdraw me from the war, since my mother bare not even me wholly a coward. For from the time that thou didst gather the battle of thy comrades about the ships, from that hour do we abide here, and war with the Danaans ceaselessly; and our comrades concerning whom thou inquirest are slain. Only Deïphobos and the strong prince Helenos have both withdrawn, both of them being wounded in the hand with long spears, for Kronion kept death away from them. But now lead on, wheresoever thy heart and spirit bid thee, and we will follow with thee eagerly, nor methinks shall we lack for valour, as far as we have strength; but beyond his strength may no man fight, howsoever eager he be."

So spake the hero, and persuaded his brother's heart, and they went forth where the war and din were thickest, round Kebriones, and noble Polydamas, and Phalkes, and Orthaios, and godlike Polyphetes, and Palmys, and Askanios, and Morys, son of Hippotion, who had come in their turn, out of deepsoiled Askanie, on the morn before, and now Zeus urged them to fight. And these set forth like the blast of violent winds, that rushes earthward beneath the

thunder of father Zeus, and with marvellous din doth
mingle with the salt sea, and therein are many swelling
waves of the loud roaring sea, arched over and white with
foam, some vanward, others in the rear; even so the Trojans
arrayed in van and rear and shining with bronze, followed
after their leaders.

BOOK XIV

How Sleep and Hera beguiled Zeus to slumber on the heights of
Ida, and Poseidon spurred on the Achaians to resist Hector,
and how Hector was wounded.

YET the cry of battle escaped not Nestor, albeit at his
wine, but he spake winged words to the son of
Asklepios: "Bethink thee, noble Machaon, what had best
be done; lo, louder waxes the cry of the strong warriors by
the ships. Nay, now sit where thou art, and drink the bright
wine, till Hekamede of the fair tresses shall heat warm
water for the bath, and wash away the clotted blood, but I
will speedily go forth and come to a place of outlook."

Therewith he took the well-wrought shield of his son,
horse-taming Thrasymedes, which was lying in the hut, all
glistering with bronze, for the son had the shield of his
father. And he seized a strong spear, with a point of keen
bronze, and stood outside the hut, and straightway beheld a
deed of shame, the Achaians fleeing in rout, and the high-
hearted Trojans driving them, and the wall of the Achaians
was overthrown. And as when the great sea is troubled
with a dumb wave, and dimly bodes the sudden paths of the
shrill winds, but is still unmoved nor yet rolled forward or to
either side, until some steady gale comes down from Zeus,
even so the old man pondered,—his mind divided this way
and that,—whether he should fare into the press of the

Danaans of the swift steeds, or go after Agamemnon, son of Atreus, shepherd of the host. And thus as he pondered, it seemed to him the better counsel to go to the son of Atreus.

Now the kings, the fosterlings of Zeus, encountered Nestor, as they went up from the ships, even they that were wounded with the bronze, Tydeus' son, and Odysseus, and Agamemnon, son of Atreus. For far apart from the battle were their ships drawn up, on the shore of the grey sea, for these were the first they had drawn up to the plain, but had builded the wall in front of the hindmost. For in no wise might the beach, wide as it was, hold all the ships, and the host was straitened. Wherefore they drew up the ships row within row, and filled up the wide mouth of all the shore that the headlands held between them. Therefore the kings were going together, leaning on their spears, to look on the war and fray, and the heart of each was sore within his breast. And the old man met them, even Nestor, and caused the spirit to fail within the breasts of the Achaians.

And mighty Agamemnon spake and accosted him: "O Nestor, son of Neleus, great glory of the Achaians, wherefore dost thou come hither and hast deserted the war, the bane of men? Lo, I fear the accomplishment of the word that dread Hector spake, and the threat wherewith he threatened us, speaking in the assembly of the Trojans, namely, that never would he return to Ilios from the ships, till he had burned the ships with fire, and slain the men."

Then Nestor of Gerenia the knight answered him, saying: "Verily these things are now at hand, and being accomplished. For, lo, the wall is overthrown, wherein we trusted that it should be an unbroken bulwark of the ships and of our own bodies. But let us take counsel, how these things may best be done, if wit may do aught: but into the war I counsel not that we should go down, for in no wise may a wounded man do battle."

Then Agamemnon king of men answered him again: "Let us drag down the ships that are drawn up in the first line near to the sea, and speed them all forth to the salt sea divine, and moor them far out with stones, till the divine night comes, if even at night the Trojans will refrain from war, and then might we drag down all the ships. For there is no shame in fleeing from ruin, yea, even in the night. Better doth he fare who flees from trouble, than he that is overtaken."

Then, looking on him sternly, spake Odysseus of many counsels: "Atreus' son, what word hath passed the door of thy lips? Man of mischief, sure thou shouldst lead some other inglorious army, not be king among us, to whom Zeus hath given it, from youth even unto age, to wind the skein of grievous wars, till every man of us perish. Art thou indeed so eager to leave the wide-wayed city of the Trojans, the city for which we endure with sorrow so many evils? Be silent, lest some other of the Achaians hear this word, that no man should so much as suffer to pass through his mouth, none that understandeth in his heart how to speak fit counsel, none that is a sceptred king, and hath hosts obeying him so many as the Argives over whom thou reignest. For the Achaians will not make good the war, when the ships are drawn down to the salt sea, but will look round about to flee, and withdraw from battle. There will thy counsel work a mischief, O marshal of the host!"

Then the king of men, Agamemnon, answered him: "Odysseus, right sharply hast thou touched my heart with thy stern reproof: nay, I do not bid the sons of the Achaians to drag, against their will, the well-timbered ships to the salt sea. Now perchance there may be one who will utter a wiser counsel than this of mine,—a young man or an old,—welcome would it be to me."

Then Diomedes of the loud war-cry spake also among them: "The man is near,—not long shall we seek him, if ye be willing to be persuaded of me, and each of you be not resentful at all, because in years I am the youngest among you. Let us go down to the battle, wounded as we are, since we needs must; and then might we hold ourselves aloof from the battle, beyond the range of darts, lest any take wound upon wound; but the others will we spur on, even them that aforetime gave place to their passion, and stand apart, and fight not."

So he spake, and they all heard him readily, and obeyed him. And they set forth, led by Agamemnon the king of men.

Now the renowned Earth-shaker held no vain watch, but went with them in the guise of an ancient man, and he seized the right hand of Agamemnon, Atreus' son, and uttering winged words he spake to him, saying: "Atreides, now methinks the ruinous heart of Achilles rejoices in his breast, as he beholds the slaughter and flight of the Achaians, since he hath no wisdom, not a grain. Nay, even so may he perish likewise, and god mar him. But with thee the blessed gods are not utterly wroth, nay, even yet methinks the leaders and rulers of the Trojans will cover the wide plain with dust, and thyself shalt see them fleeing to the city from the ships and the huts."

So spake he, and shouted mightily, as he sped over the plain. And loud as nine thousand men, or ten thousand cry in battle, when they join the strife of war, so mighty was the cry that the strong Shaker of the earth sent forth from his breast, and great strength he put into the heart of each of the Achaians, to strive and war unceasingly.

Now Hera of the golden throne stood on the peak of Olympus, and saw with her eyes, and anon knew him that was her brother and her lord's going to and fro through the glorious fight, and she rejoiced in her heart. And she beheld Zeus sitting on the topmost crest of many-fountained Ida, and to her heart he was hateful. Then she took thought, the ox-eyed lady Hera, how she might beguile the mind of aegis-bearing Zeus. And this seemed to her in her heart to be the best counsel, namely to fare to Ida, when she had well adorned herself, if perchance a sweet sleep and a kindly she could pour on his eye lids and his crafty wits. And she set forth to her bower, that her dear son Hephaistos had fashioned, and therein had made fast strong doors on the pillars, with a secret bolt, that no other god might open. There did she enter in and closed the shining doors. With ambrosia first did she cleanse every stain from her winsome body, and anointed her with olive oil, ambrosial, soft, and of a sweet savour; if it were but shaken, in the bronze-floored mansion of Zeus, the savour thereof went right forth to earth and heaven. Therewith she anointed her fair body, and combed her hair, and with her hands plaited her shining tresses, fair and ambrosial, flowing from her immortal head. Then she clad her in her fragrant robe that Athene wrought delicately for her, and therein set many things beautifully made, and fastened it over her breast with clasps of gold. And she girdled it with a girdle arrayed with a hundred tassels, and she set earrings in her pierced ears, earrings of three drops, and glistering, therefrom shone grace abundantly. And with a veil over all the peerless goddess veiled herself, a fair new veil, bright as the sun, and beneath her shining feet she bound goodly sandals. But when she had adorned her body with all her array, she went forth from her bower, and called Aphrodite apart from the other gods, and spake to her, saying: "Wilt thou obey me, dear child, in that which I shall tell thee? or wilt thou refuse, with a grudge in thy heart, because I succour the Danaans, and thou the Trojans?"

Then Aphrodite the daughter of Zeus answered her: "Hera, goddess queen, daughter of mighty Kronos, say the thing that is in thy mind, my heart bids me fulfil it, if fulfil it I may, and if it may be accomplished."

Then with crafty purpose the lady Hera answered her: "Give me now Love and Desire wherewith thou dost overcome all the Immortals, and mortal men. For I am going to visit the limits of the bountiful Earth, and Okeanos, father of the gods, and mother Tethys, who reared me well and nourished me in their halls, having taken me from Rhea, when far-seeing Zeus imprisoned Kronos beneath the earth and the unvintaged sea. Them am I going to visit, and their endless strife will I loose, for already this long time they hold apart from each other, since wrath hath settled in their hearts. If with words I might persuade their hearts, and bring them back to love, ever should I be called dear to them and worshipful."

Then laughter-loving Aphrodite answered her again: "It may not be, nor seemly were it, to deny that thou askest, for thou sleepest in the arms of Zeus, the chief of gods."

Therewith from her breast she loosed the broidered girdle, fair-wrought, wherein are all her enchantments; therein are love, and desire, and loving converse, that steals the wits even of the wise. This girdle she laid in her hands, and spake, and said: "Lo now, take this girdle and lay it up in thy bosom, this fair-wrought girdle, wherein all things are fashioned; methinks thou wilt not return with that unaccomplished, which in thy heart thou desirest."

So spake she, and the ox-eyed lady Hera smiled, and smiling laid up the zone within her breast.

Then the daughter of Zeus, Aphrodite, went to her house, and Hera, rushing down, left the peak of Olympus, and sped over the snowy hills of the Thracian horsemen, even over the topmost crests, nor grazed the ground with her feet, and from Athos she fared across the foaming sea, and came to Lemnos, the city of godlike Thoas. There she met Sleep, the brother of Death, and clasped her hand in his, and spake and called him by name: "Sleep, lord of all gods and of all men, if ever thou didst hear my word, obey me again even now, and I will be grateful to thee always. Lull me, I pray thee, the shining eyes of Zeus beneath his brows. And gifts I will give to thee, even a fair throne, imperishable for ever, a golden throne, that Hephaistos the Lame, mine own child, shall fashion skilfully, and will set beneath it a footstool for the feet, for thee to set thy shining feet upon, when thou art at a festival. Nay come, and I will give thee one of the younger of the Graces, to wed and to be called thy wife."

So she spake, and Sleep was glad, and answered and said: "Come now, swear to me by the inviolable water of Styx, and with one of thy hands grasp the bounteous earth, and with the other the shining sea, that all may be witnesses to us, even all the gods below that are with Kronos, that verily thou wilt give me one of the younger of the Graces, even Pasithea, that myself do long for all my days."

So spake he, nor did she disobey, the white-armed goddess Hera; she sware as he bade her, and called all the gods by name, even those below Tartaros that are called Titans. But when she had sworn and ended that oath, the twain left the citadel of Lemnos, and of Imbros, clothed on in mist, and swiftly they accomplished the way. To many-fountained Ida they came, the mother of wild beasts, to Lekton, where first they left the sea, and they twain fared above the dry land, and the topmost forest waved beneath their feet. There Sleep halted, ere the eyes of Zeus beheld him, and alighted on a tall pine tree, the loftiest pine that then in all Ida rose through the nether to the upper air. But Hera swiftly drew nigh to topmost Gargaros, the highest crest of Ida, and Zeus the cloud-gatherer beheld her. And as he saw her, so love came over his deep heart, and he stood before her, and spoke, and said: "Hera, with what desire comest thou thus hither from Olympus, and thy horses and chariot are not here, whereon thou mightst ascend?"

Then with crafty purpose lady Hera answered him: "I am going to visit the limits of the bountiful Earth, and

Okeanos, father of the gods, and mother Tethys, who reared me well and cherished me in their halls. Them am I going to visit, and their endless strife will I loose, for already this long time they hold apart from each other, since wrath hath settled in their hearts. But my horses are standing at the foot of many-fountained Ida, my horses that shall bear me over wet and dry. And now it is because of thee that I am thus come hither, down from Olympus, lest perchance thou mightest be wroth with me hereafter, if silently I were gone to the mansion of deep-flowing Okeanos."

Then Zeus, the gatherer of the clouds, answered her and said: "Hera, thither mayst thou go on a later day. For never once as thus did the love of goddess or woman so mightily overflow and conquer the heart within my breast."

Thus slept the Father in quiet on the crest of Gargaros, by Sleep and love overcome. But sweet Sleep started and ran to the ships of the Achaians, to tell his tidings to the god that holdeth and shaketh the earth. And he stood near him, and spake winged words: "Eagerly now, Poseidon, do thou aid the Danaans, and give them glory for a little space, while yet Zeus sleepeth, for over him have I shed soft slumber, and Hera hath beguiled him."

So he spake, and passed to the renowned tribes of men, and still the more did he set on Poseidon to aid the Danaans, who straightway sprang far afront of the foremost, and called to them: "Argives, are we again to yield the victory to Hector, son of Priam, that he may take our ships and win renown? Nay, even so he saith and declareth that he will do, for that Achilles by the hollow ships abides angered at heart. But for him there will be no such extreme regret, if we spur us on to aid each the other. Nay come, as I command, let us all obey. Let us harness us in the best shields that are in the host, and the greatest, and cover our heads with shining helms, and take the longest spears in our hands, and so go forth. Yea, and I will lead the way, and methinks that Hector, son of Priam, will not long await us, for all his eagerness. And whatsoever man is steadfast in battle, and hath a small buckler on his shoulder, let him give it to a worse man, and harness him in a large shield."

So spake he, and they heard him eagerly and obeyed him. And them the kings themselves arrayed, wounded as they were, Tydeus' son, and Odysseus, and Agamemnon, son of Atreus. They went through all the host, and made exchange of weapons of war. The good arms did the good warrior harness him in, the worse he gave to the worse. But when they had done on the shining bronze about their bodies, they started on the march, and Poseidon led them, the Shaker of the earth, with a dread sword of fine edge in his strong hand, like unto lightning; wherewith it is not permitted that any should mingle in woful war, but fear holds men afar therefrom. But the Trojans on the other side was renowned Hector arraying. Then did they now strain the fiercest strife of war, even dark-haired Poseidon and glorious Hector, one succouring the Trojans, the other with the Argives. And the sea washed up to the huts and ships of the Argives, and they gathered together with a mighty cry. Not so loudly bellows the wave of the sea against the land, stirred up from the deep by the harsh breath of the north wind, nor so loud is the roar of burning fire in the glades of a mountain, when it springs to burn up the forest, nor calls the wind so loudly in the high leafy tresses of the trees, when it rages and roars its loudest, as then was the cry of the Trojans and Achaians, shouting dreadfully as they rushed upon each other.

First glorious Hector cast with his spear at Aias, who was facing him full, and did not miss, striking him where two belts were stretched across his breast, the belt of his shield, and of his silver-studded sword; these guarded his tender flesh. And Hector was enraged because his swift spear had flown vainly from his hand, and he retreated into the throng of his fellows, avoiding Fate.

Then as he was departing the great Telamonian Aias smote him with a huge stone; for many stones, the props of swift ships, were rolled among the feet of the fighters; one of these he lifted, and smote Hector on the breast, over the shield-rim, near the neck, and made him spin like a top with the blow, that he reeled round and round. And even as when an oak falls uprooted beneath the stroke of father Zeus, and a dread savour of brimstone arises therefrom, and whoso stands near and beholds it has no more courage, for dread is the bolt of great Zeus, even so fell mighty Hector straightway in the dust. And the spear fell from his hand, but his shield and helm were made fast to him, and round him rang his arms adorned with bronze.

Then with a loud cry they ran up, the sons of the Achaians, hoping to drag him away, and they cast showers of darts. But not one availed to wound or smite the shepherd of the host, before that might be the bravest gathered about him, Polydamas, and Aineias, and goodly Agenor, and Sarpedon, leader of the Lykians, and noble Glaukos, and of the rest not one was heedless of him, but they held their round shields in front of him, and his comrades lifted him in their arms, and bare him out of the battle, till he reached his swift horses that were standing waiting for him, with the charioteer and the fair-dight chariot at the rear of the combat and the war. These toward the city bore him heavily moaning. Now when they came to the ford of the fair-flowing river, of eddying Xanthos, that immortal Zeus begat, there they lifted him from the chariot to the ground, and poured water over him, and he gat back his breath, and looked up with his eyes, and sitting on his heels kneeling, he vomited black blood. Then again he sank back on the ground, and black night covered his eyes, the stroke still conquering his spirit.

BOOK XV

Zeus awakening, biddeth Apollo revive Hector, and restore the fortunes of the Trojans. Fire is thrown on the ship of Protesilaos.

Now when they had sped in flight across the palisade and trench, and many were overcome at the hands of the Danaans, the rest were stayed, and abode beside the chariots in confusion, and pale with terror, and Zeus awoke, on the peaks of Ida, beside Hera of the golden throne. Then he leaped up, and stood, and beheld the Trojans and Achaians, those in flight, and these driving them on from the rear, even the Argives, and among them the prince Poseidon. And Hector he saw lying on the plain, and around him sat his comrades, and he was gasping with difficult breath, and his mind wandering, and was vomiting blood, for it was not the weakest of the Achaians that had smitten him. Beholding him, the father of men and gods had pity on him, and terribly he spoke to Hera, with fierce look: "O thou ill to deal with, Hera, verily it is thy crafty wile that has made noble Hector cease from the fight, and has terrified the host. Nay, but yet I know not whether thou mayst not be the first to reap the fruits of thy cruel treason, and I beat thee with stripes. Dost thou not remember, when thou wert hung from on high, and from thy feet I suspended two anvils, and round thy hands fastened a golden bond that might not be broken? And thou didst hang in the clear air and the clouds and the gods were wroth in high Olympus, but they could not come round and unloose thee."

So spake he, and the ox-eyed lady Hera shuddered, and spake unto him winged words, saying: "Let earth now be witness hereto, and wide heaven above, and that falling water of Styx, the greatest oath and the most terrible to the blessed gods, and thine own sacred head, and our own bridal bed, whereby never would I forswear myself, that not by my will does earth-shaking Poseidon trouble the Trojans and Hector, and succour them of the other part. Nay, it is his own soul that urgeth and commandeth him, and he had pity on the Achaians, when he beheld them hard pressed beside the ships. I would even counsel him also to go even where thou, lord of the storm-cloud, mayst lead him."

So spake she, and the father of gods and men smiled, and answering her he spake winged words: "If thou, of a truth, O ox-eyed lady Hera, wouldst hereafter abide of one mind with me among the immortal gods, thereon would Poseidon, howsoever much his wish be contrariwise, quickly turn his mind otherwhere, after thy heart and mine. But if indeed thou speakest the truth and soothly, go thou now among the tribes of the gods, and call Iris to come hither, and Apollo, the renowned archer, that Iris may go among the host of mail-clad Achaians and tell Poseidon the prince to cease from the war, and get him unto his own house. But let Phoebus Apollo spur Hector on to the war, and breathe strength into him again, and make him forget his anguish, that now wears down his heart, and drive the Achaians back again, when he hath stirred in them craven fear. Let

them flee and fall among the many-benched ships of Achilles
son of Peleus, and he shall rouse his own comrade, Patroklos; and him shall renowned Hector slay with the spear, in
front of Ilios, after that he has slain many other youths, and
among them my son, noble Sarpedon. In wrath therefor
shall goodly Achilles slay Hector. From that hour verily
will I cause a new pursuit from the ships that shall endure
continually, even until the Achaians take steep Ilios,
through the counsels of Athene. But before that hour
neither do I cease in my wrath, nor will I suffer any other
of the Immortals to help the Danaans there, before I
accomplish that desire of the son of Peleus, as I promised
him at the first, and confirmed the same with a nod of my
head, on that day when the goddess Thetis clasped my
knees, imploring me to honour Achilles, the sacker of
cities."

So spake he, nor did the white-armed goddess Hera disobey him, and she sped down from the hills of Ida to high
Olympus, and went among the gathering of the immortal
gods. And she called Apollo without the hall and Iris, that
is the messenger of the immortal gods, and she spake
winged words, and addressed them, saying: "Zeus bids you
go to Ida as swiftly as may be, and when ye have gone, and
looked on the face of Zeus, do ye whatsoever he shall order
and command."

And these twain came before the face of Zeus the cloud
gatherer, and stood there, and he was nowise displeased at
heart when he beheld them, for that speedily they had
obeyed the words of his dear wife. And to Iris first he spake
winged words: "Go, get thee, swift Iris, to the prince Posei-

don, and tell him all these things, nor be a false messenger. Command him to cease from war and battle, and to go among the tribes of the gods, or into the bright sea. But if he will not obey my words, but will hold me in no regard, then let him consider in his heart and mind, lest he dare not for all his strength to abide me when I come against him, since I deem me to be far mightier than he, and elder born."

So spake he, nor did the wind-footed fleet Iris disobey him, but went down the hills of Ida to sacred Ilios. And as when snow or chill hail fleets from the clouds beneath the stress of the North Wind born in the clear air, so fleetly she fled in her eagerness, swift Iris, and drew near the renowned Earth-shaker and spake to him the message of Zeus. And he left the host of the Achaians, and passed to the sea, and sank, and sorely they missed him, the heroes of the Achaians.

Then Zeus, the gatherer of the clouds, spake to Apollo, saying: "Go now, dear Phoebus, to Hector of the helm of bronze. Let glorious Hector be thy care, and rouse in him great wrath even till the Achaians come in their flight to the ships, and the Hellespont. And from that moment will I devise word and deed wherewithal the Achaians may take breath again from their toil."

So spake he, nor was Apollo deaf to the word of the Father, but he went down the hills of Ida like a fleet falcon, the bane of doves, that is the swiftest of flying things. And he found the son of wise-hearted Priam, noble Hector, sitting up, no longer lying, for he had but late got back his life, and knew the comrades around him, and his gasping and his sweat had ceased, from the moment when the will of aegis-bearing Zeus began to revive him. Then far-darting Apollo stood near him, and spake to him: "Hector, son of Priam, why dost thou sit fainting apart from the others? Is it perchance that some trouble cometh upon thee?"

Then, with faint breath answered him Hector of the glancing helm: "Nay, but who art thou, best of the gods, who enquirest of me face to face? Dost thou not know that by the hindmost row of the ships of the Achaians, Aias of the loud war-cry smote me on the breast with a stone, as I was slaying his comrades, and made me cease from mine impetuous might? And verily I deemed that this very day I should pass to the dead, and the house of Hades, when I had gasped my life away."

Then prince Apollo the Far-darter answered him again: "Take courage now, so great an ally hath the son of Kronos sent thee out of Ida, to stand by thee and defend thee, even Phoebus Apollo of the golden sword, me who of old defend thee, thyself and the steep citadel. But come now, bid thy many charioteers drive their swift steeds against the hollow ships, and I will go before and make smooth all the way for the chariots, and will put to flight the Achaian heroes."

So he spake, and breathed great might into the shepherd of the host, and even as when a stalled horse, full fed at the manger, breaks his tether and speedeth at the gallop over the plain exultingly, being wont to bathe in the fair-flowing stream, and holds his head on high, and the mane floweth about his shoulders, and he trusteth in his glory, and nimbly his knees bear him to the haunts and pasture of the mares, even so Hector lightly moved his feet and knees, urging on his horsemen, when he heard the voice of the god. But as when hounds and country folk pursue a horned stag, or a wild goat, that steep rock and shady wood save from them, nor is it their lot to find him, but at their clamour a bearded lion hath shown himself on the way, and lightly turned them all despite their eagerness, even so the Danaans for a while followed on always in their companies, smiting with swords and double-pointed spears, but when they saw Hector going up and down the ranks of men, then were they afraid, and the hearts of all fell to their feet.

Then to them spake Thoas, son of Andraimon, far the best of the Aitolians, skilled in throwing the dart, and good in close fight, and in council did few of the Achaians surpass him, when the young men were striving in debate; he made harangue and spake among them: "Alas, and verily a great marvel is this I behold with mine eyes, how he hath again arisen, and hath avoided the Fates, even Hector. Surely each of us hoped in his heart, that he had died beneath the hand of Aias, son of Telamon. But some one of the gods again hath delivered and saved Hector, who verily hath loosened the knees of many of the Danaans, as methinks will befall even now, for not without the will of loud-thundering Zeus doth he rise in the front ranks, thus eager for battle. But come, as I declare let us all obey. Let us bid the throng turn back to the ships, but let us as many as avow us to be the best in the host, take our stand, if perchance first we may meet him, and hold him off with outstretched spears, and he, methinks, for all his eagerness, will fear at heart to enter into the press of the Danaans."

So spake he, and they heard him eagerly, and obeyed him. They that were with Aias and the prince Idomeneus, and Teukros, and Neriones, and Meges the peer of Ares, called to all the best of the warriors and sustained the fight with Hector and the Trojans, but behind them the multitude returned to the ships of the Achaians.

Now the Trojans drave forward in close ranks, and with long strides Hector led them, while in front of him went Phoebus Apollo, his shoulders wrapped in cloud, and still he held the fell aegis, dread, circled with a shaggy fringe, and gleaming, that Hephaistos the smith gave to Zeus, to bear for the terror of men; with this in his hands did he lead the host.

Now the Argives abode them in close ranks, and shrill the cry arose on both sides, and the arrows leaped from the bow-strings, and many spears from stalwart hands, whereof some stood fast in the flesh of young men swift in fight, but many halfway, ere ever they reached the white flesh, stuck in the ground, longing to glut themselves with flesh. Now so long as Phoebus Apollo held the aegis unmoved in his hands, so long the darts smote either side amain, and the folk fell. But when he looked face to face on the Danaans of the swift steeds, and shook the aegis, and himself shouted mightily, he quelled their heart in their breast, and they forgot their impetuous valour. And as when two wild beasts drive in confusion a herd of kine, or a great flock of sheep, in the dark hour of black night, coming swiftly on them when the herdsman is not by, even so were the Achaians terror-stricken and strengthless, for Apollo sent a panic among them, but still gave renown to the Trojans and Hector.

And Hector smote his horses on the shoulder with the lash, and called aloud on the Trojans along the ranks. And they all cried out, and level with his held the steeds that drew their chariots, with a marvellous din, and in front of them Phoebus Apollo lightly dashed down with his feet the banks of the deep ditch, and cast them into the midst thereof, making a bridgeway long and wide as is a spear-cast, when a man throws to make trial of his strength. Thereby the Trojans poured forward in their battalions, while in their van Apollo held the splendid aegis. And most easily did he cast down the wall of the Achaians, as when a boy scatters the sand beside the sea, first making sand build-ings for sport in his childishness, and then again, in his sport, confounding them with his feet and hands; even so didst thou, archer Apollo, confound the long toil and labour of the Argives, and among them rouse a panic fear.

So they were halting, and abiding by the ships, calling each to other; and lifting their hands to all the gods did each man pray vehemently, and chiefly prayed Nestor, the Warden of the Achaians, stretching his hand towards the starry heaven: "O father Zeus, if ever any one of us in wheat-bearing Argos did burn to thee fat thighs of bull or sheep, and prayed that he might return, and thou didst promise and assent thereto, of these things be thou mindful, and avert, Olympian, the pitiless day, nor suffer the Trojans thus to overcome the Achaians."

So spake he in his prayer, and Zeus, the Lord of counsel, thundered loudly, hearing the prayers of the ancient son of Neleus.

But the Trojans when they heard the thunder of aegis-bearing Zeus, rushed yet the more eagerly upon the Argives, and were mindful of the joy of battle. And as when a great wave of the wide sea sweeps over the bulwarks of a ship, the might of the wind constraining it, which chiefly swells the waves, even so did the Trojans with a great cry bound over the wall, and drave their horses on, and at the hindmost row of the ships were fighting hand to hand with double-pointed spears, the Trojans from the chariots, but the Achaians climbing up aloft, from the black ships with long pikes that they had lying in the ships for battle at sea, jointed pikes shod at the head with bronze.

Now the Trojans, like ravening lions, rushed upon the ships, fulfilling the behests of Zeus, that ever was rousing their great wrath, but softened the temper of the Argives, and took away their glory, while he spurred on the others. For the heart of Zeus was set on giving glory to Hector, the son of Priam, that withal he might cast fierce-blazing fire, unwearied, upon the beaked ships, and so fulfil all the presumptuous prayer of Thetis; wherefore wise-counselling Zeus awaited, till his eyes should see the glare of a burning ship. For even from that hour was he to ordain the backward chase of the Trojans from the ships, and to give glory to the Danaans. With this design was he rousing Hector, Priam's son, that himself was right eager, against the hollow ships. For short of life was he to be, yea, and already Pallas Athene was urging against him the day of destiny, at the hand of the son of Peleus. And fain he was to break the ranks of men, trying them wheresoever he saw the thickest press, and the goodliest harness. Yet not even so might he break them for all his eagerness. Nay, they stood firm, and embattled like a steep rock and a great, hard by the hoary sea, a rock that abides the swift paths of the shrill winds, and the swelling waves that roar against it. Even so the Danaans steadfastly abode the Trojans and fled not away. But Hector shining with fire on all sides leaped on the throng, and fell upon them, as when beneath the storm-clouds a fleet wave reared of the winds falls on a swift ship, and she is all hidden with foam, and the dread blast of the wind roars against the sail, and the sailors fear, and tremble in their hearts, for by but a little way are they borne forth from death, even so the spirit was torn in the breasts of the Achaians.

So again keen battle was set by the ships. Thou wouldst deem that unwearied and unworn they met each other in war, so eagerly they fought. And in their striving they were minded thus; the Achaians verily deemed that never would they flee from the danger, but perish there, but the heart of each Trojan hoped in his breast, that they should fire the ships, and slay the heroes of the Achaians. With these imaginations they stood to each other, and Hector seized the stern of a seafaring ship, a fair ship, swift on the brine, that had borne Protesilaos to Troia, but brought him not back again to his own country. Now round his ship the Achaians and Trojans warred on each other hand to hand, nor far apart did they endure the flights of arrows, nor of darts, but standing hard each by other, with one heart, with sharp axes and hatchets they fought, and with great swords, and double-pointed spears. And many fair brands, dark-scabbarded and hilted, fell to the ground, some from the hands, some from off the shoulders of warring men, and the black earth ran with blood. But Hector, after that once he had seized the ship's stern, left not his hold, keeping the ensign in his hands, and he called to the Trojans: "Bring fire, and all with one voice do ye raise the war-cry; now hath Zeus given us the dearest day of all,—to take the ships that came hither against the will of the gods, and brought many woes upon us, by the cowardice of the elders, who withheld me when I was eager to fight at the sterns of the ships, and kept back the host. But if even then far-seeing Zeus did harm our wits, now he himself doth urge and command us onwards."

So spake he, and they set yet the fiercer on the Argives. And Aias no longer abode their onset, for he was driven back by the darts, but he withdrew a little,—thinking that now he should die,—on to the oarsman's bench of seven feet long, and he left the decks of the trim ship. There then he stood on the watch, and with his spear he ever drave the Trojans from the ships, whosoever brought unwearied fire, and ever he shouted terribly, calling to the Danaans: "O friends, Danaan heroes, men of Ares' company, play the man, my friends, and be mindful of impetuous valour. Do we deem that there be allies at our backs, or some wall stronger than this to ward off death from men? Verily there is not hard by any city arrayed with towers, whereby we might defend ourselves, having a host that could turn the balance of battle. Nay, but we are set down in the plain of the mailed men of Troy, with our backs against the sea, and far off from our own land. Therefore is safety in battle, and not in slackening from the fight."

So spake he, and rushed on ravening for battle, with his keen spear. And whosoever of the Trojans was coming against the ship with blazing fire, to pleasure Hector at his urging, him would Aias wound, awaiting him with his long spear, and twelve men in front of the ships at close quarters did he wound.

BOOK XVI

How Patroklos fought in the armour of Achilles, and drove the Trojans from the ships, but was slain at last by Hector.

So they were warring round the well-timbered ship, but Patroklos drew near Achilles, shepherd of the host, and he shed warm tears, even as a fountain of dark water that down a steep cliff pours its cloudy stream. And noble swift-footed Achilles when he beheld him was grieved for his sake, and accosted him, and spake winged words, saying: "Wherefore weepest thou, Patroklos, like a fond little maid, that runs by her mother's side, and bids her mother take her up, snatching at her gown, and hinders her in her going, and tearfully looks at her, till the mother takes her up? like her, Patroklos, dost thou let fall soft tears. Hast thou aught to tell to the Myrmidons, or to me myself, or is it some tidings out of Phthia that thou alone hast heard? Or dost thou lament for the sake of the Argives,—how they perish by the hollow ships through their own transgression? Speak out, and hide it not within thy spirit, that we may both know all."

But with a heavy groan didst thou speak unto him, O knight Patroklos: "O Achilles, son of Peleus, far the bravest of the Achaians, be not wroth, seeing that so great calamity has beset the Achaians. For verily all of them that aforetime were the best are lying among the ships, smitten

and wounded. Smitten is the son of Tydeus, strong
Diomedes, and wounded is Odysseus, spearman renowned,
and Agamemnon; and smitten is Eurypylos on the thigh
with an arrow. And about them the leeches skilled in medi-
cines are busy, healing their wounds, but thou art hard to
reconcile, Achilles. Never then may such wrath take hold of
me as that thou nursest; thou brave to the hurting of others.
What other men later born shall have profit of thee, if thou
dost not ward off base ruin from the Argives? Pitiless that
thou art, the knight Peleus was not then thy father, nor
Thetis thy mother, but the grey sea bare thee, and the sheer
cliffs, so untoward is thy spirit. But if in thy heart thou art
shunning some oracle, and thy lady mother hath told thee
somewhat from Zeus, yet me do thou send forth quickly,
and make the rest of the host of the Myrmidons follow me,
if yet any light may arise from me to the Danaans. And give
me thy harness to buckle about my shoulders, if perchance
the Trojans may take me for thee, and so abstain from
battle, and the warlike sons of the Achaians may take
breath, wearied as they be, for brief is the breathing in war.
And lightly might we that are fresh drive men wearied with
the battle back to the citadel, away from the ships and the
huts."

So he spake and besought him, in his unwittingness, for
truly it was to be his own evil death and fate that he prayed
for. Then to him in great heaviness spake swift-footed
Achilles: "Ah me, Patroklos of the seed of Zeus, what word
hast thou spoken? Neither take I heed of any oracle that I
wot of, nor yet has my lady mother told me somewhat from
Zeus, but this dread sorrow comes upon my heart and spirit,

from the hour that a man wishes to rob me who am his equal, and to take away my prize, for that he excels me in power. A dread sorrow to me is this, after all the toils that my heart hath endured. The maiden that the sons of the Achaians chose out for me as my prize, and that I won with my spear when I sacked a well-walled city, her has mighty Agamemnon the son of Atreus taken back out of my hands, as though I were but some sojourner dishonourable. But we will let bygones be bygones. No man may be angry of heart for ever, yet verily I said that I would not cease from my wrath, until that time when to mine own ships should come the war-cry and the battle. But do thou on thy shoulders my famous harness, and lead the war-loving Myrmidons to the fight, to ward off destruction from the ships, lest they even burn the ships with blazing fire, and take away our desired return. But when thou hast driven them from the ships, return, and even if the loud-thundering lord of Hera grant thee to win glory, yet long not thou apart from me to fight with the war-loving Trojans; thereby wilt thou minish mine honour. Neither do thou, exulting in war and strife, and slaying the Trojans, lead on toward Ilios, lest one of the eternal gods from Olympus come against thee; right dearly doth Apollo the Far-darter love them. Nay, return back when thou hast brought safety to the ships, and suffer the rest to fight along the plain. For would, O father Zeus, and Athene, and Apollo, would that not one of all the Trojans might escape death, nor one of the Argives, but that we twain might avoid destruction, that alone we might undo the sacred coronal of Troy."

So spake they each to other, but Aias no longer abode the

onset, for he was overpowered by darts; the counsel of Zeus was subduing him, and the shafts of the proud Trojans; and his bright helmet, being smitten, kept ringing terribly about his temples: for always it was smitten upon the fair-wrought cheek-pieces. Moreover his left shoulder was wearied, as steadfastly he held up his glittering shield, nor yet could they make him give ground, as they pressed on with their darts around him. And ever he was worn out with difficult breath, and much sweat kept running from all his limbs, nor had he a moment to draw breath, so on all sides was evil heaped on evil.

Tell me now, ye Muses that have mansions in Olympus, how first fire fell on the ships of the Achaians. Hector drew near, and the ashen spear of Aias he smote with his great sword, hard by the socket, behind the point, and shore it clean away, and the son of Telamon brandished in his hand no more than a pointless spear, and far from him the head of bronze fell ringing on the ground.

And Aias knew in his noble heart, and shuddered at the deeds of the gods, even how Zeus that thundereth on high did utterly cut off from him avail in war, and desired victory for the Trojans. Then Aias gave back out of the darts. But the Trojans cast on the swift ship unwearying fire, and instantly the inextinguishable flame streamed over her: so the fire begirt the stern, whereon Achilles smote his thighs, and spake to Patroklos: "Arise, Patroklos of the seed of Zeus, commander of the horsemen, for truly I see by the ships the rush of the consuming fire. Up then, lest they take the ships, and there be no more retreat; do on thy harness speedily, and I will summon the host."

So spake he, while Patroklos was harnessing him in shining bronze. His goodly greaves, fitted with silver clasps, he
first girt round his legs, and next did on around his breast
the well-dight starry corslet of the swift-footed son of
Aiakos. And round his shoulders he cast a sword of bronze,
with studs of silver, and next took the great and mighty
shield, and on his proud head set a well-wrought helm with
a horse-hair crest, and terribly nodded the crest from above.
Then seized he two strong lances that fitted his grasp, only
he took not the spear of the noble son of Aiakos, heavy, and
huge, and stalwart, that none other of the Achaians could
wield. And Patroklos bade Automedon to yoke the horses
speedily, even Automedon whom most he honoured after
Achilles, the breaker of the ranks of men, and whom he
held trustiest in battle to abide his call. And for him Automedon led beneath the yoke the swift horses, Xanthos and
Balios, that fly as swift as the winds, the horses that the
harpy Podarge bare to the West Wind, as she grazed on the
meadow by the stream of Okeanos. And in the sidetraces he
put the goodly Pedasos, that Achilles carried away, when
he took the city of Eetion; and being but a mortal steed, he
followed with the immortal horses.

Meanwhile Achilles went and harnessed all the Myrmidons in the huts with armour, and they gathered like ravening wolves with strength in their hearts unspeakable. And
among them all stood warlike Achilles urging on the horses
and the targeteers. And he aroused the heart and valour of
each of them, and the ranks were yet the closer serried when
they heard the prince. And as when a man builds the wall of
a high house with close-set stones, to avoid the might of the

winds, even so close were arrayed the helmets and bossy shields, and shield pressed on shield, helm on helm, and man on man, and the horse-hair crests on the bright helmet-ridges touched each other when they nodded, so close they stood by each other.

And straightway they poured forth like wasps that have their dwelling by the wayside, and that boys are ever wont to vex, always tormenting them in their nests beside the way in childish sport, and a common evil they make for many. With heart and spirit like theirs the Myrmidons poured out now from the ships, and a cry arose unquenchable, and Patroklos called on his comrades, shouting aloud: "Myrmidons, ye comrades of Achilles son of Peleus, be men, my friends, and be mindful of your impetuous valour, that so we may win honour for the son of Peleus, that is far the bravest of the Argives by the ships, and whose close-fighting squires are the best. And let wide-ruling Agamemnon the son of Atreus learn his own blindness of heart, in that he nothing honoured the best of the Achaians."

So spake he, and aroused each man's heart and courage, and all in a mass they fell on the Trojans, and the ships around echoed wondrously to the cry of the Achaians. But when the Trojans beheld the strong son of Menoitios, himself and his squire, shining in their armour, the heart was stirred in all of them, and the companies wavered, for they deemed that by the ships the swift-footed son of Peleus had cast away his wrath, and chosen reconcilement: then each man glanced round, to see where he might flee sheer destruction.

But Patroklos first with a shining spear cast straight into

the press, where most men were thronging, even by the stern of the ship of great-hearted Protesilaos, and he smote Pyraichmes, who led his Paionian horsemen out of Amydon, from the wide water of Axios; him he smote on the right shoulder, and he fell on his back in the dust with a groan, and his comrades around him, the Paionians, were afraid, for Patroklos sent fear among them all, when he slew their leader that was ever the best in fight. Then he drove them out from the ships, and quenched the burning fire. And the half-burnt ship was left there, and the Trojans fled, with a marvellous din, and the Danaans poured in among the hollow ships, and ceaseless was the shouting. And as when from the high crest of a great hill Zeus, the gatherer of the lightning, hath stirred a dense cloud, and forth shine all the peaks, and sharp promontories, and glades, and from heaven the infinite air breaks open, even so the Danaans, having driven the blazing fire from the ships, for a little while took breath, but there was no pause in the battle. For not yet were the Trojans driven in utter rout by the Achaians, dear to Ares, from the black ships, but they still stood up against them, and only perforce gave ground from the ships.

But even as robber wolves fall on the lambs or kids, choosing them out of the herds, when they are scattered on hills by the witlessness of the shepherd, and the wolves behold it, and speedily harry the younglings that have no heart of courage,—even so the Danaans fell on the Trojans, and they were mindful of ill-sounding flight, and forgot their impetuous valour.

But that great Aias ever was fain to cast his spear at

Hector of the helm of bronze, but he, in his cunning of war, covered his broad shoulders with his shield of bulls' hide, and watched the hurtling of the arrows, and the noise of spears. And verily well he knew the change in the mastery of war, but even so he abode, and was striving to rescue his trusty comrades.

And as when from Olympus a cloud fares into heaven, from the sacred air, when Zeus spreadeth forth the tempest, even so from the ships came the war-cry and the rout, nor in order due did they cross the ditch again. But his swift-footed horses bare Hector forth with his arms, and he left the host of Troy, whom the delved trench restrained against their will. And in the trench did many swift steeds that draw the car break the fore-part of the pole, and leave the chariots of their masters.

But Patroklos followed after, crying fiercely to the Danaans, and full of evil will against the Trojans, while they with cries and flight filled all the ways, for they were scattered, and on high the storm of dust was scattered below the clouds, and the whole-hooved horses strained back towards the city, away from the ships and the huts.

But even where Patroklos saw the folk thickest in the rout, thither did he guide his horses with a cry, and under his axle-trees men fell prone from their chariots, and the cars were overturned with a din of shattering. But straight over the ditch, in forward flight, leaped the swift horses. And the heart of Patroklos urged him against Hector, for he was eager to smite him, but his swift steeds bore Hector forth and away. And even as beneath a tempest the whole black earth is oppressed, on an autumn day, when Zeus pours forth rain most vehemently, and all the rivers run full, and many a scaur the torrents tear away, and down to the dark sea they rush headlong from the hills, roaring mightily, and minished are the works of men, even so mighty was the roar of the Trojan horses as they ran.

Now Patroklos when he had cloven the nearest companies, drave them backward again to the ships, nor suffered them to approach the city, despite their desire, but between the ships, and the river, and the lofty wall, he rushed on them, and slew them, and avenged many a comrade slain. There first he smote Pronoos with a shining spear, where the shield left bare the breast, and loosened his limbs, and he fell with a crash. Then Thestor the son of Enops he next assailed, as he sat crouching in the polished chariot, for he was struck distraught, and the reins flew from his hands. Him he drew near, and smote with the lance on the right jaw, and clean pierced through his teeth. And Patroklos caught hold of the spear and dragged him over the rim of the car, as when a man sits on a jutting rock, and drags a sacred fish forth from the sea, with line and glittering hook of bronze; so on the bright spear dragged he Thestor gaping from the chariot, and cast him down on his face and life left him as he fell. Next, as Euryalos came on, he smote him on the midst of the head with a stone, and all his head was shattered within the strong helmet, and prone on the earth he fell, and death that slayeth the spirit overwhelmed him. Next Erymas, and Amphoteros, and Epaltes and Tlepolemos son of Damastor, and Echios and Pyris, and Ipheus and Euippos, and Polymelos son of Argeas, all these in turn he brought low to the bounteous earth. But when Sarpedon beheld his comrades with ungirdled doublets, subdued beneath the hands of Patroklos son of Menoitios, he cried aloud, upbraiding the godlike Lykians: "Shame, ye Lykians, whither do ye flee? Now be ye strong, for I will encounter this man that I may know who he is that conquers here, and verily many evils hath he wrought the Trojans, in that he hath loosened the knees of many men and noble."

So spake he, and leaped with his arms from the chariot to the ground. But Patroklos, on the other side, when he beheld him leaped from his chariot. And they, like vultures of crooked talons and curved beaks, that war with loud yells on some high cliff, even so they rushed with cries against each other. And beholding then the son of Kronos of the crooked counsels took pity on them, and he spake to Hera, his sister and wife: "Ah woe is me for that it is fated that Sarpedon, the best-beloved of men to me, shall be subdued under Patroklos son of Menoitios. And in two ways my heart within my breast is divided, as I ponder whether I should catch him up alive out of the tearful war, and set him down in the rich land of Lykia, or whether I should now subdue him beneath the hands of the son of Menoitios."

Then the ox-eyed lady Hera made answer to him: "Most dread son of Kronos, what word is this thou hast spoken? A mortal man long doomed to fate dost thou desire to deliver again from death of evil name? Work thy will, but all we other gods will in no wise praise thee. And another thing I will tell thee, and do thou lay it up in thy heart; if thou dost send Sarpedon living to his own house, consider lest thereon some other god likewise desire to send his own dear son away out of the strong battle. For round the great citadel of Priam war many sons of the Immortals, and among the Immortals wilt thou send terrible wrath. But if he be dear to thee, and thy heart mourns for him, truly then suffer him to be subdued in the strong battle beneath the hands of Patroklos son of Menoitios, but when his soul and life leave that warrior, send Death and sweet Sleep to bear him, even till they come to the land of wide Lykia, there will his kindred and friends bury him, with a barrow and a pillar, for this is the due of the dead."

So spake she, nor did the father of gods and men disregard her. But he shed bloody raindrops on the earth, honouring his dear son, that Patroklos was about to slay in the deep-soiled land of Troia, far off from his own country. Now when they were come near each other in onset, there verily did Patroklos smite the renowned Thrasymelos, the good squire of the prince Sarpedon, on the lower part of the belly, and loosened his limbs. But Sarpedon missed him with his shining javelin, as he in turn rushed on, but wounded the horse Pedasos on the right shoulder with the spear, and he shrieked as he breathed his life away, and fell crying in the dust, and his spirit fled from him. But the other twain reared this way and that, and the yoke creaked, and the reins were confused on them, when their trace-horse lay in the dust. But thereof did Automedon, the spearman renowned, find a remedy, and drawing his long-edged sword from his stout thigh, he leaped forth, and cut adrift the horse, with no delay, and the pair righted themselves, and strained in the reins, and they met again in life-devouring war.

Then again Sarpedon missed with his shining dart, and the point of the spear flew over the left shoulder of Patroklos and smote him not, but he in turn arose with the bronze, and his javelin flew not vainly from his hand, but struck Sarpedon even where the midriff clasps the beating heart. And he fell as falls an oak, or a silver poplar, or a slim pine tree, that on the hills the shipwrights fell with whetted axes, to be timber for shipbuilding; even so before the horses and chariot he lay at length, moaning aloud, and clutching at the bloody dust. And as when a lion hath fallen on a herd, and slain a bull, tawny and high of heart, among the kine of trailing gait, and he perishes groaning beneath the claws of the lion, even so under Patroklos did the leader of the Lykian shieldmen rage, even in death, and he called to his dear comrade: "Dear Glaukos, warrior among warlike men, now most doth it behove thee to be a spearman, and a hardy fighter: now let baneful war be dear to thee, if indeed thou art a man of might. First fare all about and urge on the heroes that be leaders of the Lykians, to fight for Sarpedon, and thereafter thyself do battle for me with the sword. For to thee even in time to come shall I be shame and disgrace for ever, all thy days, if the Achaians strip me of mine armour, fallen in the gathering of the ships. Nay, hold out manfully, and spur on all the host."

Even as he spake thus, the end of death veiled over his eyes and his nostrils, but Patroklos, setting foot on his breast drew the spear out of his flesh, and the midriff followed with the spear, so that he drew forth together the spear point, and the soul of Sarpedon; and the Myrmidons held there his panting steeds, eager to fly afar, since the chariot was reft of its lords.

Then dread sorrow came on Glaukos, when he heard the voice of Sarpedon, and his heart was stirred, that he availed not to succour him. And with his hand he caught and held his arm, for the wound galled him, the wound of the arrow wherewith, as he pressed on towards the lofty wall, Teukros had smitten him, warding off destruction from his fellows. Then in prayer spake Glaukos to far-darting Apollo: "Hear, O Prince that art somewhere in the rich land of Lykia, or in Troia, for thou canst listen everywhere to the man that is in need, as even now need cometh upon me. For I have this stark wound, and mine arm is thoroughly pierced with sharp pains, nor can my blood be stanched, and by the wound is my shoulder burdened, and I cannot hold my spear firm, nor go and fight against the enemy. And the best of men has perished, Sarpedon, the son of Zeus, and he succours not even his own child. But do thou, O Prince, heal me this stark wound, and lull my pains, and give me strength, that I may call on my Lykian kinsmen, and spur them to the war, and myself may fight about the dead man fallen."

So spake he in his prayer, and Phoebus Apollo heard him. Straightway he made his pains to cease, and in the grievous wound stanched the black blood, and put courage into his heart. And Glaukos knew it within him, and was glad, for that the great god speedily heard his prayer. First went he all about and urged on them that were leaders of the Lykians to fight around Sarpedon, and thereafter he went with long strides among the Trojans, to Polydamas son of Panthoös and noble Agenor, and he went after Aineias, and Hector of the helm of bronze, and standing by them spake winged words: "Hector, now surely art thou utterly forgetful of the allies, that for thy sake, far from their friends and their own country, breathe their lives away! but thou carest not to aid them! Sarpedon lies low, the leader of the Lykian shieldmen, he that defended Lykia by his dooms and his might, yea him hath mailed Ares subdued beneath the spear of Patroklos. But, friends, stand by him, and be angry in your hearts lest the Myrmidons strip him of his harness, and dishonour the dead, in wrath for the sake of the Danaans, even them that perished, whom we slew with spears by the swift ships."

So spake he, and sorrow seized the Trojans utterly, ungovernable and not to be borne; for Sarpedon was ever the stay of their city, all a stranger as he was, for many people followed with him, and himself the best warrior of them all. Then they made straight for the Danaans eagerly, and Hector led them, being wroth for Sarpedon's sake. But the fierce heart of Patroklos son of Menoitios urged on the Achaians. And he spake first to the twain Aiantes that themselves were right eager: "Aiantes, now let defence be your desire, and be such as afore ye were among men, or even braver yet. That man lies low who first leaped on to the wall of the Achaians, even Sarpedon. Nay, let us strive to take him, and work his body shame, and strip the harness from his shoulders, and many a one of his comrades fighting for his sake let us subdue with the pitiless bronze."

So spake he, and they themselves were eager in defence.

So on both sides they strengthened the companies, Trojans and Lykians, Myrmidons and Achaians, and they joined battle to fight around the dead man fallen; terribly they shouted, and loud rang the harness of men. And as the din ariseth of woodcutters in the glades of a mountain, and the sound thereof is heard far away, so rose the din of them from the wide-wayed earth, the noise of bronze and of well-tanned bulls' hides smitten with swords and double-pointed spears. And now not even a clear-sighted man could any longer have known noble Sarpedon, for with darts and blood and dust was he covered wholly from head to foot. And ever men thronged about the dead, as in a steading flies buzz around the full milk-pails, in the season of spring, when the milk drenches the bowls, even so thronged they about the dead. Nor ever did Zeus turn from the strong fight his shining eyes, but ever looked down on them, and much in his heart he debated of the slaying of Patroklos, whether there and then above divine Sarpedon glorious Hector should slay him likewise in strong battle with the sword, and strip his harness from his shoulders, or whether to more men yet he should deal sheer labour of war. And thus to him as he pondered it seemed the better way, that the gallant squire of Achilles, Peleus' son, should straightway drive the Trojans and Hector of the helm of bronze towards the city, and should rob many of their life. And in Hector first he put a weakling heart, and leaping into his car Hector turned in flight, and cried on the rest of the Trojans to flee, for he knew the turning of the sacred scales of Zeus. Thereon neither did the strong Lykians abide, but fled all in fear, when they beheld their king stricken to the heart, lying in the company of the dead, for many had fallen above him, when Kronion made fierce the fight. Then the others stripped from the shoulders of Sarpedon his shining arms of bronze, and these the strong son of Menoitios gave to his comrades to bear to the hollow ships. Then Zeus that gathereth the clouds spake to Apollo: "Prithee, dear Phoebus, go take Sarpedon out of range of darts, and cleanse the black blood from him, and thereafter bear him far away, and bathe him in the streams of the river, and anoint him with ambrosia, and clothe him in garments that wax not old, and send him to be wafted by fleet convoy, by the twin brethren Sleep and Death, that quickly will set him in the rich land of wide Lykia. There will his kinsmen and clansmen give him burial, with barrow and pillar, for such is the due of the dead."

So spake he, nor was Apollo disobedient to his father. He went down the hills of Ida to the dread battle din, and straightway bore goodly Sarpedon out of the darts, and carried him far away, and bathed him in the streams of the river, and anointed him with ambrosia, and clad him in garments that wax not old, and sent him to be wafted by fleet convoy, the twin brethren Sleep and Death, that swiftly set him down in the rich land of wide Lykia. But Patroklos cried to his horses and Automedon, and after the Trojans and Lykians went he, and so was blindly forgetful, in his witlessness, for if he had kept the saying of the son of Peleus, verily he should have escaped the evil fate of black death. But ever is the wit of Zeus stronger than the wit of men, so now he roused the spirit of Patroklos in his breast. There whom first, whom last didst thou slay, Patroklos, when the gods called thee deathward? Adrestos first, and Autonoos, and Echeklos, and Perimos, son of Megas, and Epistor, and Melanippos, and thereafter Elasos, and Moulios, and Pylartes; these he slew, but the others were each man of them fain of flight. Then would the sons of the Achaians have taken high-gated Troy, by the hands of Patroklos, for around and before him he raged with the spear, but that Phoebus Apollo stood on the well-builded wall, with baneful thoughts towards Patroklos, and suc-couring the Trojans. Thrice clomb Patroklos on the corner of the lofty wall, and thrice did Apollo force him back and smote the shining shield with his immortal hands. But when for the fourth time he came on like a god, then cried far-darting Apollo terribly, and spake winged words: "Give back, Patroklos of the seed of Zeus! Not beneath thy spear is it fated that the city of the valiant Trojans shall fall, nay nor beneath Achilles, a man far better than thou."

So spake he, and Patroklos retreated far back, avoiding the wrath of far-darting Apollo. But Hector within the Skaian gates was restraining his whole-hooved horses, pondering whether he should drive again into the din and fight, or should call unto the host to gather to the wall. While thus he was thinking, Phoebus Apollo stood by him in the guise of a young man and a strong, Asios, who was the mother's brother of horse-taming Hector, being own brother of Hekabe, and son of Dymas, who dwelt in Phrygia, on the streams of Sangarios. In his guise spake

Apollo, son of Zeus, to Hector: "Hector, wherefore dost thou cease from fight? It doth not behove thee. Would that I were as much stronger than thou as I am weaker, thereon quickly shouldst thou stand aloof from war to thy hurt. But come, turn against Patroklos thy strong-hooved horses, if perchance thou mayst slay him, and Apollo give thee glory."

So spake the god, and went back again into the moil of men. But renowned Hector bade wise-hearted Kebriones to lash his horses into the war. Then Apollo went and passed into the press, and sent a dread panic among the Argives, but to the Trojans and Hector gave he renown. And Hector let the other Argives be, and slew none of them, but against Patroklos he turned his strong-hooved horses, and Patroklos on the other side leaped from his chariot to the ground, with a spear in his left hand, and in his other hand grasped a shining jagged stone, that his hand covered. Firmly he planted himself and hurled it, nor long did he shrink from his foe, nor was his cast in vain, but he struck Kebriones the charioteer of Hector, the bastard son of renowned Priam, on the brow with the sharp stone, as he held the reins of the horses. Both his brows the stone drave together, and his bone held not, but his eyes fell to the ground in the dust, there, in front of his feet. Then he, like a diver, fell from the well-wrought car, and his spirit left his bones. Then taunting him didst thou address him, knightly Patroklos: "Out on it, how nimble a man, how lightly he diveth! Yea, if perchance he were on the teeming deep, this man would satisfy many by seeking for oysters, leaping from the ship, even if it were stormy weather, so lightly now he diveth from the chariot into the plain. Verily among the Trojans too there be diving men."

So speaking he set on the hero Kebriones with the rush of a lion, that while wasting the cattle-pens is smitten in the breast, and his own valour is his bane, even so against Kebriones, Patroklos, didst thou leap furiously. But Hector, on the other side, leaped from his chariot to the ground. And these twain strove for Kebriones like lions, that on the mountain peaks fight, both hungering, both high of heart, for a slain hind. Even so for Kebriones' sake these two masters of the war-cry, Patroklos son of Menoitios, and re-nowned Hector, were eager each to hew the other's flesh with the ruthless bronze.

Hector then seized him by the head, and slackened not hold, while Patroklos on the other side grasped him by the foot, and thereon the others, Trojans and Danaans, joined strong battle. And as the East wind and the South contend with one another in shaking a deep wood in the dells of a mountain, shaking beech, and ash, and smooth-barked cornel tree, that clash against each other their long boughs with marvellous din, and a noise of branches broken, so the Trojans and Achaians were leaping on each other and slaying, nor had either side any thought of ruinous flight. And many sharp darts were fixed around Kebriones, and winged arrows leaping from the bow-string, and many mighty stones smote the shields of them that fought around him. But he in the whirl of dust lay mighty and mightily fallen, forgetful of his chivalry.

Now while the sun was going about mid-heaven, so long

the darts smote either side, and the host fell, but when the sun turned to the time of the loosing of oxen, lo, then beyond their doom the Achaians proved the better. The hero Kebriones drew they forth from the darts, out of the tumult of the Trojans, and stripped the harness from his shoulders, and with ill design against the Trojans, Patroklos rushed upon them. Three times then rushed he on, peer of swift Ares, shouting terribly, and thrice he slew nine men. But when the fourth time he sped on like a god, thereon to thee, Patroklos, did the end of life appear, for Phoebus met thee in the strong battle, in dreadful wise. And Patroklos was not ware of him coming through the press, for hidden in thick mist did he meet him, and stood behind him, and smote his back and broad shoulders with a down-stroke of his hand, and his eyes were dazed. And from his head Phoebus Apollo smote the helmet that rolled rattling away with a din beneath the hooves of the horses, the helm with upright socket, and the crests were defiled with blood and dust. And all the long-shadowed spear was shattered in the hands of Patroklos, the spear great and heavy and strong, and sharp, while from his shoulders the tasselled shield with the baldric fell to the ground.

And the prince Apollo, son of Zeus, loosed his corslet, and blindness seized his heart and his shining limbs were unstrung, and he stood in amaze, and at close quarters from behind a Dardanian smote him on the back, between the shoulders, with a sharp spear, even Euphorbos, son of Panthoös, who excelled them of his age in casting the spear, and in horsemanship, and in speed of foot. Even thus, verily, had he cast down twenty men from their chariots, though then first had he come with his car to learn the lesson of war. He it was that first smote a dart into thee, knightly Patroklos, nor overcame thee, but ran back again and mingled with the throng, first drawing forth from the flesh his ashen spear, nor did he abide the onset of Patroklos, unarmed as he was, in the strife. But Patroklos being overcome by the stroke of the god, and by the spear, gave ground, and retreated to the host of his comrades, avoiding Fate. But Hector, when he beheld great-hearted Patroklos give ground, being smitten with the keen bronze, came nigh unto him through the ranks, and wounded him with a spear, in the lowermost part of the belly, and drave the bronze clean through. And he fell with a crash, and sorely grieved the host of Achaians. And as when a lion hath overcome in battle an untiring boar, they twain fighting with high heart on the crests of a hill, about a little well, and both are desirous to drink, and the lion hath by force overcome the boar that draweth difficult breath; so after that he had slain many did Hector son of Priam take the life away from the strong son of Menoitios, smiting him at close quarters with the spear; and boasting over him he spake winged words: "Patroklos, surely thou saidst that thou wouldst sack my town, and from Trojan women take away the day of freedom, and bring them in ships to thine own dear country: fool! nay, in front of these were the swift horses of Hector straining their speed for the fight; and myself in wielding the spear excel among the war-loving Trojans, even I who ward from them the day of destiny: but thee shall vultures here devour. Ah, wretch, surely Achilles for all his valour, availed thee not, who straitly charged thee as thou camest, he abiding there, saying, 'Come not to me, Patroklos lord of steeds, to the hollow ships, till thou hast torn the gory doublet of man-slaying Hector about his breast;' so, surely, he spake to thee, and persuaded the wits of thee in thy witlessness."

Then faintly didst thou answer him, knightly Patroklos: "Boast greatly, as now, Hector, for to thee have Zeus, son of Kronos, and Apollo given the victory, who lightly have subdued me; for themselves stripped my harness from my shoulders. But if twenty such as thou had encountered me, here had they all perished, subdued beneath my spear. But me have ruinous Fate and the son of Leto slain, and of men Euphorbos, but thou art the third in my slaying. But another thing will I tell thee, and do thou lay it up in thy heart; verily thou thyself art not long to live, but already doth Death stand hard by thee, and strong Fate, that thou art to be subdued by the hands of noble Achilles, of the seed of Aiakos."

Even as so he spake the end of death overshadowed him. And his soul, fleeting from his limbs, went down to the house of Hades, wailing its own doom, leaving manhood and youth.

Then renowned Hector spake to him even in his death: "Patroklos, wherefore to me dost thou prophesy sheer destruction? who knows but that Achilles, the child of fair-tressed Thetis, will first be smitten by my spear, and lose his life?"

So spake he, and drew the spear of bronze from the wound, setting his foot on the dead, and cast him off on his back from the spear. And straightway with the spear he went after Automedon, the godlike squire of the swift-footed Aiakides, for he was eager to smite him; but his swift-footed immortal horses bare him out of the battle, horses that the gods gave to Peleus, a splendid gift.

BOOK XVII

Of the battle around the body of Patroklos.

B UT Atreus' son, Menelaos dear to Ares, was not unaware of the slaying of Patroklos by the Trojans in
the fray. He went up through the front of the fight harnessed in flashing bronze, and strode over the body as above
a first-born calf standeth lowing its mother. Thus above
Patroklos strode fair-haired Menelaos, and before him held
his spear and the circle of his shield, eager to slay whoever
should encounter him. Then was Panthoös' son of the stout
ashen spear not heedless of noble Patroklos as he lay, and
he smote on the circle of the shield of Menelaos, but the
bronze spear brake it not, but the point was bent back in
the stubborn shield. And Menelaos Atreus' son in his turn
made at him with his bronze spear, having prayed unto
father Zeus, and as he gave back pierced the nether part of
his throat, and threw his weight into the stroke, following
his heavy hand; and sheer through the tender neck went
the point of the spear. And he fell with a crash, and his
armour rang upon him. In blood was his hair drenched
that was like unto the hair of the Graces, and his tresses
closely knit with bands of silver and gold.

Then easily would the son of Atreus have borne off the
noble spoils of Panthoös' son, had not Phoebus Apollo
grudged it to him, and aroused against him Hector, peer of

swift Ares, putting on the semblance of a man, of Mentes, chief of the Kikones. And he spake aloud to him winged words: "Hector, now art thou hasting after things unattainable, even the horses of wise Aiakides; for hard are they to be tamed or driven by mortal man, save only Achilles whom an immortal mother bare. Meanwhile hath warlike Menelaos Atreus' son stridden over Patroklos and slain the best of the Trojans there, even Panthoös' son Euphorbos, and hath stayed him in his impetuous might."

Thus saying the god went back into the strife of men, but dire grief darkened Hector's inmost soul, and then he gazed searchingly along the lines, and straightway was aware of the one man stripping off the noble arms, and the other lying on the earth; and blood was flowing about the gaping wound. Then he went through the front of the fight harnessed in flashing bronze, crying a shrill cry, like unto Hephaistos' flame unquenchable. Not deaf to his shrill cry was Atreus' son, and sore troubled he spake to his great heart: "Ay me, if I shall leave behind me these goodly arms, and Patroklos who here lieth for my vengeance' sake, I fear lest some Danaan beholding it be wroth against me. But if for honour's sake I do battle alone with Hector and the Trojans, I fear lest they come about me many against one; for all the Trojans is bright-helmed Hector leading hither. But if I might somewhere find Aias of the loud war-cry, then both together would we go and be mindful of battle even were it against the power of heaven, if haply we might save his dead for Achilles Peleus' son: that were best among these ills."

While thus he communed with his mind and heart, therewithal the Trojan ranks came onward, and Hector at their head. Then Menelaos gave backward, and left the dead man, turning himself ever about like a deep-maned lion which men and dogs chase from a fold with spears and cries; and his strong heart within him groweth chill, and loth goeth he from the steading; so from Patroklos went fairhaired Menelaos, and turned and stood, when he came to the host of his comrades, searching for mighty Aias Telamon's son. Him very speedily he espied on the left of the whole battle, cheering his comrades and rousing them to fight, for great terror had Phoebus Apollo sent on them; and he hasted him to run, and straightway stood by him and said: "This way, beloved Aias; let us bestir us for the dead Patroklos, if haply his naked corpse at least we may carry to Achilles, though his armour is held by Hector of the glancing helm."

Thus spake he, and aroused the heart of wise Aias. And he went up through the front of the fight, and with him fairhaired Menelaos. Now Hector, when he had stripped from Patroklos his noble armour, was dragging him thence that he might cut off the head from the shoulders with the keen bronze and carry his body to give to the dogs of Troy. But Aias came anigh, and the shield that he bare was as a tower; then Hector gave back into the company of his comrades, and sprang into his chariot; and the goodly armour he gave to the Trojans to carry to the city, to be great glory unto him. But Aias spread his broad shield over the son of Menoitios and stood as it were a lion before his whelps when huntsmen in a forest encounter him as he leadeth his young. And by his side stood Atreus' son, Menelaos dear to Ares, nursing great sorrow in his breast.

Then Hector called on the Trojans with a mighty shout: "Trojans and Lykians and Dardanians that fight hand to hand, be men, my friends, and bethink you of impetuous valour, until I do on me the goodly arms of noble Achilles that I stripped from brave Patroklos when I slew him."

Thus having spoken went Hector of the glancing helm forth out of the strife of war, and ran and speedily with fleet feet following overtook his comrades, not yet far off, who were bearing to the city Peleides' glorious arms. And standing apart from the dolorous battle he changed his armour; his own he gave the warlike Trojans to carry to sacred Ilios, and he put on the divine arms of Achilles, Peleus' son.

But when Zeus that gathereth the clouds beheld from afar off Hector arming him in the armour of Peleus' godlike son, he shook his head and spake thus unto his soul: "Ah, hapless man, no thought is in thy heart of death that yet draweth nigh unto thee; thou doest on thee the divine armour of a peerless man before whom the rest have terror. His comrade, gentle and brave, thou hast slain, and unmeetly hast stripped the armour from his head and shoulders; yet now for a while at least I will give into thy hands great might, in recompense for this, even that nowise shalt thou come home out of the battle, for Andromache to receive from thee Peleides' glorious arms."

Thus spake the son of Kronos, and bowed his dark brows therewithal.

But the armour fitted itself unto Hector's body, and Ares

the dread war-god entered into him, and his limbs were filled within with valour and strength. Then he sped among the noble allies with a mighty cry, and in the flashing of his armour he seemed to all of them like unto Peleus' great-hearted son. And he came to each and encouraged him with his words—Mesthles and Glaukos and Medon and Thersilochos and Asteropaios and Deisenor and Hippothoös and Phorkys and Chromios and the augur Ennomos—these encouraged he and spake to them winged words: "Listen, ye countless tribes of allies that dwell round about. It was not for mere numbers that I sought or longed when I gathered each of you from your cities, but that ye might zealously guard the Trojans' wives and infant little ones from the war-loving Achaians. For this end am I wearying my people by taking gifts and food from them, and nursing thereby the courage of each of you. Now therefore let all turn straight against the foe and live or die, for such is the dalliance of war. And whoso shall drag Patroklos, dead though he be, among the horse-taming men of Troy, and make Aias yield, to him will I award half the spoils and keep half myself; so shall his glory be great as mine."

Thus spake he, and they against the Danaans charged with all their weight, levelling their spears, and their hearts were high of hope to drag the corpse from under Aias, Telamon's son. Fond men! from full many reft he life over that corpse. And then spake Aias to Menelaos of the loud war-cry: "Dear Menelaos, fosterling of Zeus, no longer count I that we two of ourselves shall return home out of the war. Nor have I so much dread for the corpse of Patroklos, that shall soon glut the dogs and birds of the men of Troy, as for thy head and mine lest some evil fall thereon, for all is shrouded by a storm-cloud of war, even by Hector, and sheer doom stareth in our face. But come, call thou to the best men of the Danaans, if haply any hear."

Thus spake he, and Menelaos of the loud war-cry disregarded him not, but shouted unto the Danaans, crying a far-heard cry: "O friends, ye leaders and counsellors of the Argives, who by the side of the sons of Atreus, Agamemnon and Menelaos, drink at the common cost and are all commanders of the host, on whom wait glory and honour from Zeus, hard is it for me to distinguish each chief amid the press—such blaze is there of the strife of war. But let each go forward of himself and be wroth at heart that Patroklos should become a sport among the dogs of Troy."

Thus spake he, and Oïleus' son fleet Aias heard him clearly, and was first to run along the melee to meet him, and after him Idomeneus, and Idomeneus' brother-in-arms, Meriones, peer of the man-slaying war-god. And who shall of his own thought tell the names of the rest, even of all that after these aroused the battle of the Achaians?

Now the Trojans charged forward in close array, and Hector led them. And as when at the mouth of some heaven-born river a mighty wave roareth against the stream, and arouseth the high cliffs' echo as the salt sea belloweth on the beach, so loud was the cry wherewith the Trojans came. But the Achaians stood firm around Menoitios' son with one soul all, walled in with shields of bronze. And over their bright helmets the son of Kronos shed thick darkness, for in the former time was Menoitios' son not unloved of him, while he was yet alive and squire of Aiakides. So was Zeus loth that he should become a prey of the dogs of his enemies at Troy, and stirred his comrades to do battle for him.

Now first the Trojans thrust back the glancing-eyed Achaians, who shrank before them and left the dead, yet the proud Trojans slew not any of them with spears, though they were fain, but set to hale the corpse. But little while would the Achaians hold back therefrom, for very swiftly Aias rallied them, Aias the first in presence and in deeds of all the Danaans after the noble son of Peleus. Right through the fighters in the forefront rushed he like a wild boar in his might that in the mountains when he turneth at bay scattereth lightly dogs and lusty young men through the glades. Thus did proud Telamon's son the glorious Aias press on the Trojan battalions and lightly scatter them, as they had bestrode Patroklos and were full fain to drag him to their city and win renown.

Then would the Trojans in their turn in their weakness overcome have been driven back into Ilios by the Achaians dear to Ares, and the Argives would have won glory even against the appointment of Zeus by their power and might. But Apollo himself aroused Aineias, putting on the semblance of Periphas the herald, the son of Epytos, who grew old with his old father in his heraldship, of friendly thought toward Aineias. In his similitude spake Apollo, son of Zeus: "Aineias, how could ye ever guard high Ilios if it were against the will of God? Other men have I seen that trust in their own might and power and valour, and in their host, even though they have scant folk to lead. But here, albeit

Zeus is fainer far to give victory to us than to the Danaans, yet ye are dismayed exceedingly and fight not."

Thus spake he, and Aineias knew far-darting Apollo when he looked upon his face, and spake unto Hector, shouting loud: "Hector and ye other leaders of the Trojans and their allies, shame were this if in our weakness overcome we were driven back into Ilios by the Achaians dear to Ares. Nay, thus saith a god, who standeth by my side: Zeus, highest Orderer, is our helper in this fight. Therefore let us go right onward against the Danaans. Not easily at least let them take the dead Patroklos to the ships."

Thus spake he, and leapt forth far before the fighters in the front. And the Trojans rallied and stood up against the Achaians. Thus strove they as it had been fire, nor wouldst thou have thought there was still sun or moon, for over all the battle where the chiefs stood around the slain son of Menoitios they were shrouded in darkness, while the other Trojans and well-greaved Achaians fought at ease in the clear air, and piercing sunlight was spread over them, and on all the earth and hills there was no cloud seen; and they ceased fighting now and again, avoiding each other's dolorous darts and standing far apart. But they who were in the midst endured affliction of the darkness and the battle, and all the best men of them were wearied by the pitiless weight of their bronze arms.

Thus all day long waxed the mighty fray of their sore strife, and unabatingly ever with the sweat of toil were the knees and legs and feet of each man and arms and eyes bedewed as the two hosts did battle around the brave squire of fleet Aiakides. And as when a man giveth the hide of a great bull to his folk to stretch, all soaked in fat, and they take and stretch it standing in a circle, and straightway the moisture thereof departeth and the fat entereth in under the haling of many hands, and it is all stretched throughout,— thus they on both sides haled the dead man this way and that in narrow space, for their hearts were high of hope, the Trojans that they should drag him to Ilios and the Achaians to the hollow ships; and around him the fray waxed wild, nor might Ares rouser of hosts nor Athene despise the sight thereof, albeit their anger were exceeding great.

Such was the grievous travail of men and horses over Patroklos that Zeus on that day wrought. But not as yet knew noble Achilles aught of Patroklos' death, for far away from the swift ships they were fighting beneath the wall of the men of Troy. Therefore never deemed he in his heart that he was dead, but that he should come back alive, after that he had touched the gates; for neither that other thought had he anywise, that Patroklos should sack the stronghold without his aid.

Now the rest continually around the dead man with their keen spears made onset relentlessly and slew each the other. And thus would one speak among the mail-clad Achaians: "Friends, it were verily not glorious for us to go back to the hollow ships; rather let the black earth yawn for us all beneath our feet. Far better were that straightway for us if we suffer the horse-taming Trojans to hale this man to their city and win renown."

And thus on the other side would one of the great-hearted

Trojans say: "Friends, though it were our fate that all together we be slain beside this man, let none yet give backward from the fray."

Thus would one speak, and rouse the spirit of each. So they fought on, and the iron din went up through the high desert air unto the brazen heaven. But the horses of Aiakides that were apart from the battle were weeping, since first they were aware that their charioteer was fallen in the dust beneath the hand of man-slaying Hector. Verily Automedon, Diores' valiant son, plied them oft with blows of the swift lash, and oft with gentle words he spake to them and oft with chiding, yet would they neither go back to the ships at the broad Hellespont nor yet to the battle after the Achaians, but as a pillar abideth firm that standeth on the tomb of a man or woman dead, so abode they immovably with the beautiful chariot, abasing their heads unto the earth. And hot tears flowed from their eyes to the ground as they mourned in sorrow for their charioteer, and their rich manes were soiled as they drooped from beneath the yoke-cushion on both sides beside the yoke. And when the son of Kronos beheld them mourning he had compassion on them, and shook his head and spake to his own heart: "Ah, hapless pair, why gave we you to king Peleus, a mortal man, while ye are deathless and ever young? Was it that ye should suffer sorrows among ill-fated men? For methinketh there is nothing more piteous than a man among all things that breathe and creep upon the earth. But verily Hector Priam's son shall not drive you and your deftly-wrought car; that will I not suffer. Is it a small thing that he holdeth the armour and vaunteth himself vainly thereupon? Nay, I will put courage into your knees and heart that ye may bring Automedon also safe out of the war to the hollow ships. For yet further will I increase victory to the men of Troy, so that they slay until they come unto the well-timbered ships, and the sun set and divine night come down."

Thus saying he breathed good courage into the horses. And they shook to earth the dust from their manes, and lightly bare the swift car amid Trojans and Achaians. And behind them fought Automedon, albeit in grief for his comrade, swooping with his chariot as a vulture on wild geese; for lightly he would flee out of the onset of the Trojans and lightly charge, pursuing them through the thick melee. Yet could he not slay any man as he hasted to pursue them, for it was impossible that being alone in his sacred car he should at once assail them with the spear and hold his fleet horses. Then at last espied him a comrade, even Alkimedon son of Laerkes, son of Haimon, and he halted behind the car and spake unto Automedon: "Automedon, what god hath put into thy breast unprofitable counsel and taken from thee wisdom, that thus alone thou art fighting against the Trojans in the forefront of the press? Thy comrade even now was slain, and Hector goeth proudly, wearing on his own shoulders the armour of Aiakides."

And Automedon son of Diores answered him, saying: "Alkimedon, what other Achaian hath like skill to guide the spirit of immortal steeds, save only Patroklos, peer of gods in counsel, while he yet lived? but now have death and fate overtaken him. But take thou the lash and shining reins, and I will get me down from my horses, that I may fight."

Thus spake he, and Alkimedon leapt on the fleet war-chariot and swiftly took the lash and reins in his hands, and Automedon leapt down. And noble Hector espied them, and straightway spake unto Aineias as he stood near: "Aineias, counsellor of mail-clad Trojans, I espy here the two horses of fleet Aiakides come forth to battle with feeble charioteers. Therefore might I hope to take them if thou in thy heart art willing, since they would not abide our onset and stand to do battle against us."

Thus spake he, and the brave son of Anchises disregarded him not. And they twain went right onward, their shoulders shielded by ox-hides dried and tough, and bronze thick overlaid. And with them went both Chromios and godlike Aretos, and their hearts were of high hope to slay the men and drive off the strong-necked horses—fond hope, for not without blood lost were they to get them back from Automedon. He praying to father Zeus was filled in his inmost heart with valour and strength. And straightway he spake to Alkimedon, his faithful comrade: "Alkimedon, hold the horses not far from me, but with their very breath upon my back; for I deem that Hector the son of Priam will not refrain him from his fury until he mount behind Achilles' horses of goodly manes after slaying us twain, and dismay the ranks of Argive men, or else himself fall among the foremost."

Thus said he, and called upon the Aiantes and Menelaos: "Aiantes, leaders of the Argives, and Menelaos, lo now, commit ye the corpse unto whoso may best avail to bestride it and resist the ranks of men, and come ye to ward the day of doom from us who are yet alive, for here in the dolorous war are Hector and Aineias, the best men of the Trojans, pressing hard. Yet verily these issues lie in the lap of the gods: I too will cast my spear, and the rest shall Zeus decide."

He said, and poised his far-shadowing spear and hurled it, and smote on the circle of the shield of Aretos, and the shield sustained not the spear, but right through went the bronze, and he forced it into his belly low down through his belt. And as when a strong man with a sharp axe smiting behind the horns of an ox of the homestead cleaveth the sinew asunder, and the ox leapeth forward and falleth, so leapt Aretos forward and fell on his back; and the spear in his entrails very piercingly quivering unstrung his limbs. And Hector hurled at Automedon with his bright spear, but he looked steadfastly on the bronze javelin as it came at him and avoided it, for he stooped forward, and the long spear fixed itself in the ground behind, and the javelin-butt quivered, and there dread Ares took away its force. And then had they lashed at each other with their swords hand to hand, had not the Aiantes parted them in their fury, when they were come through the melee at their comrades' call. Before them Hector and Aineias and godlike Chromios shrank backward and gave ground and left Aretos wounded to the death as he lay. And Automedon, peer of swift Ares, stripped off the armour of the dead, and spake exultingly: "Verily, I have a little eased my heart of grief for the death of Menoitios' son, albeit a worse man than him have I slain."

Thus saying he took up the gory spoils and set them in his car, and gat him thereon, with feet and hands all bloody, as a lion that hath devoured a bull.

Now great-hearted Aias and Menelaos were aware of Zeus how he gave the Trojans their turn to victory. First of these to speak was great Aias son of Telamon: "Ay me, now may any man, even though he be a very fool, know that father Zeus himself is helping the Trojans. Come, let us ourselves devise some excellent means, that we may both hale the corpse away and ourselves return home to the joy of our friends, who grieve as they look hitherward and deem that no longer shall the fury of man-slaying Hector's unapproachable hand refrain itself, but fall upon the black ships. And would there were some comrade to carry tidings with all speed unto the son of Peleus, since I deem that he hath not even heard the grievous tidings, how his dear comrade is slain. But nowhere can I behold such an one among the Achaians, for themselves and their horses likewise are wrapped in darkness. O father Zeus, deliver thou the sons of the Achaians from the darkness, and make clear sky and vouchsafe sight unto our eyes. In the light be it that thou slayest us, since it is thy good pleasure that we die."

Then fair-haired Menelaos departed glancing everywhither, as an eagle which men say hath keenest sight of all birds under heaven, and though he be far aloft the fleet footed hare eludeth him not by crouching beneath a leafy bush, but the eagle swoopeth thereon and swiftly seizeth her and taketh her life. Thus in that hour, Menelaos fosterling of Zeus, ranged thy shining eyes everywhither through the multitude of the host of thy comrades, if haply they might behold Nestor's son yet alive. Him quickly he perceived at the left of the whole battle, heartening his comrades and rousing them to fight. And fair-haired Menelaos came and stood nigh and said unto him: "Antilochos, fosterling of Zeus, come hither that thou mayest learn woful tidings— would it had never been. Ere now, I ween, thou too hast known by thy beholding that God rolleth mischief upon the Danaans, and with the Trojans is victory. And slain is the best man of the Achaians, Patroklos, and great sorrow is wrought for the Danaans. But run thou to the ships of the Achaians and quickly tell this to Achilles, if haply he may straightway rescue to his ship the naked corpse: but his armour is held by Hector of the glancing helmet."

Thus spake he, and Antilochos had horror of the word he heard. And long time speechlessness possessed him, and his eyes were filled with tears, and his full voice choked. Yet for all this disregarded he not the bidding of Menelaos, but set him to run, when he had given his armour to a noble comrade, Laodokos, who close anigh him was wheeling his whole-hooved horses.

So him his feet bare out of the battle weeping, to Achilles son of Peleus carrying an evil tale. But thy heart, Menelaos fosterling of Zeus, chose not to stay to aid the wearied comrades from whom Antilochos departed, and great sorrow was among the Pylians. But to them Menelaos sent noble Thrasymedes, and himself went again to bestride the hero Patroklos. And he hasted and stood beside the Aiantes and straightway spake to them: "So have I sent that man to the swift ships to go to fleet-footed Achilles. Yet deem I not that he will now come, for all his wrath against noble Hector, for he could not fight unarmed against the men of Troy. But let us ourselves devise some excellent means, both how we may hale the dead away, and how we ourselves may escape death and fate amid the Trojans' battle-cry."

Then answered him great Aias Telamon's son, saying: "All this hast thou said well, most noble Menelaos. But do thou and Meriones put your shoulders beneath the dead and lift him and bear him swiftly out of the fray, while we twain behind you shall do battle with the Trojans and noble Hector, one in heart as we are in name, for from of old time we are wont to await fierce battle side by side."

Thus spake he, and the others took the dead man in their arms and lifted him mightily on high. But the Trojan host behind cried aloud when they saw the Achaians lifting the corpse, and charged like hounds that spring in front of hunter-youths upon a wounded wild boar, and for a while run in haste to rend him, but when he wheeleth round among them, trusting in his might, then they give ground and shrink back here and there. Thus for a while the Trojans pressed on with all their power, striking with swords and double-headed spears, but when the Aiantes turned about and halted over against them, then they changed colour, and none dared farther onset to do battle around the dead.

BOOK XVIII

How Achilles grieved for Patroklos, and how Thetis asked for
him new armour of Hephaistos; and of the making of the
armour.

THUS fought the rest in the likeness of blazing fire, while
to Achilles came Antilochos, a messenger fleet of
foot. Him found he in front of his ships of upright horns,
boding in his soul the things which even now were accomplished. And sore troubled he spake to his great heart: "Ay
me, wherefore again are the flowing-haired Achaians flocking to the ships and flying in rout over the plain? May the
gods not have wrought against me the grievous fears at my
heart, even as my mother revealed and told me that while
I am yet alive the best man of the Myrmidons must by deed
of the men of Troy forsake the light of the sun. Surely now
must Menoitios' valiant son be dead—foolhardy! surely I
bade him when he should have beaten off the fire of the foe
to come back to the ships nor with Hector fight amain."

While thus he held debate in his heart and soul, there
drew nigh unto him noble Nestor's son, shedding hot tears,
and spake his grievous tidings: "Ay me, wise Peleus' son,
very bitter tidings must thou hear, such as I would had
never been. Fallen is Patroklos, and they are fighting
around his body, naked, for his armour is held by Hector of
the glancing helm."

275

Thus spake he, and a black cloud of grief enwrapped Achilles, and with both hands he took dark dust and poured it over his head and defiled his comely face, and on his fragrant doublet black ashes fell. And himself in the dust lay mighty and mightily fallen, and with his own hands tore and marred his hair. And the handmaidens, whom Achilles and Patroklos took captive, cried aloud in the grief of their hearts, and ran forth around valiant Achilles, and all beat on their breasts with their hands, and the knees of each of them were unstrung. And Antilochos on the other side wailed and shed tears, holding Achilles' hands while he groaned in his noble heart, for he feared lest he should cleave his throat with the sword. Then terribly moaned Achilles; and his lady mother heard him as she sate in the depths of the sea beside her ancient sire. And thereon she uttered a cry, and the goddesses flocked around her, all the daughters of Nereus that were in the deep of the sea. With these the bright cave was filled, and they all beat together on their breasts, and Thetis led the lament: "Listen, sister Nereids, that ye all hear and know well what sorrows are in my heart. Ay me unhappy, ay me that bare to my sorrow the first of men! For after I had borne a son noble and strong, the chief of heroes, and he shot up like a young branch, then when I had reared him as a plant in a very fruitful field I sent him in beaked ships to Ilios to fight against the men of Troy; but never again shall I welcome him back to his home, to the house of Peleus. And while he yet liveth in my sight and beholdeth the light of the sun, he sorroweth, neither can I help him any whit though I go unto him. But I will go, that I may look upon my dear child, and learn what sorrow hath come to him though he abide aloof from the war."

Thus spake she and left the cave; and the nymphs went with her weeping, and around them the surge of the sea was sundered. And when they came to deep-soiled Troy-land they went up upon the shore in order, where the ships of the Myrmidons were drawn up thickly around fleet Achilles. And as he groaned heavily his lady mother stood beside him, and with a shrill cry clasped the head of her child, and spake unto him winged words of lamentation: "My child, why weepest thou? what sorrow hath come to thy heart? Tell it forth, hide it not. One thing at least hath been accomplished of Zeus according to the prayer thou madest, holding up to him thy hands, that the sons of the Achaians should all be pent in at the ships, through lack of thee, and should suffer hateful things."

Then groaning heavily spake unto her Achilles fleet of foot: "My mother, that prayer truly hath the Olympian accomplished for me. But what delight have I therein, since my dear comrade is dead, Patroklos, whom I honoured above all my comrades as it were my very self! Him have I lost, and Hector that slew him hath stripped from him the armour great and fair, a wonder to behold, that the gods gave to Peleus a splendid gift, on the day when they laid thee in the bed of a mortal man. Would thou hadst abode among the deathless daughters of the sea, and Peleus had wedded a mortal bride! But now, that thou mayest have sorrow a thousand fold in thy heart for a dead son, never shalt thou welcome him back home, since my soul biddeth me also live no longer nor abide among men, if Hector be not first smitten by my spear and yield his life, and pay for his slaughter of Patroklos, Menoitios' son."

Then answered unto him Thetis shedding tears: "Short-lived, I ween, must thou be then, my child, by what thou sayest, for straightway after Hector is death appointed unto thee."

Then mightily moved spake unto her Achilles fleet of foot: "Straightway may I die, since I might not succour my comrade at his slaying. He hath fallen afar from his country and lacked my help in his sore need. Now therefore, since I go not back to my dear native land, neither have at all been succour to Patroklos nor to all my other comrades that have been slain by noble Hector, but I sit beside my ships a profit-less burden of the earth, I that in war am such an one as is none else of the mail-clad Achaians, though in council are others better—may strife perish utterly among gods and men, and wrath that stirreth even a wise man to be vexed, wrath that far sweeter than trickling honey waxeth like smoke in the breasts of men, even as I was wroth even now against Agamemnon king of men. But bygones will we let be, for all our pain, curbing the heart in our breasts under necessity. Now go I forth, that I may light on the destroyer of him I loved, on Hector: then will I accept my death whensoever Zeus willeth to accomplish it and the other im-mortal gods. For not even the mighty Herakles escaped death, albeit most dear to Kronian Zeus the king, but Fate overcame him and Hera's cruel wrath. So also shall I, if my fate hath been fashioned likewise, lie low when I am dead. But now let me win high renown, let me set some Trojan woman, some deep-bosomed daughter of Dardanos, staunching with both hands the tears upon her tender cheeks and wailing bitterly; yea, let them know that I am come back, though I tarried long from the war. Hold not me then from the battle in thy love, for thou shalt not prevail with me."

Then Thetis the silver-footed goddess answered him, saying: "Yea verily, my child, no blame is in this, that thou ward sheer destruction from thy comrades in their distress. But thy fair glittering armour of bronze is held among the Trojans. Hector of the glancing helm beareth it on his shoulders in triumph, yet not for long, I ween, shall he glory therein, for death is hard anigh him. But thou, go not yet down into the melee of war until thou see me with thine eyes come hither. In the morning will I return, at the coming up of the sun, bearing fair armour from the king Hephaistos."

Thus spake she and turned to go from her son, and as she turned she spake among her sisters of the sea: "Ye now go down within the wide bosom of the deep, to visit the Ancient One of the Sea and our father's house, and tell him all. I am going to high Olympus to Hephaistos of noble skill, if haply he will give unto my son noble armour shining gloriously."

Thus spake she, and they forthwith went down beneath the surge of the sea. And the silver-footed goddess Thetis went on to Olympus that she might bring noble armour to her son.

So her unto Olympus her feet bore. But the Achaians with terrible cries were fleeing before man-slaying Hector till they came to the ships and to the Hellespont. Nor might the well-greaved Achaians drag the corpse of Patroklos Achilles' squire out of the darts, for now again overtook him the host and the horses of Troy, and Hector son of Priam, in might as it were a flame of fire. Thrice did glorious Hector seize him from behind by the feet, resolved to drag him away, and mightily called upon the men of Troy. Thrice did the two Aiantes, clothed on with impetuous might, beat him off from the dead man, but he nathless, trusting in his might, anon would charge into the press, anon would stand and cry aloud, but he gave ground never a whit. As when shepherds in the field avail nowise to chase a fiery lion in fierce hunger away from a carcase, so availed not the two warrior Aiantes to scare Hector son of Priam from the dead. And now would he have won the body and gained renown unspeakable, had not fleet wind-footed Iris come speeding from Olympus with a message to the son of Peleus to array him, unknown of Zeus and the other gods, for Hera sent her. And she stood anigh and spake to him winged words: "Rouse thee, son of Peleus, of all men most redoubtable! Succour Patroklos, for whose body is terrible battle afoot before the ships. There slay they one another, these guarding the dead corpse, while the men of Troy are fierce to hale him unto windy Ilios, and chiefliest noble Hector is fain to drag him, and his heart biddeth him fix the head on the stakes of the wall when he hath sundered it from the tender neck. But arise, lie thus no longer! let awe enter thy heart to forbid that Patroklos become the sport of dogs of Troy. Thine were the shame if he go down mangled amid the dead."

Then answered her fleet-footed noble Achilles: "Goddess Iris, what god sent thee a messenger unto me?"

And to him again spake wind-footed fleet Iris: "It was Hera that sent me, the wise wife of Zeus, nor knoweth the high-throned son of Kronos nor any other of the Immortals that on snowy Olympus have their dwelling-place."

And Achilles fleet of foot made answer to her and said: "And how may I go into the fray? The Trojans hold my arms; and my dear mother bade me forbear to array me until I behold her with my eyes returned, for she promised to bring fair armour from Hephaistos. Other man know I none whose noble armour I might put on, save it were the shield of Aias Telamon's son. But himself, I ween, is in the forefront of the press, dealing death with his spear around Patroklos dead."

Then again spake unto him wind-footed fleet Iris: "Well are we also aware that thy noble armour is held from thee. But go forth unto the trench as thou art and show thyself to the men of Troy, if haply they will shrink back and refrain them from battle, and the warlike sons of the Achaians take breath."

Thus spake fleet-footed Iris and went her way. But Achilles dear to Zeus arose, and around his strong shoulders Athene cast her tasselled aegis, and around his head the bright goddess set a crown of a golden cloud, and kindled therefrom a blazing flame. And as when a smoke issueth from a city and riseth up into the upper air, from an island afar off that foes beleaguer, while the others from their city fight all day in hateful war,—but with the going down of the sun blaze out the beacon-fires in line, and high aloft rusheth up the glare for dwellers round about to behold, if haply they may come with ships to help in need—thus from the head of Achilles soared that blaze toward the heavens. And he went and stood beyond the wall beside the trench, yet mingled not among the Achaians, for he minded the wise bidding of his mother. There stood he and shouted aloud, and afar off Pallas Athene uttered her voice, and spread terror unspeakable among the men of Troy. Clear as the voice of a clarion when it soundeth by reason of slaughterous foemen that beleaguer a city, so clear rang forth the voice of Aiakides. And when they heard the brazen voice of Aiakides, the souls of all of them were dismayed, and the horses of goodly manes were fain to turn the chariots backward, for they boded anguish in their hearts. And the charioteers were amazed when they saw the unwearying fire blaze fierce on the head of the great-hearted son of Peleus, for the bright-eyed goddess Athene made it blaze. Thrice from over the trench shouted mightily noble Achilles, and thrice were the men of Troy confounded and their proud allies. Yea there and then perished twelve men of their best by their own chariot wheels and spears. But the Achaians with joy drew Patroklos forth of the darts and laid him on a litter, and his dear comrades stood around lamenting him; and among them followed fleet-footed Achilles, shedding hot tears for his true comrade he saw lying on the bier, mangled by the keen bronze. Him sent he forth with chariot and horses unto the battle, but home again welcomed never more.

Then Hera the ox-eyed queen sent down the unwearying Sun to be gone unwillingly unto the streams of Ocean. So the Sun set, and the noble Achaians made pause from the stress of battle and the hazardous war.

But the Achaians all night made moan in lamentation for Patroklos. And first of them in the loud lamentation was the son of Peleus, laying upon the breast of his comrade his man-slaying hands and moaning very sore, even as a deep-bearded lion whose whelps some stag-hunter hath snatched away out of a deep wood; and the lion coming afterward grieveth and through many glens he rangeth on the track of the footsteps of the man, if anywhere he might find him, for most bitter anger seizeth him;—thus Achilles moaning heavily spake among the Myrmidons: "Ay me, vain verily was the word I uttered on that day when I cheered the hero Menoitios in his halls and said that I would bring back to Opoeis his son in glory from the sack of Ilios with the share of spoil that should fall unto him. Not all the purposes of men doth Zeus accomplish for them. It is appointed that both of us redden the same earth with our blood here in Troy-land, for neither shall the old knight Peleus welcome me back home within his halls, nor my mother Thetis, but even here shall earth keep hold on me. Yet now, O Patroklos, since I follow thee under earth, I will not hold thy funeral till I have brought hither the armour and the head of Hector, thy high-hearted slayer, and before thy pyre I will cut the throats of twelve noble sons of the men of Troy, for mine anger thou art slain. Till then beside the beaked ships shalt thou lie as thou art, and around thee deep-bosomed women, Trojan and Dardanian, shall mourn thee weeping night and day, even they whom we toiled to win by our strength and our long spears when we sacked rich cities of mortal men."

Thus spake noble Achilles, and bade his comrades set a great tripod on the fire, that with all speed they might wash from Patroklos the bloody gore. So they set a tripod of ablution on the burning fire, and poured therein water and took wood and kindled it beneath; and the fire wrapped the belly of the tripod, and the water grew hot. And when the water boiled in the bright bronze, then washed they him and anointed with olive oil, and filled his wounds with fresh ointment, and laid him on a bier and covered him with soft cloth from head to foot, and thereover a white robe. Then all night around Achilles fleet of foot the Myrmidons made lament and moan for Patroklos.

Meanwhile Zeus spake unto Hera his sister and wife: "Thou hast accomplished this, O Hera, ox-eyed queen, thou hast aroused Achilles fleet of foot. Verily of thine own children must the flowing-haired Achaians be."

Then answered unto him Hera the ox-eyed queen: "Most dread son of Kronos, what is this word thou hast said? Truly even a man, I ween, is to accomplish what he may for another man, albeit he is mortal and hath not wisdom as we. How then was I who avow me the first of goddesses both by birth and for that I am called thy wife, and thou art king among all Immortals—how was I not in mine anger to devise evil against the men of Troy?"

So debated they on this wise with one another. But Thetis of the silver feet came unto the house of Hephaistos, imperishable, starlike, far seen among the dwellings of Immortals, a house of bronze, wrought by the crook-footed god himself. Him found she sweating in toil and busy about his bellows, for he was forging tripods twenty in all to stand around the wall of his stablished hall, and beneath the base of each he had set golden wheels, that of their own motion they might enter the assembly of the gods and again return unto his house, a marvel to look upon. Thus much were they finished that not yet were the ears of cunning work set thereon; these was he making ready, and welding chains. While hereat he was labouring with wise intent, then drew nigh unto him Thetis, goddess of the silver feet. And Charis went forward and beheld her, fair Charis of the shining chaplet whom the renowned lame god had wedded. And she clasped her hand in hers and spake and called her by her name: "Wherefore, long-robed Thetis, comest thou to our house, honoured that thou art and dear? No frequent comer art thou hitherto. But come onward with me that I may set guest-cheer before thee."

Thus spake the bright goddess and led her on. Then set she her on a silver-studded throne, goodly, of cunning work, and a footstool was beneath her feet; and she called to Hephaistos, the famed artificer, and said unto him: "Hephaistos, come forth hither, Thetis hath need of thee."

And the renowned lame god made answer to her: "Verily a dread and honoured goddess in my sight is she that is within, seeing that she delivered me when pain came upon me from my great fall though the ill-will of my shameless mother who would fain have hid me away, for that I was lame. Then had I suffered anguish of heart had not Eurynome and Thetis taken me into their bosom—Eurynome daughter of Ocean that floweth back ever upon himself. Nine years with them I wrought much cunning work of bronze, brooches and spiral arm-bands and cups and necklaces, in the hollow cave, while around me the stream of Ocean with murmuring foam flowed infinite. Neither knew thereof any other of gods or of mortal men, save only Thetis and Eurynome who delivered me. And now cometh Thetis to our house; wherefore behoveth it me verily in all wise to repay fair-tressed Thetis for the saving of my life. But do thou now set beside her fair entertainment, while I put away my bellows and all my gear."

He said, and from the anvil rose limping, a huge bulk, but under him his slender legs moved nimbly. The bellows he set away from the fire, and gathered all his gear wherewith he worked into a silver chest; and with a sponge he wiped his face and hands and sturdy neck and shaggy breast, and did on his doublet, and took a stout staff and went forth limping; but there were handmaidens of gold that moved to help their lord, the semblances of living maids. In them is understanding at their hearts, in them are voice and strength, and they have skill of the immortal gods. These moved beneath their lord, and he gat him haltingly near to where Thetis was, and set him on a bright seat, and clasped her hand in his and spake and called her by her name: "Wherefore, long-robed Thetis, comest thou to our house, honoured that thou art and dear? No frequent comer art thou hitherto. Speak what thou hast at heart; my soul is fain to accomplish it, if accomplish it I can, and if it be appointed for accomplishment."

Then answered unto him Thetis shedding tears: "Hephaistos, hath there verily been any of all goddesses in Olympus
that hath endured so many grievous sorrows at heart as are
the woes that Kronian Zeus hath laid upon me above all
others? He chose me from among the sisters of the sea to
enthrall me to a man, even Peleus Aiakos' son, and with a
man I endured wedlock sore against my will. Now lieth he
in his halls forspent with grievous age, but other griefs are
mine. A son he gave me to bear and nourish, the chief of
heroes, and he shot up like a young branch. Like a plant in
a very fruitful field I reared him and sent him forth on
beaked ships to Ilios to fight against the men of Troy, but
never again shall I welcome him back to his home within
the house of Peleus. And while he yet liveth in my sight and
beholdeth the light of the sun, he sorroweth, neither can I
help him any whit though I go unto him. The maiden whom
the sons of the Achaians chose out to be his prize, her hath
the lord Agamemnon taken back out of his hands. In grief
for her wasted he his heart, while the men of Troy were
driving the Achaians on their ships, nor suffered them to
come forth. And the elders of the Argives entreated him,
and told over many noble gifts. Then albeit himself he refused to ward destruction from them, he put his armour on
Patroklos and sent him to the war, and much people with
him. All day they fought around the Skaian gates and that
same day had sacked the town, but that when now Menoitios' valiant son had wrought much harm, Apollo slew him
in the forefront of the battle, and gave glory unto Hector.
Therefore now come I a suppliant unto thy knees, if haply
thou be willing to give my short-lived son shield and helmet,

and goodly greaves fitted with ankle-pieces, and cuirass. For the armour that he had erst, his trusty comrade lost when he fell beneath the men of Troy; and my son lieth on the earth with anguish in his soul."

Then made answer unto her the lame god of great renown: "Be of good courage, let not these things trouble thy heart. Would that so might I avail to hide him far from dolorous death, when dread fate cometh upon him, as surely shall goodly armour be at his need, such as all men afterward shall marvel at, whatsoever may behold."

Thus saying he left her there and went unto his bellows and turned them upon the fire and bade them work. And the bellows, twenty in all, blew on the crucibles, sending deft blasts on every side, now to aid his labour and now anon howsoever Hephaistos willed and the work went on. And he threw bronze that weareth not into the fire, and tin and precious gold and silver, and next he set on an anvil-stand a great anvil, and took in his hand a sturdy hammer, and in the other he took the tongs.

First fashioned he a shield great and strong, adorning it all over, and set thereto a shining rim, triple, bright-glancing, and therefrom a silver baldric. Five were the folds of the shield itself; and therein fashioned he much cunning work from his wise heart.

There wrought he the earth, and the heavens, and the sea, and the unwearying sun, and the moon waxing to the full, and the signs every one wherewith the heavens are crowned, Pleiads and Hyads and Orion's might, and the Bear that men call also the Wain, her that turneth in her place and watcheth Orion, and alone hath no part in the baths of Ocean.

Also he fashioned therein two fair cities of mortal men. In the one were espousals and marriage feasts, and beneath the blaze of torches they were leading the brides from their chambers through the city, and loud arose the bridal song. And young men were whirling in the dance, and among them flutes and viols sounded high; and women standing each at her door were marvelling. But the folk were gathered in the assembly place; for there a strife was arisen, two men striving about the blood-price of a man slain; the one claimed to pay full atonement, expounding to the people, but the other denied him and would take naught. And the folk were cheering both, as they took part on either side. And heralds kept order among the folk, while the elders on polished stones were sitting in the sacred circle, and holding in their hands staves from the loud-voiced heralds. Then before the people they rose up and gave judgment each in turn. And in the midst lay two talents of gold, to be given unto him who should plead among them most righteously.

But around the other city were two armies in siege with glittering arms. And two counsels found favour among them, either to sack the town or to share all with the townsfolk even whatsoever substance the fair city held within. But the besieged were not yet yielding, but arming for an ambushment. On the wall there stood to guard it their dear wives and infant children, and with these the old men; but the rest went forth, and their leaders were Ares and Pallas Athene, both wrought in gold, and golden was the vesture they had on. Goodly and great were they in their armour, even as gods, far seen around, and the folk at their feet were smaller. And when they came where it seemed good to them to lay ambush, in a river bed where there was a common watering-place of herds, there they set them, clad in glittering bronze. And two scouts were posted by them afar off to spy the coming of flocks and of oxen with crooked horns. And presently came the cattle, and with them two herdsmen playing on pipes, that took no thought of the guile. Then the others when they beheld these ran upon them and quickly cut off the herds of oxen and fair flocks of white sheep, and slew the shepherds withal. But the besiegers, as they sat before the speech-places and heard much din among the oxen, mounted forthwith behind their high-stepping horses, and came up with speed. Then they arrayed their battle and fought beside the river banks, and smote one another with bronze-shod spears. And among them mingled Strife and Tumult, and fell Death, grasping one man alive fresh-wounded, another without wound, and dragging another dead through the melee by the feet; and the raiment on her shoulders was red with the blood of men. Like living mortals they hurled together and fought, and haled the corpses each of the other's slain.

Furthermore he set in the shield a soft fresh-ploughed field, rich tilth and wide, the third time ploughed; and many ploughers therein drave their yokes to and fro as they wheeled about. Whensoever they came to the boundary of the field and turned, then would a man come to each and give into his hands a goblet of sweet wine, while others would be turning back along the furrows, fain to reach the boundary of the deep tilth. And the field grew black behind and seemed as it were a-ploughing, albeit of gold, for this was the great marvel of the work.

Furthermore he set therein the demesne-land of a king, where hinds were reaping with sharp sickles in their hands. Some armfuls along the swathe were falling in rows to the earth, whilst others the sheaf-binders were binding in twisted bands of straw. Three sheaf-binders stood over them, while behind boys gathering corn and bearing it in their arms gave it constantly to the binders; and among them the king in silence was standing at the swathe with his staff, rejoicing in his heart. And henchmen apart beneath an oak were making ready a feast, and preparing a great ox they had sacrificed; while the women were strewing much white barley to be a supper for the hinds.

Also he set therein a vineyard teeming plenteously with clusters, wrought fair in gold; black were the grapes, but the vines hung throughout on silver poles. And around it he ran a ditch of cyanus, and round that a fence of tin; and one single pathway led to it, whereby the vintagers might go when they should gather the vintage. And maidens and striplings in childish glee bare the sweet fruit in plaited baskets. And in the midst of them a boy made pleasant music on a clear-toned viol, and sang thereto a sweet Linos-song with delicate voice; while the rest with feet falling together kept time with the music and song.

Also he wrought therein a herd of kine with upright horns, and the kine were fashioned of gold and tin, and with lowing they hurried from the byre to pasture beside a murmuring river, beside the waving reed. And herdsmen of gold were following with the kine, four of them, and nine dogs fleet of foot came after them. But two terrible lions among the foremost kine had seized a loud-roaring bull that bellowed mightily as they haled him, and the dogs and the young men sped after him. The lions rending the great bull's hide were devouring his vitals and his black blood; while the herdsmen in vain tarred on their fleet dogs to set on, for they shrank from biting the lions but stood hard by and barked and swerved away.

Also the glorious lame god wrought therein a pasture in a fair glen, a great pasture of white sheep, and a steading, and roofed huts, and folds.

Also did the glorious lame god devise a dancing-place like unto that which once in wide Knosos Daidalos wrought for Ariadne of the lovely tresses. There were youths dancing and maidens of costly wooing, their hands upon one another's wrists. Fine linen the maidens had on, and the youths well-woven doublets faintly glistening with oil. Fair wreaths had the maidens, and the youths daggers of gold hanging from silver baldrics. And now would they run round with deft feet exceeding lightly, as when a potter sitting by his wheel that fitteth between his hands maketh trial of it whether it run: and now anon they would run in lines to meet each other. And a great company stood round the lovely dance in joy; and through the midst of them, leading the measure, two tumblers whirled.

Also he set therein the great might of the River of Ocean around the uttermost rim of the cunningly-fashioned shield.

Now when he had wrought the shield great and strong, then wrought he him a corslet brighter than a flame of fire, and he wrought him a massive helmet to fit his brows, goodly and graven, and set thereon a crest of gold, and he wrought him greaves of pliant tin.

So when the renowned lame god had finished all the armour, he took and laid it before the mother of Achilles. Then she like a falcon sprang down from snowy Olympus, bearing from Hephaistos the glittering arms.

BOOK XIX

How Achilles and Agamemnon were reconciled before the
assembly of the Achaians, and Achilles went forth with them
to battle.

Now Morning saffron-robed arose from the streams of
Ocean to bring light to gods and men, and Thetis
came to the ships, bearing his gift from the god. Her dear
son she found fallen about Patroklos and uttering loud
lament; and round him many of his company made moan.
And the bright goddess stood beside him in their midst,
and clasped her hand in his and spake and called upon his
name: "My child, him who lieth here we must let be, for all
our pain, for by the will of gods from the beginning was he
brought low. But thou take from Hephaistos arms of pride,
arms passing goodly, such as no man on his shoulders yet
hath borne."

Thus spake the goddess and in front of Achilles laid the
arms, and they rang all again in their glory. And awe fell on
all the Myrmidons, nor dared any to gaze thereon, for they
were awe-stricken. But when Achilles looked thereon, then
came fury upon him the more, and his eyes blazed terribly
forth as it were a flame beneath their lids: glad was he as he
held in his hands that splendid gift of a god. But when he
had satisfied his soul in gazing on the glory of the arms,
straightway to his mother spake he winged words: "My

mother, the arms the god has given are such as it beseemeth that the work of Immortals should be, and that no mortal man should have wrought. Now therefore will I arm me in them, but I have grievous fear lest meantime on the gashed wounds of Menoitios' valiant son flies light and breed worms therein, and defile his corpse—for the life is slain out of him—and so all his flesh shall rot."

Then answered him Thetis, goddess of the silver feet: "Child, have no care for this within thy mind. I will see to ward from him the cruel tribes of flies which prey on men slain in fight: for even though he lie till a whole year's course be run, yet his flesh shall be sound continually, or better even than now. But call thou the Achaian warriors to the place of assembly, and unsay thy wrath against Agamemnon shepherd of the host, and then arm swiftly for battle, and clothe thee with thy strength."

Thus saying she filled him with adventurous might, while on Patroklos she shed ambrosia and red nectar through his nostrils, that his flesh might abide the same continually.

But noble Achilles went down the beach of the sea, crying his terrible cry, and roused the Achaian warriors. And they who before were wont to abide in the circle of the ships, and they who were helmsmen and kept the steerage of the ships, or were stewards there and dealt out food, even these came then to the place of assembly, because Achilles was come forth, after long ceasing from grievous war. Limping came two of Ares' company, Tydeus' son staunch in fight and noble Odysseus, each leaning on his spear, for their wounds were grievous still; and they went and sate them down in the forefront of the assembly. And last came

Agamemnon king of men, with his wound upon him, for him too in the stress of battle Koön Antenor's son had wounded with his bronze-tipped spear. But when all the Achaians were gathered, then uprose fleet-footed Achilles and spake in their midst: "Son of Atreus, was this in any wise the better way for both thee and me, what time with grief at our hearts we waxed fierce in soul-devouring strife for the sake of a girl? Would that Artemis had slain her with her arrow at the ships, on the day whereon I took her to me, when I had spoiled Lyrnessos; so should not then so many Achaians have bitten the wide earth beneath their enemies' hands, by reason of my exceeding wrath. It hath been well for Hector and the Trojans, but the Achaians I think shall long remember the strife that was betwixt thee and me. But bygones will we let be, for all our pain, and curb under necessity the spirit within our breasts. I now will stay my anger: it beseems me not implacably for ever to be wroth; but come rouse speedily to the fight the flowing-haired Achaians, that I may go forth against the men of Troy and put them yet again to the proof, if they be fain to couch hard by the ships. Methinks that some among them shall be glad to rest their knees when they are fled out of the fierceness of the battle, and from before our spear."

He spake, and the well-greaved Achaians rejoiced that the great-hearted son of Peleus had made renouncement of his wrath. Then among them spake Agamemnon king of men, speaking from the place where he sat, not arisen to stand forth in their midst: "O Danaan friends and heroes, to the son of Peleus I will declare myself, but ye other Argives give heed, and each mark well my word. Oft have the

Achaians spoken thus to me, and upbraided me; but it is not I who am the cause, but Zeus and Destiny and Erinys that walketh in the darkness, who put into my soul fierce madness on the day when in the assembly I, even I, bereft Achilles of his meed. But since thus blinded was I, and Zeus bereft me of my wit, fain am I to make amends, and recompense manifold for the wrong. Only arise thou to the battle and rouse the rest of the host. Gifts am I ready to offer, even all that noble Odysseus went yesterday to promise in thy hut. So, if thou wilt, stay awhile, though eager, from battle, and squires shall take the gifts from my ship and carry them to thee, that thou mayest see that what I give sufficeth thee."

Then answered him Achilles swift of foot: "Most noble son of Atreus, Agamemnon king of men, for the gifts, to give them as it beseemeth, if so thou wilt, or to withhold, is in thy choice. But now let us bethink us of battle with all speed; this is no time to dally here with subtleties, for a great work is yet undone. Once more must Achilles be seen in the forefront of the battle, laying waste with his brazen spear the battalions of the men of Troy. Thereof let each of you think as he fighteth with his man."

Then Odysseus of many counsels answered him and said: "Nay yet, for all thy valour, godlike Achilles, not against Ilios lead thou the sons of Achaians fasting to fight the men of Troy, since not of short spell shall the battle be, when once the ranks of men are met, and God shall breathe valour into both. But bid the Achaians taste at the swift ships food and wine; for thence is vigour and might."

Then to him spake Agamemnon king of men: "Let Achilles abide for a space, eager for battle though he be, and all ye others abide together, until the gifts come forth from my hut, and we make faithful oath with sacrifice. But thee thyself I thus charge and bid. Choose thee young men, princes of the Achaian folk, and bear my gifts from my ship, even all that we promised yesterday to Achilles, and take with thee the women. And let Talthybios speedily make me ready a boar-swine in the midst of the wide Achaian host, to sacrifice to Zeus and to the Sun."

And to him in answer swift-footed Achilles spake: "Most noble son of Atreus, Agamemnon king of men, at some other time were it even better ye should be busied thus, when haply there shall be some pause of war, and the spirit within my breast shall be less fierce. But now they lie mangled on the field—even they whom Hector son of Priam slew, when Zeus gave him glory—and ye call men to their food. Verily for my part I would bid the sons of the Achaians to fight now unfed and fasting, and with the setting sun make ready a mighty meal, when we shall have avenged the shame. Till then down my throat at least nor food nor drink shall go, since my comrade is dead, who in my hut is lying mangled by the sharp spear, with his feet toward the door, and round him our comrades mourn, wherefore in my heart is no thought of those matters, but of slaying, and blood, and grievous moans of men."

Then answered him Odysseus of many counsels: "O Achilles, Peleus' son, mightiest of Achaians far, better and mightier not a little art thou than I with the spear, but in counsel I may surpass thee greatly, since I was born first and know more things: wherefore let thy heart endure to listen to my speech. Quickly have men surfeit of battle, of that wherein the sword streweth most straw yet is the harvest scantiest, when Zeus inclineth his balance, who is disposer of the wars of men. But it cannot be that the Achaians fast to mourn a corpse; for exceeding many and thick fall such on every day; when then should there be rest from toil? Nay, it behoveth to bury him who is dead, steeling our hearts, when once we have wept him for a day; but such as are left alive from hateful war must take thought of meat and drink, that yet more against our foes we may fight relentlessly ever, clad in unyielding bronze. Then let none of the host hold back awaiting other summons; this is the summons, and ill shall it be for whoso is left behind at the Argive ships; but all together as one we will rouse against the horse-taming Trojans the fury of war."

He spoke, and took with him the sons of noble Nestor, and Meges son of Phyleus, and Thoas, and Meriones, and Lykomedes son of Kreiontes, and Melanippos. And they went on their way to the hut of Agamemnon, Atreus' son. Forthwith as the word was spoken so was the deed done. Seven tripods they bare from the hut, as he promised him, and twenty bright caldrons, and twelve horses, and anon they led forth women skilled in goodly arts, seven, and the eighth was fair-faced Briseis. Then Odysseus, having weighed ten talents of gold in all, led the way, and with him young men of the Achaians bare the gifts. These they set in the midst of the place of assembly, and Agamemnon rose up, and beside that shepherd of the host stood Talthybios, whose voice was like a god's, and held a boar between his hands. And the son of Atreus drawing with his hands his knife, which ever hung beside the mighty scabbard of his sword, cut off the first hairs from the boar, and lifting up his hands he prayed to Zeus, and cut the boar's throat with the pitiless knife. And the body Talthybios whirled and threw into the great wash of the hoary sea, to be the food of fishes; but Achilles arose up and spake in the midst of the warrior Argives: "Father Zeus, sore madness dealest thou verily to men. Never could the son of Atreus have stirred the soul within my breast, nor led off the damsel implacably against my will, had not Zeus willed that on many of the Achaians death should come. But now go forth to your meal, that we may join battle thereupon."

Thus he spake and dispersed the assembly with all speed. The rest were scattered each to his own ship, but the great-hearted Myrmidons took up the gifts, and bare them to the ship of godlike Achilles. And they laid them in the huts and set the women there, and gallant squires drave the horses among their troop.

But Briseis that was like unto golden Aphrodite, when she beheld Patroklos mangled by the keen spear, fell about him and made shrill lament, and tore with her hands her breast and tender neck, and beautiful face. And she spake amid her weeping, that woman like unto goddesses: "Patroklos, dearest to my hapless heart, alive I left thee when I left this hut, but now, O prince of the people, I am come back to find thee dead; thus evil ever followeth evil in my lot. My husband, unto whom my father and lady mother gave me, I beheld before your city mangled with the keen spear, and my three brothers whom my own mother bore, my near and dear, who all met their day of doom. But thou, when swift Achilles slew my husband and wasted godlike Mynes' city, wouldst ever that I should not even weep, and saidest that thou wouldst make me godlike Achilles' wedded wife, and that ye would take me in your ships to Phthia and make me a marriage feast among the Myrmidons. Therefore with all my soul I mourn thy death, for thou wert ever kind."

Thus spake she weeping, and thereon the women wailed, in semblance for Patroklos, but each for her own woe. But round Achilles gathered the elders of the Achaians, praying him that he would eat; but he denied them with a groan: "I pray you, if any kind comrade will hearken to me, bid me not sate my heart with meat and drink, since terrible grief is come upon me. Till the sun go down I will abide, and endure continually until then."

Thus spake he weeping, and the elders mourned with him. And when the son of Kronos beheld them sorrowing he pitied them, and forthwith to Athene spake he winged words: "My child, thou hast then left utterly the man of thy heart. Hath Achilles then no longer a place within thy thought? He before the steep-prowed ships sits mourning his dear comrade; the rest are gone to their meal, but he is fasting and unfed. But go, distil into his breast nectar and pleasant ambrosia, that no pains of hunger come on him."

Thus saying he sped forward Athene who before was fain. And she, like a falcon wide-winged and shrill-voiced, hurled herself forth from heaven through the upper air. So while the Achaians were arming presently throughout the camp, she in Achilles' breast distilled nectar and pleasant ambrosia, that grievous hunger might not assail his knees, and then herself was gone to the firm house of her mighty father. Then the Achaians poured forth from the swift ships. As when thick snowflakes flutter down from Zeus, chill beneath the blast of Boreas born in the upper air, so thick from the ships streamed forth bright glittering helms and bossy shields, strong-plaited cuirasses and ashen spears. And the sheen thereof went up to heaven and all the earth around laughed in the flash of bronze, and there went a sound beneath the feet of the men, and in the midst of them noble Achilles harnessed him. His teeth gnashed together, and his eyes blazed as it were the flame of a fire, for into his heart was intolerable anguish entered in. Thus wroth against the men of Troy he put on the gift of the god, which Hephaistos wrought him by his art. First on his legs he set the fair greaves fitted with silver ankle-pieces, and next he donned the cuirass about his breast. Then round his shoulders he slung the bronze sword silver-studded; then lastly he took the great and strong shield, and its brightness shone afar off as the moon's. Or as when over the sea there appeareth to sailors the brightness of a burning fire, and it burneth on high among the mountains in some lonely steading—sailors whom storm-blasts bear unwilling over the sea, the home of fishes, afar from them they love:—so from Achilles' goodly well-dight shield the brightness thereof shot up toward heaven. And he lifted the stout helmet and set it on his head, and like a star it shone, the horse-hair crested helmet, and around it waved plumes of gold that Hephaistos had set thick about the crest. Then noble Achilles proved him in his armour to know whether it fitted unto him, and whether his glorious limbs ran free; and it became to him as it were wings, and buoyed up the shepherd of hosts.

And forth from its stand he drew his father's spear, heavy and great and strong: that spear could none other of the Achaians wield, but Achilles alone awaited to wield it, the Pelion ashen spear that Cheiron gave to his father dear, from a peak of Pelion, to be the death of warriors. And Automedon and Alkimos went about to yoke the horses, and put on them fair breast-straps, and bits within their jaws, and stretched the reins behind to the firm-built chariot. Then Automedon took the bright lash, fitted to his hand, and sprang up behind the horses, and after him mounted Achilles armed, effulgent in his armour like bright Hyperion. And terribly he called upon the horses of his sire: "Xanthos and Balios, famed children of Podarge, in other sort take heed to bring your charioteer safe back to the Danaan host, when we have done with battle, and leave him not as ye left Patroklos to lie there dead."

Then the horse Xanthos of glancing feet made answer unto him from beneath the yoke;—and he bowed with his head, and all his mane fell from the yoke-cushion beside the yoke and touched the ground;—for the white-armed goddess Hera gave him speech: "Yea verily for this hour, dread Achilles, we will still bear thee safe, yet is thy death day nigh at hand, neither shall we be cause thereof, but a mighty god, and forceful Fate. For not through sloth or heedlessness of ours did the men of Troy from Patroklos' shoulders strip his arms, but the best of the gods, whom bright-haired Leto bore, slew him in the forefront of the battle, and to Hector gave renown. We even with the wind of Zephyr, swiftest, they say, of all winds, well might run; nathless to thee thyself it is appointed to be slain in fight by a god and by a man."

Now when he had thus spoken the Erinyes stayed his voice. And sore troubled did fleet-footed Achilles answer him: "Xanthos, why prophesiest thou my death? nowise behoveth it thee. Well know I of myself that it is appointed me to perish here, far from my father dear and mother; howbeit anywise I will not refrain till I give the Trojans surfeit of war."

He said, and with a cry among the foremost held on his whole-hooved steeds.

BOOK XX

How Achilles made havoc among the men of Troy.

So by the beaked ships around thee, son of Peleus, hungry for war, the Achaians armed; and over against them the men of Troy, upon the high ground of the plain.

But Zeus bade Themis call the gods to council from many-folded Olympus' brow; and she ranged all about and bade them to the house of Zeus. There was no River came not up, save only Ocean, nor any nymph, of all that haunt fair thickets and springs of rivers and grassy water-meadows. And they came to the house of Zeus who gathereth the clouds, and sat them down in the polished colonnades which Hephaistos in the cunning of his heart had wrought for father Zeus.

Thus gathered they within the doors of Zeus; nor was the Earthshaker heedless of the goddess' call, but from the salt sea came up after the rest, and set him in the midst, and inquired concerning the purpose of Zeus: "Wherefore, O Lord of the bright lightning, hast thou called the gods again to council? Say, ponderest thou somewhat concerning the Trojans and Achaians? for lo, the war and the fighting of them are kindled very nigh."

And Zeus, who gathered the clouds, answered him, saying: "Thou knowest, O Earthshaker, the purpose within my breast, wherefor I gathered you hither; even in their perish-

305

ing have I regard unto them. But for me I will abide here, sitting within a fold of Olympus, where I will gladden my heart with gazing; but go all ye forth that ye come among the Trojans and Achaians and succour these or those, howsoever each of you hath a mind. For if Achilles alone shall fight against the Trojans, not even a little while shall they hold back the son of Peleus, the fleet of foot. Nay, but even aforetime they trembled when they looked upon him; now therefore that his wrath for his friend is waxen terrible I fear me lest he overleap the bound of fate, and storm the wall."

Thus spake the son of Kronos, and roused unabating war. For on this side and on that the gods went forth to war: to the company of the ships went Hera, and Pallas Athene, and Poseidon, Earth-enfolder, and the Helper Hermes, pre-eminent in subtle thoughts; and with these went Hephaistos in the greatness of his strength, halting, but his shrunk legs moved nimbly under him: but to the Trojans went Ares of the glancing helm, and with him Phoebus of the unshorn hair, and archer Artemis, and Leto and Xanthos and laughter-loving Aphrodite.

Now for so long as gods were afar from mortal men, so long waxed the Achaians glorious, for that Achilles was come forth among them, and his long ceasing from grim battle was at an end. And the Trojans were smitten with sore trembling in the limbs of every one of them, in terror when they beheld the son of Peleus, fleet of foot, blazing in his arms, peer of man-slaying Ares. But when among the melee of men the Olympians were come down, then leapt up in her might Strife, rouser of hosts, then sent forth

Athene a cry, now standing by the hollowed trench without the wall, and now on the echoing shores she shouted aloud. And a shout uttered Ares against her, terrible as the blackness of the storm, now from the height of the city to the Trojans calling clear, or again along Simois shore over Kallikolonë he sped.

So urged the blessed gods both hosts to battle, then themselves burst into fierce war. And terribly thundered the father of gods and men from heaven above; and from beneath Poseidon made the vast earth shake and the steep mountain tops. Then trembled all the spurs of many-fountained Ida, and all her crests, and the city of the Trojans, and the ships of the Achaians. And the Lord of the Underworld, Aïdoneus, had terror in hell, and leapt from his throne in that terror and cried aloud, lest the world be cloven above him by Poseidon, Shaker of earth, and his dwelling-place be laid bare to mortals and immortals—grim halls, and vast, and lothly to the gods. So loud the roar rose of that battle of gods. For against King Poseidon stood Phoebus Apollo with his winged arrows, and against Enyalios stood Athene, bright-eyed goddess, and against Hera she of the golden shafts and echoing chase, even archer Artemis, sister of the Far-darter; and against Leto the strong Helper Hermes, and against Hephaistos the great deep-eddying River, whom gods call Xanthos and men Skamandros.

Thus gods with gods were matched. Meanwhile Achilles yearned above all to meet Hector, son of Priam, in the fray; for with that blood chiefliest his spirit bade him sate Ares, stubborn lord of war. But straightway Apollo, rouser of hosts, moved Aineias to go to meet the son of Peleus, and filled him with brave spirit: and he made his own voice like the voice of Lykaon the son of Priam; in his semblance spake Apollo, son of Zeus: "Aineias, counsellor of Trojans, where now are thy threats wherewith thou didst boast to the Trojan lords over thy wine, saying thou wouldest stand up in battle against Achilles, Peleus' son?"

And to him Aineias answered and said: "Son of Priam, why biddest thou me thus face the fierce son of Peleus in battle, though I be not fain thereto? It is impossible for man to face Achilles in fight, for that ever some god is at his side to ward off death. Ay, and at any time his spear flieth straight, neither ceaseth till it have pierced through flesh of man. But if God once give us fair field of battle, not lightly shall he overcome me, not though he boast him made of bronze throughout."

And to him in answer spake Apollo son of Zeus: "Yea, hero, pray thou too to the everliving gods; for thou too, men say, wast born of Aphrodite daughter of Zeus, and Achilles' mother is of less degree among the gods. For thy mother is child of Zeus, his but of the Ancient One of the Sea. Come, bear up thy unwearying spear against him, let him nowise turn thee back with revilings and bitter words."

He said, and breathed high spirit into the shepherd of the host, and he went onward through the forefront of the fighting, harnessed in flashing bronze. But white-armed Hera failed not to discern Anchises' son as he went through the press of men to meet the son of Peleus, and gathering the gods about her she spake among them thus: "Consider ye twain, Poseidon and Athene, within your hearts, what shall come of these things that are done. Here is Aineias gone forth harnessed in flashing bronze, to meet the son of Peleus, and it is Phoebus Apollo that hath sent him. Come then, be it ours to turn him back straightway; or else let some one of us stand likewise beside Achilles and give him mighty power, so that he fail not in his spirit, but know that they who love him are the best of the Immortals, and that they who from of old ward war and fighting from the Trojans are vain as wind. All we from Olympus are come down to mingle in this fight that he take no hurt among the Trojans on this day—afterward he shall suffer whatsoever things Fate span for him with her thread, at his beginning, when his mother bare him. If Achilles learn not this from voice divine, then shall he be afraid when some god shall come against him in the battle; for gods revealed are hard to look upon."

Then to her made answer Poseidon, Shaker of the earth: "Hera, be not fierce beyond wisdom; it behoveth thee not. Not fain am I at least to match gods with gods in strife. Let us go now into some high place apart and seat us there to watch, and battle shall be left to men. Only if Ares or Phoebus Apollo fall to fighting, or put constraint upon Achilles and hinder him from fight, then straightway among us too shall go up the battle-cry of strife; right soon, methinks, shall they hie them from the issue of the fray back to Olympus to the company of the gods, overcome by the force of our hands."

Thus spake the blue-haired god, and led the way to the mounded wall of heaven-sprung Herakles. There sate them down Poseidon and the other gods, and clothed their shoulders with impenetrable cloud. And they of the other part sat down on the brows of Kallikolonë around thee, Archer Phoebus, and Ares waster of cities. Thus they on either side sat devising counsels, but shrank all from falling to grievous war, and Zeus from his high seat commanded them.

Meanwhile the whole plain was filled with men and horses, and ablaze with bronze; and the earth rang with the feet of them as they rushed together in the fray. Two men far better than the rest were meeting in the midst between the hosts, eager for battle, Aineias, Anchises' son, and noble Achilles. First came on Aineias threateningly, tossing his strong helm; his rapid shield he held before his breast, and brandished his bronze spear. And on the other side the son of Peleus rushed to meet him like a lion. And when they were come near against each other, then first to Aineias spake fleet-footed noble Achilles: "Aineias, wherefore hast thou so far come forward from the crowd to stand against me: doth thy heart bid thee fight with me in hope of holding Priam's honour and lordship among the horse-taming Trojans? Nay, though thou slay me, not for that will Priam lay his kingdom in thy hands, for he hath sons, and is sound and of unshaken mind. Or have the Trojans allotted thee some lot of ground more choice than all the rest, fair land of tilth and orchard, that thou mayest dwell therein, if thou slay me? But methinks thou wilt find the slaying hard; for once ` before, I ween, have I made thee flee before my spear. Hast thou forgotten the day when thou wert alone with the kine, and I made thee run swift-footed down Ida's steeps in haste? —then didst thou not look behind thee in thy flight. Thence fleddest thou to Lernessos, but I wasted it, having fought against it with the help of Athene and of father Zeus, and carried away women captive, bereaving them of their day of freedom: only thee Zeus shielded, and other gods. But not this time, methinks, shall they shield thee, as thou imaginest in thy heart: therefore I bid thee go back into the throng and come not forth against me, while as yet thou art unhurt—after the event even a fool is wise."

Then to him in answer again Aineias spake: "Son of Peleus, think not with words to affright me as a child, since I too well know myself how to speak taunts and unjust speech. We know each other's race and lineage in that we have heard the fame proclaimed by mortal men, but never hast thou set eyes on my parents, or I on thine. Thou, they say, art son of noble Peleus, and of Thetis of the fair tresses, the daughter of the sea: the sire I boast is Anchises great of heart, and my mother is Aphrodite. Of these shall one pair or the other mourn their dear son to-day; for verily not with idle words shall we two satisfy our strife and depart out of the battle."

He said, and against the other's dread and mighty shield hurled his great spear, and the shield rang loud beneath the spear-point. And the son of Peleus held away the shield from him with his stout hand, in fear, for he thought that the far-shadowing spear of Aineias great of heart would lightly pierce it through—fond man, and knew not in his mind and heart that not lightly do the glorious gifts of gods yield to force of mortal men. So did not the great spear of wise Aineias pierce that shield, for the gold resisted it, even the gift of the god. Yet through two folds he drave it, but three remained, for five folds had the lame god welded, two bronze, and two inside of tin, and one of gold; therein was stayed the ashen spear.

Then Achilles in his turn hurled his far-shadowing spear, and smote upon the circle of the shield of Aineias, beneath the edge of the rim, where the bronze ran thinnest round, and the bull-hide was thinnest thereon; and right through sped the Pelion ashen spear, and the shield cracked under it. And Aineias crouched and held up the shield away from him in dread; and the spear flew over his back and fixed itself in the earth, having divided asunder the two circles of the sheltering shield. And having escaped the long spear he stood still, and a vast anguish drowned his eyes, affrighted that the spear was planted by him so nigh. But Achilles drew his sharp sword and furiously made at him, crying his terrible cry: then Aineias grasped in his hand a stone (a mighty deed) such as two men, as men now are, would not avail to lift, but he with ease wielded it all alone. Then would Aineias have smitten him with the stone as he charged, either on helm or shield, which had warded from him bitter death, and then would the son of Peleus have closed and slain him with his sword, had not Poseidon, Shaker of earth, marked it with speed, and straightway spoken among the immortal gods: "Alas, woe is me for Aineias great of heart, who quickly will go down to Hades slain by the son of Peleus, for that he will obey the words of Apollo the far-darter, fond man, but nowise shall the god help him from grievous death. Come, let us guide him out of death's way, lest the son of Kronos be wroth, if Achilles slay him."

And him then answered Hera the ox-eyed queen: "Shaker

of earth, thyself with thine own mind take counsel, whether thou wilt save Aineias, or leave him. For by many oaths among all the Immortals have we two sworn, even Pallas Athene and I, never to help the Trojans from their evil day, not even when all Troy shall burn in the burning of fierce fire, and they that burn her shall be the warlike sons of the Achaians."

Now when Poseidon Shaker of earth heard that, he went up amid the battle and the clash of spears, and came where Aineias and renowned Achilles were. Then presently he shed mist over the eyes of Achilles, Peleus' son, and drew the bronze-headed ashen spear from the shield of Aineias great of heart, and set it before Achilles' feet, and lifted Aineias and swung him high from off the earth. Over many ranks of warriors, of horses many, sprang Aineias soaring in the hand of the god, and lighted at the farthest verge of the battle of many onsets, where the Kaukones were arraying them for the fight. Then hard beside him came Poseidon, Shaker of earth, and spake aloud to him winged words: "Aineias, what god is it that biddeth thee fight infatuate against Peleus' vehement son, who is both a better man than thou and dearer to Immortals? Rather withdraw thee whensoever thou fallest in with him, lest even contrary to thy fate thou enter the house of Hades. But when Achilles shall have met his death and doom, then be thou of good courage to fight among the foremost, for there shall none other of the Achaians slay thee."

He spoke, and left him there, when he had shown him all these things. Then quickly from Achilles' eyes he purged the magic mist; and he stared with wide eyes, and in trouble spake unto his proud soul: "Ha! verily a great marvel behold I here with mine eyes. My spear lieth here upon the ground, nor can I anywise see the man at whom I hurled it with intent to slay him. Truly then is Aineias likewise dear to the immortal gods, howbeit I deemed that his boasting thereof was altogether vanity. Away with him! not again will he find heart to make trial of me, now that once more he has escaped death to his joy. But come, I will call on the warlike Danaans and go forth to make trial of some other Trojan face to face."

He said, and leapt along the lines, and called upon each man: "No longer stand afar from the men of Troy, noble Achaians, but come let man match man and throw his soul into the fight. Hard is it for me, though I be strong, to assail so vast a folk and fight them all: not even Ares, though an immortal god, nor Athene, could plunge into the jaws of such a fray and toil therein. But to my utmost power with hands and feet and strength no whit, I say, will I be slack, nay, never so little, but right through their line will I go forward, nor deem I that any Trojan shall be glad who shall come nigh my spear."

Thus spake he urging them. But to the Trojans glorious Hector called aloud, and proclaimed that he would go forth against Achilles: "High-hearted Trojans, fear not Peleus' son. I too in words could fight even Immortals, but with the spear it were hard, for they are stronger far. Neither shall Achilles accomplish all his talk, but part thereof he is to accomplish, and part to break asunder in the midst. And against him will I go forth, though the hands of him be even as fire, yea though his hands be as fire and his fierceness as the flashing steel."

Thus spake he urging them, and the Trojans raised their spears for battle; and their fierceness was mingled confusedly, and the battle-cry arose. Then Phoebus Apollo stood by Hector and spake to him: "Hector, no longer challenge Achilles at all before the lines, but in the throng await him and from amid the roar of the battle, lest haply he spear thee or come near and smite thee with his sword."

Thus spake he, and Hector again fell back into the crowd of men, for he was amazed when he heard the sound of a god's voice.

But Achilles sprang in among the Trojans, his heart clothed with strength, crying his terrible cry, and fell upon godlike Polydoros, Priam's son. Him would his sire continually forbid to fight, for that among his children he was youngest born and best beloved, and overcame all in fleetness of foot. Just then in boyish folly, displaying the swiftness of his feet, he was rushing through the forefighters, until he lost his life. Him in the midst did fleet-footed noble Achilles smite with a javelin, in his back as he darted by, where his belt's golden buckles clasped, and the breast and back plates overlapped: and right through beside the navel went the spear-head, and he fell on his knee with a cry, and dark cloud covered him round about, and he clasped his bowels to him with his hands as he sank.

Then when Hector saw his brother Polydoros clasping his bowels with his hands, and sinking to the earth, a mist fell over his eyes, nor longer might he endure to range so far apart, but he came up against Achilles brandishing his sharp spear, and like flame of fire. And Achilles when he saw him, sprang up, and spake exultingly: "Behold the man who hath deepest stricken into my soul, who slew my dear prized friend; not long shall we now shrink from each other along the highways of the war."

He said, and looking grimly spake unto goodly Hector: "Come thou near, that the sooner thou mayest arrive at the goal of death."

Then to him, unterrified, said Hector of the glancing helm: "Son of Peleus, think not with words to affright me as a child, since I too know myself how to speak taunts and unjust speech. And I know that thou art a man of might, and a far better man than I. Yet doth this issue lie in the lap of the gods, whether I though weaker shall take thy life with my hurled spear, for mine too hath been found keen ere now."

He said, and poised his spear and hurled it, and Athene with a breath turned it back from glorious Achilles, breathing very lightly; and it came back to goodly Hector, and fell there before his feet. Then Achilles set fiercely upon him, eager to slay him, crying his terrible cry. But Apollo caught Hector up, very easily, as a god may, and hid him in thick mist. Thrice then did fleet-footed noble Achilles make onset with his spear of bronze, and thrice smote the thick mist. Then with dread shout he spake to him winged words: "Dog, thou art now again escaped from death; yet came ill very nigh thee; but now hath Phoebus Apollo saved thee, to whom thou must surely pray when thou goest forth amid the clash of spears. Verily I will slay thee yet when I meet thee hereafter, if any god is helper of me too. Now will I make after the rest, whomsoever I may seize."

As through deep glens rageth fierce fire on some parched mountain-side, and the deep forest burneth, and the wind driving it whirleth every way the flame, so raged he every way with his spear, as it had been a god, pressing hard on the men he slew; and the black earth ran with blood. For even as when one yoketh wide-browed bulls to tread white barley in a stablished threshing-floor, and quickly is it trodden out beneath the feet of the loud-lowing bulls, thus beneath great-hearted Achilles his whole-hooved horses trampled corpses and shields together; and with blood all the axletree below was sprinkled and the rims that ran around the car, for blood-drops from the horses' hooves splashed them, and blood-drops from the tires of the wheels. But the son of Peleus pressed on to win him glory, flecking with gore his irresistible hands.

BOOK XXI

How Achilles fought with the River, and chased the men of Troy
within their gates.

B UT when now they came unto the ford of the fair-flowing river, seen eddying Xanthos, whom immortal
Zeus begat, there sundering them he chased the one part to
the plain toward the city, even where the Achaians were
flying in affright the day before, when glorious Hector was
in his fury—thither poured some in flight, and Hera spread
before them thick mist to hinder them:—but half were pent
into the deep-flowing silver-eddied river, and fell therein
with a mighty noise, and the steep channel sounded, and
the banks around rang loudly; for with shouting they swam
therein hither and thither, whirled round the eddies. And
as when at the rush of fire locusts take wing to fly unto a
river, and the unwearying fire flameth forth on them with
sudden onset, and they huddle in the water; so before
Achilles was the stream of deep-eddying Xanthos filled with
the roar and the throng of horses and men.

Then the seed of Zeus left behind him his spear upon the
bank, leant against tamarisk bushes, and leapt in, as it were
a god, keeping his sword alone, and devised grim work at
heart, and smote as he turned him every way about: and
their groaning went up ghastly as they were stricken by the
sword, and the water reddened with blood. As before a

dolphin of huge maw fly other fish and fill the nooks of some fair-havened bay, in terror, for he devoureth amain whichsoever of them he may catch; so along the channels of that dread stream the Trojans crouched beneath the precipitous sides. And when his hands were weary of slaughter he chose twelve young men alive out of the river, an atonement for Patroklos, Menoitios' son that was dead. These brought he forth amazed like fawns, and bound behind them their hands with well-cut thongs, which they themselves wore on their pliant doublets, and gave them to his comrades to lead down to the hollow ships. Then again he made his onset, athirst for slaying.

But the River waxed ever more wroth in his heart, and sought in his soul how he should stay goodly Achilles from his work, and ward destruction from the Trojans. Meanwhile the son of Peleus with his far-shadowing spear leapt, fain to slay him, upon Asteropaios son of Pelegon, whom wide-flowing Axios begat of Periboia eldest of the daughters of Akessamenos. Upon him set Achilles, and Asteropaios stood against him from the river, holding two spears; for Xanthos put courage into his heart, being angered for the slaughtered youths whom Achilles was slaughtering along the stream and had no pity on them. Then when the twain were come nigh in onset on each other, unto him first spake fleet-footed noble Achilles: "Who and whence art thou of men, that darest to come against me? Ill-fated are they whose children match them with my might."

And to him made answer Pelegon's noble son: "Highhearted son of Peleus, why askest thou my lineage? I come from deep-soiled Paionia, a land far off, leading Paionian

men with their long spears, and this now is the eleventh
morn since I am come to Ilios. My lineage is of wide-flowing
Axios, who begat Pelegon famous with the spear, and he,
men say, was my father. Now fight we, noble Achilles!"

Thus spake he in defiance, and goodly Achilles lifted the
Pelion ash: but the warrior Asteropaios hurled with both
spears together, for he could use both hands alike, and with
the one spear smote the shield, but pierced it not right
through, for the gold stayed it, the gift of a god; and with
the other he grazed the elbow of Achilles' right arm, and
there leapt forth dark blood, but the point beyond him fixed
itself in the earth, eager to batten on flesh. Then in his turn
Achilles hurled on Asteropaios his straight-flying ash, fain
to have slain him, but missed the man and struck the high
bank, and quivering half its length in the bank he left the
ashen spear. Then the son of Peleus drew his sharp sword
from his thigh and leapt fiercely at him, and he availed not
to draw with his stout hand Achilles' ashen shaft from the
steep bank. Thrice shook he it striving to draw it forth, and
thrice gave up the strain, but the fourth time he was fain to
bend and break the ashen spear of the seed of Aiakos, but
ere that Achilles closing on him reft him of life with his
sword. For in the belly he smote him beside the navel, and
all his bowels gushed out to the earth, and darkness covered
his eyes as he lay gasping. Then Achilles trampling on his
breast stripped off his armour and spake exultingly: "Lie
there! It is hard to strive against children of Kronos' mighty
son, even though one be sprung from a River-god. Thou
truly declarest thyself the seed of a wide-flowing River, but I
avow me of the lineage of great Zeus. My sire is a man

ruling many Myrmidons, Peleus the son of Aiakos, and Aiakos was begotten of Zeus. As Zeus is mightier than seaward-murmuring rivers, so is the seed of Zeus made mightier than the seed of a river. Nay, there is hard beside thee a great river, if he may anywise avail; but against Zeus the son of Kronos it is not possible to fight."

He said, and from the steep bank drew his bronze spear, and left there Asteropaios whom he had slain, lying in the sands, and the dark water flooded him. Around him eels and fishes swarmed, tearing and gnawing the fat about his kidneys. But Achilles went on after the charioted Paiones who still along the eddying river huddled in fear, when they saw their best man in the stress of battle slain violently by the hands and the sword of the son of Peleus. There slew he Thersilochos and Mydon and Astypylos and Mnesos and Thrasios and Ainios and Ophelestes; and more yet of the Paiones would swift Achilles have slain, had not the deep-eddying River called unto him in wrath, in semblance of a man, and from an eddy's depth sent forth a voice: "O Achilles, thy might and thy evil work are beyond the measure of men; for gods themselves are ever helping thee. If indeed the son of Kronos hath delivered thee all the Trojans to destroy, at least drive them forth from me and do thy grim deeds on the plain, for filled with dead men is my pleasant bed, nor can I pour my stream to the great sea, being choked with dead, and thou slayest ruthlessly. Come then, let be; I am astonied, O captain of hosts."

And to him answered Achilles fleet of foot: "So be it, heaven-sprung Skamandros, even as thou biddest. But the proud Trojans I will not cease from slaying until I have driven them into their city, and have made trial with Hector face to face whether he is to vanquish me or I him."

Thus saying, he set upon the Trojans, like a god. Then unto Apollo spake the deep-eddying River: "Out on it, lord of the silver bow, child of Zeus, thou hast not kept the ordinance of Kronos' son, who charged thee straitly to stand by the Trojans and to help them, until eve come with light late-setting, and darken the deep-soiled earth."

He said, and spear-famed Achilles sprang from the bank and leapt into his midst; but he rushed on him in a furious wave, and stirred up all his streams in tumult, and swept down the many dead who lay thick in him, slain by Achilles; these out to land he cast with bellowing like a bull, and saved the living under his fair streams, hiding them within eddies deep and wide. But terribly around Achilles arose his tumultuous wave, and the stream smote violently against his shield, nor availed he to stand firm upon his feet. Then he grasped a tall fair-grown elm, and it fell uprooted and tore away all the bank, and reached over the fair river bed with its thick shoots, and stemmed the River himself, falling all within him: and Achilles, struggling out of the eddy, made haste to fly over the plain with his swift feet, for he was afraid. But the great god ceased not, but arose upon him with darkness on his crest, that he might stay noble Achilles from slaughter, and ward destruction from the men of Troy. And the son of Peleus rushed away a spear's throw, with the swoop of a black eagle, the mighty hunter, strongest at once and swiftest of winged birds. Like him he sped, and on his breast the bronze rang terribly as he fled from beneath the onset, and behind him the River rushed on with a mighty roar. As when a field-water from a dark spring leadeth water along a bed through crops and garden grounds, a mattock in his hands, casting forth hindrances from the ditch, and as it floweth all pebbles are swept down, and swiftly gliding it murmureth down a sloping place, and out-runneth him that is its guide:—thus ever the river wave caught up Achilles for all his speed; for gods are mightier than men. For whensoever fleet-footed noble Achilles strug-gled to stand against it, and know whether all Immortals be upon him who inhabit spacious heaven, then would a great wave of the heaven-sprung River beat upon his shoulders from above, and he sprang upward with his feet, sore vexed at heart; and the River was wearying his knees with violent rush beneath, and devouring the earth from under his feet. Then the son of Peleus cried aloud, looking up to the broad heaven: "Zeus, Father, how doth none of the gods take it on him in pity to save me from the River? after that let come to me what may. None other of the inhabitants of Heaven is chargeable so much, but only my dear mother, who be-guiled me with false words, saying that under the wall of the mail-clad men of Troy I must die by the swift arrows of Apollo. Would that Hector had slain me, the best of men bred here: then brave had been the slayer, and a brave man had he slain. But now by a sorry death am I doomed to die, pent in this mighty river, like a swineherd boy whom a torrent sweepeth down as he essayeth to cross it in a storm."

Thus spake he, and quickly Poseidon and Athene came near and stood beside him, in the likeness of men, and taking his hands in theirs pledged him in words. And the first that spake was Poseidon, Shaker of the earth: "Son of

Peleus, tremble not, neither be afraid; such helpers of thee
are we from the gods, approved of Zeus, even Pallas Athene
and I, for to be vanquished of a river is not appointed thee,
but he will soon give back, and thou wilt thyself perceive it:
but we will give thee wise counsel, if thou wilt obey it; hold
not thy hand from hazardous battle until within Ilios'
famous walls thou have pent the Trojan host, even all that
flee before thee. But do thou, when thou hast taken the
life of Hector, go back unto the ships; this glory we give
unto thee to win."

They having thus spoken departed to the immortals, but
he toward the plain—for the bidding of gods was strong
upon him—went onward; and all the plain was filled with
waterflood, and many beautiful arms and corpses of slain
youths were drifting there. So upward sprang his knees as
he rushed against the stream right on, nor stayed him the
wide-flowing River, for Athene put great strength in him.
Neither did Skamandros slacken his fierceness, but yet more
raged against the son of Peleus, and he curled crestwise the
billow of his stream, lifting himself on high, and on Simoeis
he called with a shout: "Dear brother, the strength of this
man let us both join to stay, since quickly he will lay waste
the great city of king Priam, and the Trojans abide not in
the battle. Help me with speed, and fill thy streams with
water from thy springs, and urge on all thy torrents, and
raise up a great wave, and stir huge roaring of tree-stumps
and stones, that we may stay the fierce man who now is
lording it, and deeming himself match for gods. For neither,
I ween, will strength avail him, nor comeliness anywise, nor
that armour beautiful, which deep beneath the flood shall

be o'erlaid with slime, and himself I will wrap him in my sands and pour round him countless shingle without stint, or shall the Achaians know where to gather his bones, so vast a shroud of silt will I heap over them. Where he dieth there shall be his tomb, neither shall he have need of any barrow to be raised, when the Achaians make his funeral."

He said, and rushed in tumult on Achilles, raging from on high, thundering with foam and blood and bodies of dead men. Then did a dark wave of the heaven-sprung River stand towering up and overwhelm the son of Peleus. But Hera cried aloud in terror of Achilles, lest the great deep-eddying River sweep him away, and straightway she called to Hephaistos, her dear son: "Rise, lame god, O my son; it was against thee we thought that eddying Xanthos was matched in fight. Help with all speed, put forth large blast of flame. Then will I go to raise a strong storm out of the sea of the west wind and the white south which shall utterly consume the dead Trojans and their armour, blowing the angry flame. Thou along Xanthos' banks burn up his trees and wrap himself in fire, nor let him anywise turn thee back by soft words or by threat, nor stay thy rage—only when I cry to thee with my voice, then hold the unwearying fire."

Thus spake she, and Hephaistos made ready fierce-blazing fire. First on the plain fire blazed, and burnt the many dead who lay there thick, slain by Achilles; and all the plain was parched and the bright water stayed. And as when in late summer the north wind swiftly parcheth a new watered orchard, and he that tilleth it is glad, thus was the whole plain parched, and Hephaistos consumed the dead; then against the river he turned his gleaming flame. Elms burnt

and willow trees and tamarisks, and lotos burnt and rush
and galingale which round the fair streams of the river grew
in multitude. And the eels and fishes beneath the eddies
were afflicted, which through the fair streams tumbled this
way and that, in anguish at the blast of crafty Hephaistos.
And the strong River burned, and spake and called to him
by name: "Hephaistos, there is no god can match with thee,
nor will I fight thee thus ablaze with fire. Cease strife, yea,
let noble Achilles drive the Trojans forthwith out of their
city; what have I to do with strife and succour?"

Thus spake he, burnt with fire, for his fair streams were
bubbling. Then unto Hera, earnestly beseeching her, he
spake winged words: "Hera, wherefore hath thy son assailed my stream to vex it above others? I am less chargeable than all the rest that are helpers of the Trojans. But lo,
I will give over, if thou wilt, and let thy son give over too.
And I further will swear even this, that never will I ward the
day of evil from the Trojans, not even when all Troy is
burning in the blaze of hungry fire, and the warlike sons of
Achaians are the burners thereof."

Then when the white-armed goddess Hera heard his
speech, straightway she spake unto Hephaistos her dear son:
"Hephaistos, hold, famed son; it befitteth not thus for
mortals' sake to do violence to an immortal god."

Thus said she and Hephaistos quenched the fierce-blazing
fire, and the wave once more rolled down the fair river-bed.

Now Achilles was still slaying the Trojans, both themselves and their whole-hooved horses. And as when a smoke
goeth up to the broad heaven, when a city burneth, kindled
by the wrath of gods, and causeth toil to all, and griefs to

many, thus caused Achilles toil and griefs to the Trojans. And the old man Priam stood on the sacred tower, and was aware of dread Achilles, how before him the Trojans thronged in rout, nor was any succour found of them. Then with a cry he went down from the tower, to rouse the gallant warders along the walls: "Hold open the gates in your hands until the folk come to the city in their rout, for closely is Achilles chasing them—now trow I there will be deadly deeds. And when they are gathered within the wall and are taking breath, then again shut back the gate-wings firmly builded; for I fear lest that murderous man spring in within the wall."

Thus spake he, and they opened the gates and thrust back the bolts; and the gates flung back gave safety. Then Apollo leapt forth to the front that he might ward destruction from the Trojans. They straight for the city and the high wall were fleeing, parched with thirst and dust-grimed from the plain, and Achilles chased them vehemently with his spear, for strong frenzy possessed his heart continually, and he thirsted to win him renown. Then would the sons of the Achaians have taken high-gated Troy, had not Phoebus Apollo aroused goodly Agenor, Antenor's son, a princely man and strong. In his heart he put good courage, and himself stood by his side that he might ward off the grievous visitations of death, leaning against the oak, and he was shrouded in thick mist. So when Agenor was aware of Achilles waster of cities, he halted, and his heart much wavered as he stood; and in trouble he spake to his great heart: "Ay me, if I flee before mighty Achilles, there where the rest are driven terror-struck, nathless will he overtake me and slaughter me as a coward. Or what if I leave these to be driven before Achilles the son of Peleus, and flee upon my feet from the wall by another way to the Ileian plain, until I come to the spurs of Ida, and hide me in the under-wood? So then at evening, having bathed in the river and refreshed me of sweat, I might return to Ilios. Nay, why doth my heart debate thus within me? Lest he might be aware of me as I get me from the city for the plain, and speeding after overtake me with swift feet; then will it no more be possible to avoid the visitation of death, for he is exceeding mighty above all mankind. What then if in front of the city I go forth to meet him? Surely his flesh too is penetrable by sharp bronze, and there is but one life within, and men say he is mortal, howbeit Zeus the son of Kronos giveth him renown."

Thus saying, he gathered himself to await Achilles, and within him his stout heart was set to strive and fight. As a leopardess goeth forth from a deep thicket to affront a huntsman, nor is afraid at heart, nor fleeth when she heareth the bay of hounds; for albeit the man first smite her with thrust or throw, yet even pierced through with the spear she ceaseth not from her courage until she either grapple or be slain, so noble Antenor's son, goodly Agenor, refused to flee till he should put Achilles to the proof, but held before him the circle of his shield, and aimed at him with his spear, and cried aloud: "Doubtless thou hopest in thy heart, noble Achilles, on this day to sack the city of the proud men of Troy. Fond man, there shall many woful things yet be wrought before it, for within it we are many men and staunch, who in front of our parents dear and wives and sons keep Ilios safe; but thou shalt here meet death, albeit so redoubtable and bold a man of war."

He said, and hurled his sharp spear with weighty hand, and smote him on the leg beneath the knee, nor missed his mark, and the greave of new-wrought tin rang terribly on him; but the bronze bounded back from him it smote, nor pierced him, for the god's gift drave it back. Then the son of Peleus in his turn made at godlike Agenor, but Apollo suffered him not to win renown, but caught away Agenor, and shrouded him in thick mist, and sent him in peace to be gone out of the war. Then by wile he kept the son of Peleus away from the folk, for in complete semblance of Agenor himself he stood before the feet of Achilles, who hasted to run upon him and chase him. And while he chased him over the wheat-bearing plain, edging him toward the deep-eddying river Skamandros, as he ran but a little in front of him (for by wile Apollo beguiled him that he kept ever hoping to overtake him in the race), meantime the other Trojans in common rout came gladly unto their fastness, and the city was filled with the throng of them. Neither had they heart to await one another outside the city and wall, and to know who might have escaped and who had perished in the fight, but impetuously they poured into the city, whomsoever of them his feet and knees might save.

BOOK XXII

How Achilles fought with Hector, and slew him, and brought his body to the ships.

THUS they throughout the city, scared like fawns, were cooling their sweat and drinking and slaking their thirst, leaning on the fair battlements, while the Achaians drew near the wall, setting shields to shoulders. But Hector deadly fate bound to abide in his place, in front of Ilios and the Skaian gates. Then to the son of Peleus spake Phoebus Apollo: "Wherefore, son of Peleus, pursuest thou me with swift feet, thyself being mortal and I a deathless god? Thou hast not even yet known me, that I am a god, but strivest vehemently. Truly thou regardest not thy task among the affliction of the Trojans whom thou affrightedst, who now are gathered into the city, while thou hast wandered hither. Me thou wilt never slay, for I am not subject unto death."

Then mightily moved spake unto him Achilles fleet of foot: "Thou hast baulked me, Far-darter, most mischievous of all the gods, in that thou hast turned me hither from the wall: else should full many yet have bitten the dust or ever within Ilios had they come. Now hast thou robbed me of great renown, and lightly hast saved them, because thou hadst no vengeance to fear thereafter. Verily I would avenge me on thee, had I but the power."

Thus saying toward the city he was gone in pride of heart,

330

rushing like some victorious horse in a chariot, that runneth lightly at full speed over the plain; so swiftly plied Achilles his feet and knees. Him the old man Priam first beheld as he sped across the plain, blazing as the star that cometh forth at harvest-time, and plain seen his rays shine forth amid the host of stars in the darkness of night, the star whose name men call Orion's Dog. Even so on Achilles' breast the bronze gleamed as he ran. And the old man cried aloud and beat upon his head with his hands, raising them on high, and with a cry called aloud beseeching his dear son; for he before the gates was standing, all hot for battle with Achilles. And the old man spake piteously unto him, stretching forth his hands: "Hector, beloved son, I pray thee await not this man alone with none beside thee, lest thou quickly meet thy doom, slain by the son of Peleus, since he is mightier far, a merciless man. Would the gods loved him even as do I! then quickly would dogs and vultures devour him on the field—thereby would cruel pain go from my heart—the man who hath bereft me of many valiant sons, slaying them and selling them captive into far-off isles. Nay, come within the wall, my child, that thou preserve the men and women of Troy, neither give great triumph to the son of Peleus, and be thyself bereft of sweet life. Have compassion also on me, the helpless one, who still can feel, ill-fated; whom the father, Kronos' son, will bring to naught by a grievous doom in the path of old age, having seen full many ills, his sons perishing and his daughters carried away captive, and his chambers laid waste and infant children hurled to the ground in terrible war, and his sons' wives dragged away by the ruinous hands of the Achaians. Myself then last of all at the street door will ravening dogs tear, when some one by stroke or throw of the sharp bronze hath bereft my limbs of life—even the dogs I reared in my halls about my table and to guard my door, which then having drunk my blood, maddened at heart shall lie in the gateway. A young man all beseemeth, even to be slain in war, to be torn by the sharp bronze and lie on the field; though he be dead yet is all honourable to him, whate'er be seen: but when dogs defile the hoary head and hoary beard of an old man slain, this is the most piteous thing that cometh upon hapless men."

Thus spake the old man, and grasped his hoary hairs, plucking them from his head, but he persuaded not Hector's soul. Then his mother in her turn wailed tearfully, loosening the folds of her robe, while with the other hand she showed her breast; and through her tears spake to him winged words: "Hector, my child, have regard unto this bosom and pity me, if ever I gave thee consolation of my breast. Think of it, dear child, and from this side the wall drive back the foe, nor stand in front to meet him. He is merciless; if he slay thee it will not be on a bed that I or thy wife shall bewail thee, my own dear child, but far away from us by the ships of the Argives will swift dogs devour thee."

Thus they with wailing spake to their dear son, beseeching him sore, yet they persuaded not Hector's soul, but he stood awaiting Achilles as he drew nigh in giant might. As a serpent of the mountains upon his den awaiteth a man, having fed on evil poisons, and fell wrath hath entered into him, and terribly he glared as he coileth himself about his den, so Hector with courage unquenchable gave not back, leaning his shining shield against a jutting tower. Then sore troubled he spake to his great heart: "Ay me, if I go within the gates and walls, Polydamas will be first to bring reproach against me, since he bade me lead the Trojans to the city during this ruinous night when noble Achilles arose. But I regarded him not, yet surely it had been better far. And now that I have undone the host by my wantonness, I am ashamed before the men of Troy and women of trailing robes, lest at any time some worse man than I shall say: 'Hector by trusting his own might undid the host.' So will they speak; then to me would it be better far to face Achilles and either slay him and go home, or myself die gloriously before the city. Or what if I lay down my bossy shield and my stout helm, and lean my spear against the wall, and go of myself to meet noble Achilles and promise him that Helen, and with her all possessions that Alexandros brought in hollow ships to Troy, the beginning of strife, we will give to the sons of Atreus to take away, and therewithal to divide in half with the Achaians all else that this city holdeth: and if thereafter I obtain from the Trojans an oath of the Elders that they will hide nothing but divide all in twain? But wherefore doth my heart debate thus? I might come unto him and he would not pity or regard me at all, but presently slay me unarmed as it were but a woman, if I put off my armour. Better is it to join battle with all speed: let us know upon which of us twain the Olympian shall bestow renown."

Thus pondered he as he stood, but nigh on him came Achilles, brandishing from his right shoulder the Pelion ash, his terrible spear; and all around the bronze on him flashed like the gleam of blazing fire or of the Sun as he ariseth. And trembling seized Hector as he was aware of him, nor endured he to abide in his place, but left the gates behind him and fled in fear. And the son of Peleus darted after him, trusting in his swift feet. As a falcon upon the mountains, swiftest of winged things, swoopeth fleetly after a trembling dove; and she before him fleeth, while he with shrill screams hard at hand still darteth at her, for his heart urgeth him to seize her; so Achilles in hot haste flew straight for him, and Hector fled beneath the Trojans' wall, and plied swift knees. They past the watch-place and wind-waved wild fig-tree sped ever, away from under the wall, along the waggon-track, and came to the two fair-flowing springs, where two fountains rise that feed deep-eddying Skamandros. Thereby they ran, he flying, he pursuing. Valiant was the flier but far mightier he who fleetly pursued him. For not for beast of sacrifice or for an oxhide were they striving, such as are prizes for men's speed of foot, but for the life of horse-taming Hector was their race. And as when victorious whole-hooved horses run rapidly round the turning-points, and some great prize lieth in sight, be it a tripod or a woman, in honour of a man that is dead, so thrice around Priam's city circled those twain with flying feet, and all the gods were gazing on them. Then among them spake first the father of gods and men: "Ay me, a man beloved I see pursued around the wall. My heart is woe for Hector, who hath burnt for me many thighs of oxen amid the crests of many-folded Ida, and other times on the city-height; but now is goodly Achilles pursuing him with swift feet round Priam's town. Come, give your counsel, gods, and devise whether we shall save him from death or now at last slay him, valiant though he be, by the hand of Achilles Peleus' son."

Then to him answered the bright-eyed goddess Athene: "O Father, Lord of the bright lightning and the dark cloud, what is this thou hast said? A man that is a mortal, doomed long ago by fate, wouldst thou redeem back from ill-boding death? Do it, but not all we other gods approve."

And unto her in answer spake cloud-gathering Zeus: "Be of good cheer, dear child: not in full earnest speak I, and I would fain be kind to thee. Do as seemeth good to thy mind, and draw not back."

Thus saying he roused Athene, that already was set thereon, and from the crests of Olympus she darted down.

But after Hector sped fleet Achilles chasing him vehemently. And as when on the mountains a hound hunteth the fawn of a deer, having started it from its covert, through glens and glades, and if it crouch to baffle him under a bush, yet scenting it out the hound runneth constantly until he find it; so Hector baffled not Peleus' fleet-footed son. Oft as he set himself to dart under the well-built walls over against the Dardanian gates, if haply from above they might succour him with darts, so oft would Achilles gain on him and turn him toward the plain, while himself he sped ever on the city-side. And as in a dream one faileth in chase of a flying man—the one faileth in his flight and the other in his chase—so failed Achilles to overtake him in the race, and Hector to escape. For to the host did noble Achilles sign with his head, and forbade them to hurl bitter darts against Hector, lest any smiting him should gain renown, and he himself

come second. But when the fourth time they had reached
the springs, then the Father hung his golden balances, and
set therein two lots of dreary death, one of Achilles, one of
horse-taming Hector, and held them by the midst and
poised. Then Hector's fated day sank down, and fell to the
house of Hades, and Phoebus Apollo left him. But to
Peleus' son came the bright-eyed goddess Athene, and
standing near spake to him winged words: "Now verily,
glorious Achilles dear to Zeus, I have hope that we twain
shall carry off great glory to the ships for the Achaians,
having slain Hector, for all his thirst for fight. No longer is it
possible for him to escape us, not even though far-darting
Apollo should travail sore, grovelling before the Father,
aegis-bearing Zeus. But do thou now stand and take breath,
and I will go and persuade this man to confront thee in
fight."

Thus spake Athene, and he obeyed, and was glad at
heart, and stood leaning on his bronze-pointed ashen-spear.
And she left him and came to noble Hector, like unto Deïphobos in shape and in strong voice, and standing near
spake to him winged words: "Dear brother, verily fleet
Achilles doth thee violence, chasing thee round Priam's
town with swift feet: but come let us make a stand and
await him on our defence."

Then answered her great Hector of the glancing helm:
"Deïphobos, verily aforetime wert thou far dearest of my
brothers, but now methinks I shall honour thee even more,
in that thou hast dared for my sake, when thou sawest me,
to come forth of the wall, while the others tarry within."

Then to him again spake the bright-eyed goddess Athene:

"Dear brother, of a truth my father and lady mother and my comrades around besought me much, entreating me in turn, to tarry there, so greatly do they all tremble before him; but my heart within was sore with dismal grief. And now fight we with straight-set resolve and let there be no sparing of spears, that we may know whether Achilles is to slay us and carry our bloody spoils to the hollow ships, or whether he might be vanquished by thy spear."

Thus saying Athene in her subtlety led him on. And when they were come nigh in onset on one another, to Achilles first spake great Hector of the glancing helm: "No longer, son of Peleus, will I fly thee, as before I thrice ran round the great town of Priam, and endured not to await thy onset. Now my heart biddeth me stand up against thee; I will either slay or be slain. But come hither and let us pledge us by our gods, for they shall be best witnesses and beholders of covenants: I will entreat thee in no outrageous sort, if Zeus grant me to outstay thee, and if I take thy life, but when I have despoiled thee of thy glorious armour, O Achilles, I will give back thy dead body to the Achaians, and do thou the same."

But unto him with grim gaze spake Achilles fleet of foot: "Hector, talk not to me, thou madman, of covenants. As between men and lions there is no pledge of faith, nor wolves and sheep can be of one mind, but imagine evil continually against each other, so is it impossible for thee and me to be friends, neither shall be any pledge between us until one or other shall have fallen and glutted with blood Ares, the stubborn god of war. Bethink thee of all thy soldiership: now behoveth it thee to quit thee as a good

spearman and valiant man of war. No longer is there way of
escape for thee, but Pallas Athene will straightway subdue
thee to my spear; and now in one hour shalt thou pay back
for all my sorrows for my friends whom thou hast slain in
the fury of thy spear."

He said, and poised his far-shadowing spear and hurled.
And noble Hector watched the coming thereof and avoided
it; for with his eye on it he crouched, and the bronze spear
flew over him, and fixed itself in the earth; but Pallas
Athene caught it up and gave it back to Achilles, unknown
of Hector shepherd of hosts. Then Hector spake unto the
noble son of Peleus: "Thou hast missed, so nowise yet, godlike Achilles, has thou known from Zeus the hour of my
doom, though thou thoughtest it. Cunning of tongue art
thou and a deceiver in speech, that fearing thee I might
forget my valour and strength. Not as I flee shalt thou plant
thy spear in my reins, but drive it straight through my breast
as I set on thee, if God hath given thee to do it. Now in thy
turn avoid my spear of bronze. O that thou mightst take it
all into thy flesh! Then would the war be lighter to the
Trojans, if but thou wert dead, for thou art their greatest
bane."

He said, and poised his long-shadowed spear and hurled
it, and smote the midst of the shield of Peleus' son, and
missed him not: but far from the shield the spear leapt
back. And Hector was wroth that his swift weapon had left
his hand in vain, and he stood downcast, for he had no
second ashen spear. And he called with a loud shout to Deïphobos of the white shield, and asked of him a long spear,
but he was nowise nigh. Then Hector knew the truth in his

heart, and spake and said: "Ay me, now verily the gods have summoned me to death. I deemed the warrior Deïphobos was by my side, but he is within the wall, and it was Athene who played me false. Now therefore is evil death come very nigh me, not far off, nor is there way of escape. This then was from of old the pleasure of Zeus and of the far-darting son of Zeus, who yet before were fain to succour me: but now my fate hath found me. At least let me not die without a struggle or ingloriously, but in some great deed of arms whereof men yet to be born shall hear."

Thus saying he drew his sharp sword that by his flank hung great and strong, and gathered himself and swooped like a soaring eagle that darteth to the plain through the dark clouds to seize a tender lamb or crouching hare. So Hector swooped, brandishing his sharp sword. And Achilles made at him, for his heart was filled with wild fierceness, and before his breast he made a covering with his fair graven shield, and tossed his bright four-plated helm; and round it waved fair golden plumes. As a star goeth among stars in the darkness of night, Hesperos, fairest of all stars set in heaven, so flashed there forth a light from the keen spear Achilles poised in his right hand, devising mischief against noble Hector, eyeing his fair flesh to find the fittest place. Now for the rest of him his flesh was covered by the fair bronze armour he stripped from strong Patroklos when he slew him, but there was an opening where the collar bones coming from the shoulders clasp the neck, even at the gullet, where destruction of life cometh quickliest; there, as he came on, noble Achilles drave at him with his spear, and right through the tender neck went the point. Yet the bronze-weighted ashen spear clave not the windpipe, so that he might yet speak words of answer to his foe. And he fell down in the dust, and noble Achilles spake exultingly: "Hector, thou thoughtest, whilst thou wert spoiling Patroklos, that thou wouldst be safe, and didst reck nothing of me who was afar, thou fool. But away among the hollow ships his comrade, a mightier far, even I, was left behind, who now have unstrung thy knees. Thee shall dogs and birds tear foully, but his funeral shall the Achaians make."

Then with faint breath spake unto him Hector of the glancing helm: "I pray thee by thy life and knees and parents, leave me not for dogs of the Achaians to devour by the ships, but take good store of bronze and gold, gifts that my father and lady mother shall give to thee, and give them home my body back again, that the Trojans and Trojans' wives give me my due of fire after my death."

But unto him with grim gaze spake Achilles fleet of foot: "Entreat me not, dog, by knees or parents. Would that my heart's desire could so bid me myself to carve and eat raw thy flesh, for the evil thou hast wrought me, as surely is there none that shall keep the dogs from thee, not even should they bring ten or twenty fold ransom and here weigh it out, and promise even more, not even were Priam Dardanos' son to bid pay thy weight in gold, not even so shall thy lady mother lay thee on a bed to mourn her son, but dogs and birds shall devour thee utterly."

Then dying spake unto him Hector of the glancing helm: "Verily I know thee and behold thee as thou art, nor was I destined to persuade thee; truly thy heart is iron in thy breast. Take heed now lest I draw upon thee wrath of gods, in the day when Paris and Phoebus Apollo slay thee, for all thy valour, at the Skaian gate."

He ended, and the shadow of death came down upon him, and his soul flew forth of his limbs and was gone to the house of Hades, wailing her fate, leaving her vigour and youth. Then to the dead man spake noble Achilles: "Die: for my death, I will accept it whensoever Zeus and the other immortal gods are minded to accomplish it."

He said, and from the corpse drew forth his bronze spear, and set it aside, and stripped the bloody armour from the shoulders. And other sons of Achaians ran up around, who gazed upon the stature and marvellous goodliness of Hector. Nor did any stand by but wounded him, and thus would many a man say looking toward his neighbour: "Go to, of a truth far easier to handle is Hector now than when he burnt the ships with blazing fire." Thus would many a man say, and wound him as he stood hard by. And when fleet noble Achilles had despoiled him, he stood up among the Achaians and spake winged words: "Friends, chiefs and counsellors of the Argives, since the gods have vouchsafed us to vanquish this man who hath done us more evil than all the rest together, come let us make trial in arms round about the city, that we may know somewhat of the Trojans' purpose, whether since he hath fallen they will forsake the citadel, or whether they are minded to abide, albeit Hector is no more. But wherefore doth my heart debate thus? There lieth by the ships a dead man unbewailed, unburied, Patroklos; him will I not forget, while I abide among the living and my knees can stir. Nay if even in the house of Hades the dead forget their dead, yet will I even there be

mindful of my dear comrade. But come, ye sons of the
Achaians, let us now, singing our song of victory, go back
to the hollow ships and take with us our foe. Great glory
have we won; we have slain the noble Hector, unto whom
the Trojans prayed throughout their city, as he had been a
god."

He said, and devised foul entreatment of noble Hector.
The tendons of both feet behind he slit from heel to ankle-
joint, and thrust therethrough thongs of ox-hide, and bound
him to his chariot, leaving his head to trail. And when he
had mounted the chariot and lifted therein the famous
armour, he lashed his horses to speed, and they nothing loth
flew on. And dust rose around him that was dragged, and
his dark hair flowed loose on either side, and in the dust lay
all his once fair head, for now had Zeus given him over to
his foes to entreat foully in his own native land.

Thus was his head all grimed with dust. But his mother
when she beheld her son, tore her hair and cast far from
her her shining veil, and cried aloud with an exceeding
bitter cry. And piteously moaned his father, and around
them the folk fell to crying and moaning throughout
the town. Most like it seemed as though all beetling Ilios
were burning utterly in fire. Scarcely could the folk keep
back the old man in his hot desire to get him forth of the
Dardanian gates. For he besought them all, casting himself
down in the mire, and calling on each man by his name:
"Hold, friends, and though you love me leave me to get me
forth of the city alone and go unto the ships of the Achaians. Let me pray this accursed horror-working man, if
haply he may feel shame before his age-fellows and pity an

old man. He also hath a father such as I am, Peleus, who begat and reared him to be a bane of Trojans—and most of all to me hath he brought woe. So many sons of mine hath he slain in their flower—yet for all my sorrow for the rest I mourn them all less than this one alone, for whom my sharp grief will bring me down to the house of Hades—even Hector. Would that he had died in my arms; then would we have wept and wailed our fill, his mother who bore him to her ill hap, and I myself."

Thus spake he wailing, and all the men of the city made moan with him. And among the women of Troy, Hekabe led the wild lament: "My child, ah, woe is me! wherefore should I live in my pain, now thou art dead, who night and day wert my boast through the city, and blessing to all, both men and women of Troy throughout the town, who hailed thee as a god, for verily an exceeding glory to them wert thou in thy life:—now death and fate have overtaken thee."

Thus spake she wailing. But Hector's wife knew not as yet, for no true messenger had come to tell her how her husband abode without the gates, but in an inner chamber of the lofty house she was weaving a double purple web, and broidering therein manifold flowers. Then she called to her goodly-haired handmaids through the house to set a great tripod on the fire, that Hector might have warm washing when he came home out of the battle—fond heart, and was unaware how, far from all washings, bright-eyed Athene had slain him by the hand of Achilles. But she heard shrieks and groans from the battlements, and her limbs reeled, and the shuttle fell from her hands to earth. Then again among her goodly-haired maids she spake: "Come two of ye this way with me that I may see what deeds are done. It was the voice of my husband's noble mother that I heard, and in my own breast my heart leapeth to my mouth and my knees are numbed beneath me: surely some evil thing is at hand against the children of Priam. Would that such word might never reach my ear! yet terribly I dread lest noble Achilles have cut off bold Hector from the city by himself and chased him to the plain and ere this ended his perilous pride that possessed him, for never would he tarry among the throng of men but ran out before them far, yielding place to no man in his hardihood."

Thus saying she sped through the chamber like one mad, with beating heart, and with her went her handmaidens. But when she came to the battlements and the throng of men, she stood still upon the wall and gazed, and beheld him dragged before the city:—swift horses dragged him reck-lessly toward the hollow ships of the Achaians. Then dark night came on her eyes and shrouded her, and she fell back-ward and gasped forth her spirit. From off her head she shook the bright attiring thereof, frontlet and net and woven band, and veil, the veil that golden Aphrodite gave her on the day when Hector of the glancing helm led her forth of the house of Eëtion, having given bride-gifts un-told. And around her thronged her husband's sisters and his brothers' wives, who held her up among them, distraught even to death. But when at last she came to herself and her soul returned into her breast, then wailing with deep sobs she spake among the women of Troy: "O Hector, woe is me! to one fate then were we both born, thou in Troy in the house of Priam, and I in Thebe under woody Plakos, in the house of Eëtion, who reared me from a little one—ill-fated sire of cruel-fated child. Now thou to the house of Hades beneath the secret places of the earth departest, and me in bitter mourning thou leavest a widow in thy halls: and thy son is but an infant child—son of unhappy parents, thee and me—nor shalt thou profit him, Hector, since thou art dead, neither he thee."

Thus spake she wailing, and the women joined their moan.

BOOK XXIII

Of the funeral of Patroklos, and the funeral games.

Thus they throughout the city made moan: but the Achaians when they were come to the ships and to the Hellespont were scattered each to his own ship: only the Myrmidons Achilles suffered not to be scattered, but spake among his comrades whose delight was in war: "Fleet-horsed Myrmidons, my trusty comrades, let us not yet unyoke our whole-hooved steeds from their cars, but with horses and chariots let us go near and mourn Patroklos, for such is the honour of the dead. Then when we have our fill of grievous wailing, we will unyoke the horses and all sup here."

He said, and they with one accord made lamentation, and Achilles led their mourning. So thrice around the dead they drave their well-maned steeds, moaning; and Thetis stirred among them desire of wailing. Bedewed were the sands with tears, bedewed the warriors' arms; so great a lord of fear they sorrowed for. And Peleus' son led their loud wail, laying his man-slaying hands on his comrade's breast: "All hail, Patroklos, even in the house of Hades; for all that I promised thee before am I accomplishing, seeing I have dragged hither Hector to give raw unto dogs to devour, and twelve noble children of the Trojans to slaughter before thy pyre, because of mine anger at thy slaying."

He said, and devised foul entreatment of noble Hector, stretching him prone in the dust beside the bier of Menoitios' son. And the rest put off each his glittering bronze arms, and unyoked their high-neighing horses, and sate them down numberless beside the ship of fleet-footed Aiakides, and he gave them ample funeral feast. Many sleek oxen were stretched out, their throats cut with steel, and many sheep and bleating goats, and many white-tusked boars well grown in fat were spitted to singe in the flame of Hephaistos; so on all sides round the corpse in cupfuls blood was flowing.

But the fleet-footed prince, the son of Peleus, was brought to noble Agamemnon by the Achaian chiefs, hardly persuading him thereto, for his heart was wroth for his comrade. And when they were come to Agamemnon's hut, forthwith they bade clear-voiced heralds set a great tripod on the fire, if haply they might persuade the son of Peleus to wash from him the bloody gore. But he denied them steadfastly, and sware moreover an oath: "Nay, verily by Zeus, who is highest and best of gods, not lawful is it that water should come nigh my head or ever I shall have laid Patroklos on the fire, and heaped a barrow, and shaved my hair, since never again shall second grief thus reach my heart, while I remain among the living. Yet now for the present let us yield us to our mournful meal: but with the morning, O king of men Agamemnon, rouse the folk to bring wood and furnish all that it beseemeth a dead man to have when he goeth beneath the misty gloom, to the end that untiring fire may burn him quickly from sight, and the host betake them to their work."

Thus spake he, and they listened readily to him and obeyed, and eagerly making ready each his meal they supped, and no lack had their soul of equal feast. But when they had put off from them the desire of meat and drink, the rest went down each man to his tent to take his rest, but the son of Peleus upon the beach of the sounding sea lay groaning heavily, amid the host of Myrmidons, in an open place, where waves were breaking on the shore. Now when sleep took hold on him, easing the cares of his heart, deep sleep that fell about him, (for sore tired were his glorious knees with onset upon Hector toward windy Ilios), then came there unto him the spirit of hapless Patroklos, in all things like his living self, in stature, and fair eyes, and voice, and the raiment of his body was the same; and he stood above Achilles' head and spake to him: "Thou sleepest, and hast forgotten me, O Achilles. Not in my life wast thou ever unmindful of me, but in my death. Bury me with all speed, that I pass the gates of Hades. Far off the spirits banish me, the phantoms of men outworn, nor suffer me to mingle with them beyond the River, but vainly I wander along the wide-gated dwelling of Hades. Now give me, I pray pitifully of thee, thy hand, for never more again shall I come back from Hades, when ye have given me my due of fire. Never among the living shall we sit apart from our dear comrades and take counsel together, but me hath the harsh fate swallowed up which was appointed me even from my birth. Yea and thou too thyself, Achilles peer of gods, beneath the wall of the noble Trojans art doomed to die. Yet one thing will I say, and charge thee, if haply thou wilt have regard thereto. Lay not my bones apart from thine, Achilles, but together, even as we were nurtured in your house, when Menoitios brought me yet a little one from Opöeis to your country by reason of a grievous man-slaying, on the day when I slew Amphidamas' son, not willing it, in childish wrath over the dice. Then took me the knight Peleus into his house and reared me kindly and named me thy squire: so therefore let one coffer hide our bones."

Then made answer unto him Achilles fleet of foot: "Wherefore, O my brother, hast thou come hither, and chargest me everything that I should do? Verily I will accomplish all, and have regard unto thy bidding. But stand more nigh me; for one moment let us throw our arms around each other, and take our fill of dolorous lament."

He spake, and reached forth with his hands, but clasped him not; for like a vapour the spirit was gone beneath the earth with a faint shriek. And Achilles sprang up marvelling, and smote his hands together, and spake a word of woe: "Ay me, there remaineth then even in the house of Hades a spirit and phantom of the dead, albeit the life be not anywise therein: for all night long hath the spirit of hapless Patroklos stood over me, wailing and making moan, and charged me everything that I should do, and wondrous like his living self it seemed."

Thus said he, and stirred in all of them yearning to make lament; and rosy-fingered Morn shone forth on them while they still made moan around the piteous corpse. Then lord Agamemnon sped mules and men from all the huts to fetch wood; and a man of valour watched thereover, even Meriones, squire of kindly Idomeneus. And they went forth with wood-cutting axes in their hands and well-woven ropes, and before them went the mules, and uphill and downhill and sideways and across they went. But when they came to the spurs of many-fountained Ida, straightway they set them lustily to hew high-foliaged oaks with the long-edged bronze, and with loud noise fell the trees. Then splitting them asunder the Achaians bound them behind the mules, and they tore up the earth with their feet as they made for the plain through the thick underwood. And all the wood-cutters bare logs; for thus bade Meriones, squire of kindly Idomeneus. And on the shore they threw them down in line, where Achilles purposed a mighty tomb for Patroklos and for himself.

Then when they had laid down all about great piles of wood, they sate them down all together and abode. Then straightway Achilles bade the warlike Myrmidons gird on their arms and each yoke the horses to his chariot; and they arose and put their armour on, and mounted their chariots, both fighting men and charioteers. In front were the men in chariots, and a cloud of footmen followed after, number-less; and in the midst his comrades bare Patroklos. And they heaped all the corpse with their hair that they cut off and threw thereon; and behind did goodly Achilles bear the head, sorrowing; for a noble comrade was he speeding forth unto the realm of Hades.

And when they came to the place where Achilles had bidden them, they set down the dead, and piled for him abundant wood. Then fleet-footed noble Achilles bethought him of one thing more: standing apart from the pyre he shore off a golden lock, the lock whose growth he nursed to offer unto the River Spercheios, and sore troubled spake he, looking forth over the wine-dark sea: "Spercheios, in other wise vowed my father Peleus unto thee that I returning thither to my native land should shear my hair for thee and offer a holy hecatomb, and fifty rams should sacrifice there above thy springs, where is thy sacred close and altar burning spice. So vowed the old man, but thou hast not accomplished him his desire. And now since I return not to my dear native land, unto the hero Patroklos I may give this hair to take away."

Thus saying he set the hair in the hands of his dear comrade, and stirred in all of them yearning to make lament. And so would the light of the sun have gone down on their lamentation, had not Achilles said quickly to Agamemnon as he stood beside him: "Son of Atreus—for to thy words most will the host of the Achaians have regard—of lamentation they may sate them to the full. But now disperse them from the burning and bid them make ready their meal, and we to whom the dead is dearest will take pains for these things; yet let the chiefs tarry nigh unto us."

Then when Agamemnon king of men heard that, he forthwith dispersed the host among the trim ships, but the nearest to the dead tarried there and piled the wood, and made a pyre a hundred feet this way and that, and on the pyre's top set the corpse, with anguish at their hearts. And many lusty sheep and shambling crook-horned oxen they flayed and made ready before the pyre; and taking from all of them the fat, great hearted Achilles wrapped the corpse therein from head to foot, and heaped the flayed bodies round. And he set therein two-handled jars of honey and oil, leaning them against the bier; and four strong-necked horses he threw swiftly on the pyre, and groaned aloud. Nine house-dogs had the dead chief: of them did Achilles slay twain and throw them on the pyre. And twelve valiant sons of great-hearted Trojans he slew with the sword—for he devised mischief in his heart—and he set to the merciless might of the fire, to feed thereon. Then moaned he aloud, and called on his dear comrade by his name: "All hail to thee, O Patroklos, even in the house of Hades, for all that I promised thee before am I now accomplishing. Twelve valiant sons of great-hearted Trojans, behold these all in company with thee the fire devoureth: but Hector son of Priam will I nowise give to the fire to feed upon, but to dogs."

Thus spake he threatening, but no dogs might deal with Hector, for day and night Aphrodite daughter of Zeus kept off the dogs, and anointed him with rose-sweet oil ambrosial that Achilles might not tear him when he dragged him. And over him Phoebus Apollo brought a dark cloud from heaven to earth and covered all that place whereon the dead man lay, lest meanwhile the sun's strength shrivel his flesh round about upon his sinews and limbs.

But the pyre of dead Patroklos kindled not. Then fleet-footed noble Achilles had a further thought: standing aside from the pyre he prayed to the two Winds of North and West, and promised them fair offerings, and pouring large libations from a golden cup besought them to come, that the corpses might blaze up speedily in the fire, and the wood make haste to be enkindled. Then Iris, when she heard his prayer, went swiftly with the message to the Winds. They within the house of the gusty West Wind were feasting all together at meat, when Iris sped thither, and halted on the threshold of stone. And when they saw her with their eyes, they sprang up and called to her every one to sit by him. But she refused to sit, and spake her word: "No seat for me; I must go back to the streams of Ocean, to the Ethiopians' land where they sacrifice hecatombs to the immortal gods, that I too may feast at their rites. But Achilles is praying the North Wind and the loud West to come, and promising them fair offerings, that ye may make the pyre be kindled whereon lieth Patroklos, for whom all the Achaians are making moan."

She having thus said departed, and they arose with a mighty sound, rolling the clouds before them. And swiftly they came blowing over the sea, and the wave rose beneath their shrill blast; and they came to deep-soiled Troy, and fell upon the pile, and loudly roared the mighty fire. So all night drave they the flame of the pyre together, blowing shrill; and all night fleet Achilles, holding a two-handled cup, drew wine from a golden bowl, and poured it forth and drenched the earth, calling upon the spirit of hapless Patroklos. As a father waileth when he burneth the bones of his son, new-married, whose death is woe to his hapless parents, so wailed Achilles as he burnt the bones of his comrade, going heavily round the burning pile, with many moans.

But at the hour when the Morning Star goeth forth to herald light upon the earth, the star that saffron-mantled Dawn cometh after, and spreadeth over the salt sea, then grew the burning faint, and the flame died down. And the Winds went back again to betake them home over the

Thracian main, and it roared with a violent swell. Then the son of Peleus turned away from the burning and lay down wearied, and sweet sleep leapt on him. But they who were with Atreus' son gathered all together, and the noise and clash of their approach aroused him; and he sate upright and spake a word to them: "Son of Atreus and ye other chiefs of the Achaians, first quench with gleaming wine all the burning so far as the fire's strength hath reached, and then let us gather up the bones of Patroklos, Menoitios' son, singling them well, and easy are they to discern, for he lay in the middle of the pyre, while the rest apart at the edge burnt confusedly, horses and men. And his bones let us put within a golden urn, and double-folded fat, until that I myself be hidden in Hades. But no huge barrow I bid you toil to raise—a seemly one, no more: then afterward do ye Achaians build it broad and high, whosoever of you after I am gone may be left in the benched ships."

Thus spake he, and they hearkened to the fleet-footed son of Peleus. First quenched they with gleaming wine the burning so far as the flame went, and the ash had settled deep: then with lamentation they gathered up the white bones of their gentle comrade into a golden urn and double-folded fat, and placed the urn in the hut and covered it with a linen veil. And they marked the circle of the barrow, and set the foundations thereof around the pyre, and straightway heaped thereon a heap of earth. Then when they had heaped up the barrow they were for going back. But Achilles stayed the folk in that place, and made them sit in wide assembly, and from his ships he brought forth prizes, caldrons and tripods, and horses and mules and strong oxen, and fair-girdled women, and grey iron.

First for fleet chariot-racers he ordained a noble prize, a woman skilled in fair handiwork for the winner to lead home, and an eared tripod that held two-and-twenty measures; these for the first man; and for the second he ordained a six-year-old mare unbroke; and for the third he gave a goodly caldron yet untouched by fire, holding four measures, bright as when first made; and for the fourth he ordained two talents of gold; and for the fifth a two-handled urn untouched of fire. Then he stood up and spake a word among the Argives: "Son of Atreus and ye other well-greaved Achaians, for the chariot-racers these prizes lie awaiting them in the lists. If in some other's honour we Achaians were now holding our games, it would be I who should win the first prize and bear it to my hut; for ye know how far my pair of horses are first in excellence, for they are immortal, and Poseidon gave them to my father Peleus, and he again to me. But verily I will abide, I and my whole-hooved horses, so glorious a charioteer have they lost, and one so kind, who on their manes full often poured smooth oil, when he had washed them in clear water. For him they stand and mourn, and their manes are trailing on the ground, and there stand they with sorrow at their hearts. But ye others throughout the host get ye to your places, whosoever of the Achaians hath trust in his horses and firm-jointed car."

Thus spake the son of Peleus, and the fleet chariot-racers were gathered. First of all arose up Eumelos king of men,

Admetos' son, a skilful charioteer; and next to him arose
Tydeus' son, valiant Diomedes, and yoked his horses of the
breed of Tros, which on a time he seized from Aineias,
when Apollo saved their lord. And after him arose Atreus'
son, fair-haired heaven-sprung Menelaos, and yoked him a
swift pair, Aithe, Agamemnon's mare, and his own horse
Podargos.

And Meriones was the fifth to make ready his sleek-
coated steeds. Then went they up into their chariots, and
cast in the lots: and Achilles shook them, and forth leapt
the lot of Antilochos Nestor's son, and the next lot had lord
Eumelos, and next to him the son of Atreus, spear-famed
Menelaos, and next to him drew Meriones his place; then
lastly Tydeides, far the best of all, drew his lot for his
chariot's place. Then they stood side by side, and Achilles
showed to them the turning-post, far off in the smooth plain;
and beside it he placed an umpire, godlike Phoinix, his
father's follower, that he might note the running and tell the
truth thereof.

Then all together lifted the lash above their steeds, and
smote them with the reins, and called on them eagerly with
words: and they forthwith sped swiftly over the plain, leaving the ships behind; and beneath their breasts stood the
rising dust like a cloud or whirlwind, and their manes waved
on the blowing wind. And the chariots ran sometimes on the
bounteous earth, and other whiles would bound into the air.
And the drivers stood in the cars, and the heart of every
man beat in desire of victory, and they called every man to
his horses, that flew amid their dust across the plain.

But when the fleet horses were now running the last part

of the course, back toward the grey sea, then was manifest the prowess of each, and the horses strained in the race; and presently to the front rushed the fleet mares of Pheres' grandson, and next to them Diomedes' stallions of the breed of Tros, not far apart, but hard anigh, for they seemed ever as they would mount Eumelos' car, and with their breath his back was warm and his broad shoulders, for they bent their heads upon him as they flew along. Thus would Tydeus' son have either outstripped the other or made it a dead heat, had not Phoebus Apollo been wroth with him and smitten from his hand the shining lash. Then from his eyes ran tears of anger, for that he saw the mares still at speed, even swiftlier than before, while his own horses were thrown out, as running without spur. But Athene was not unaware of Apollo's guile against Tydeides, and presently sped after the shepherd of hosts, and gave him back the lash, and put spirit into his steeds. Then in wrath after the son of Admetos was the goddess gone, and brake his steeds' yoke, and the mares ran sideways off the course, and the pole was twisted to the ground. And Eumelos was hurled out of the car beside the wheel, and his elbows and mouth and nose were flayed, and his forehead bruised above his eyebrows; and his eyes filled with tears and his lusty voice was choked. Then Tydeides held his whole-hooved horses on one side, darting far out before the rest, for Athene put spirit into his steeds and shed glory on himself. Now next after him came golden-haired Menelaos Atreus' son. But Antilochos called to his father's horses: "Go ye too in, strain to your fleetest pace. Truly I nowise bid you strive with those, the horses of wise Tydeides, unto which Athene hath now given speed, and shed glory on their charioteer. But overtake Atreides' horses with all haste, and be not outstripped by them, lest Aithe that is but a mare pour scorn on you. Why are ye outstripped, brave steeds? Thus will I tell you, and verily it shall be brought to pass—ye will find no tendance with Nestor shepherd of hosts, but straightway he will slay you with the edge of the sword if through heedlessness we win but the worse prize. Have after them at your utmost speed, and I for my part will devise a plan to pass them in the strait part of the course, and this shall fail me not."

Thus spake he, and they fearing the voice of the prince ran swiftlier some little while; and presently did the good warrior Antilochos espy a strait place in a sunk part of the way. There was a rift in the earth, where torrent water gathered and brake part of the track away, and hollowed all the place; there drave Menelaos, shunning the encounter of the wheels. But Antilochos turned his whole-hooved horses out of the track, and followed him a little at one side. And the son of Atreus took alarm and shouted to Antilochos: "Antilochos, thou art driving recklessly—hold in thy horses! The road is straitened, soon thou mayest pass me in a wider place, lest thou foul my chariot and undo us both."

Thus spake he, but Antilochos drave even fiercelier than before, plying his lash, as though he heard him not. As far as is the range of a disk swung from the shoulder when a young man hurleth it, making trial of his force, even so far ran they on; then the mares of Atreus' son gave back, for he ceased of himself to urge them on, lest the whole-hooved steeds should encounter on the track, and overset the well-knit cars, and the drivers fall in the dust in their zeal for victory. So upbraiding Antilochos spake golden-haired Menelaos: "Antilochos, no mortal man is more malicious than thou. Go thy mad way, since falsely have we Achaians called thee wise. Yet even so thou shalt not bear off the prize unchallenged to an oath."

Thus saying he called aloud to his horses: "Hold ye not back nor stand still with sorrow at heart. Their feet and knees will grow weary before yours, for they both lack youth."

Thus spake he, and they fearing the voice of the prince sped faster on, and were quickly close upon the others.

Now the Argives sitting in concourse were gazing at the horses, and they came flying amid their dust over the plain. And the first aware of them was Idomeneus, chief of the Cretans, for he was sitting outside the concourse in the highest place of view, and when he heard the voice of one that shouted, though afar off, he knew it; and he was aware of a horse showing plainly in the front, a chestnut all the rest of him, but in the forehead marked with a white star round like the moon. And he stood upright and spoke among the Argives: "Friends, chiefs, and counsellors of the Argives, is it I alone who see the horses, or do ye also? A new pair seem to me now to be in front, and a new charioteer appeareth; the mares which led in the outward course must have been thrown out there in the plain. For I saw them turning first the hither post, but now can see them nowhere, though my eyes are gazing everywhere along the Trojan plain. Did the reins escape the charioteer so that he could not drive aright round the post and failed in the turn? There, methinks, must he have been cast forth, and have broken his chariot, and the mares must have left the course, in the wildness of their heart. But stand up ye too and look, for myself I discern not certainly, but the first man seemeth to me one of Aitolian race, and he ruleth among Argives, the son of horse-taming Tydeus, stalwart Diomedes."

Then fleet Aias Oïleus' son rebuked him in unseemly sort: "Idomeneus, why art thou a braggart of old? As yet far off the high-stepping mares are coursing over the wide plain. Neither art thou so far the youngest among the Argives, nor do thy eyes look so far the keenliest from thy head, yet continually braggest thou. It beseemeth thee not to be a braggart, for there are here better men. And the mares leading are they that led before, Eumelos' mares, and he standeth and holdeth the reins within the car."

Then wrathfully in answer spake the chief of Cretans: "Aias, master of railing, ill-counselled, in all else art thou behind other Argives, for thy mind is unfriendly. Come then let us wager a tripod or caldron, and make Agamemnon Atreus' son our umpire, which mares are leading, that thou mayest pay and learn."

Thus said he, and straightway fleet Aias Oïleus' son arose angrily to answer with harsh words: and strife between the twain would have gone further, had not Achilles himself stood up and spake a word: "No longer answer each other with harsh words, Aias and Idomeneus, ill words, for it beseemeth not. Surely ye are displeased with any other who should do thus. Sit ye in the concourse and keep your eyes upon the horses; soon they in zeal for victory will come hither, and then shall ye know each of you the Argives' horses, which follow, and which lead."

He said, and the son of Tydeus came driving up, and with his lash smote now and again from the shoulder, and his horses were stepping high as they sped swiftly on their way. And sprinklings of dust smote ever the charioteer, and his chariot overlaid with gold and tin ran behind his fleet-footed steeds, and small trace was there of the wheel-tires behind in the fine dust, as they flew speeding on. Then he drew up in the mid concourse, and much sweat poured from the horses' heads and chests to the ground. And Diomedes leapt to earth from the shining car, and leant his lash against the yoke. Then stalwart Sthenelos tarried not, but promptly took the prize, and gave to his proud comrades the woman to lead and the eared tripod to bear away, and he loosed the horses from the yoke.

And next after him drave Neleian Antilochos his horses, by craft, not swiftness, having passed by Menelaos; yet even now Menelaos held his swift steeds hard anigh. As far as a horse is from the wheel, which draweth his master, straining with the car over the plain—his hindmost tail-hairs touch the tire, for the wheel runneth hard anigh nor is much space between, as he speedeth far over the plain—by so much was Menelaos behind high-born Antilochos, howbeit at first he was a whole disk-cast behind, but quickly he was catching Antilochos up, for the high mettle of Agamemnon's mare, sleek-coated Aithë, was rising in her. And if yet further both had had to run he would have passed his rival nor left it even a dead heat. But Meriones, stout squire of Idomeneus, came in a spear-throw behind famous Menelaos, for tardiest of all were his sleek-coated horses, and slowest he himself to drive a chariot in the race. Last of them all came

Admetos' son, dragging his goodly car, driving his steeds in front. Him when fleet-footed noble Achilles beheld he pitied him, and he stood up and spake winged words among the Argives: "Last driveth his whole-hooved horses the best man of them all. But come let us give him a prize, as is seemly, prize for the second place, but the first let the son of Tydeus take."

Thus spake he, and all applauded that he bade. And he would have given him the mare, for the Achaians applauded, had not Antilochos, son of great-hearted Nestor, risen up and answered Peleïan Achilles on behalf of his right: "O Achilles, I shall be sore angered with thee if thou accomplish this word, for thou art minded to take away my prize, because thou thinkest of how his chariot and fleet steeds miscarried, and himself withal, good man though he be. Nay, it behoved him to pray to the Immortals, then would he not have come in last of all in the race. But if thou pitiest him and he be dear to thy heart, there is much gold in thy hut, bronze is there and sheep, handmaids are there and whole-hooved horses. Thereof take thou and give unto him afterward even a richer prize, or even now at once, that the Achaians may applaud thee. But the mare I will not yield; for her let what man will essay the battle at my hands."

Thus spake he, and fleet-footed noble Achilles smiled, pleased with Antilochos, for he was his dear comrade; and spake in answer to him winged words: "Antilochos, if thou wouldst have me give Eumelos some other thing beside from out my house, that also will I do. I will give unto him a breast-plate that I took from Asteropaios, of bronze, whereon a casting of bright tin is overlaid, and of great worth will it be to him." He said, and bade his dear comrade Automedon bring it from the hut, and he went and brought it.

But Menelaos also arose among them, sore at heart, angered exceedingly against Antilochos; and the herald set the staff in his hand, and called for silence among the Argives; then spake among them that godlike man: "Antilochos, who once wert wise, what thing is this thou hast done? Thou hast shamed my skill and made my horses fail, thrusting thine own in front that are far worse. Come now, ye chiefs and counsellors of the Argives, give judgment between us both, and favour neither: lest some one of the mail-clad Achaians say at any time: 'By constraining Antilochos through false words hath Menelaos gone off with the mare, for his horses were far worse, howbeit he hath advantage in rank and power.' Nay, I myself will bring the issue about, and I deem that none other of the Danaans shall reproach me, for the trial shall be just. Antilochos, fosterling of Zeus, come thou hither and as it is ordained stand up before thy horses and chariot and take in thy hand the pliant lash wherewith thou dravest erst, and touching thy horses swear by the Enfolder and Shaker of the earth that not wilfully didst thou hinder my chariot by guile."

Then answered him wise Antilochos: "Bear with me now, for far younger am I than thou, king Menelaos, and thou art before me and my better. Thou knowest how a young man's transgressions come about, for his mind is hastier and his counsel shallow. So let thy heart suffer me, and I will of myself give to thee the mare I have taken. Yea, if thou shouldst ask some other greater thing from my house, I

were fain to give it thee straightway, rather than fall for
ever from my place in thy heart, O fosterling of Zeus, and
become a sinner against the gods."

Thus spake great-hearted Nestor's son, and brought the
mare and put her in the hand of Menelaos. And his heart
was gladdened as when the dew cometh upon the ears of
ripening harvest-corn, what time the fields are bristling. So
gladdened was thy soul, Menelaos, within thy heart. And he
spake unto Antilochos and uttered winged words: "Antilochos, now will I of myself put away mine anger against
thee, since nowise formerly wert thou flighty or light-
minded, howbeit now thy reason was overcome of youth-
fulness. Another time be loth to outwit better men. Not
easily should another of the Achaians have persuaded me,
but thou hast suffered and toiled greatly, and thy brave
father and brother, for my sake: therefore will I hearken to
thy prayer, and will even give unto thee the mare, though
she is mine, that these also may know that my heart was
never overweening or implacable."

He said, and gave the mare to Noëmon Antilochos' comrade to lead away, and then took the shining caldron. And
Meriones took up the two talents of gold in the fourth place,
as he had come in. So the fifth prize was left unclaimed, a
two-handled cup; to Nestor gave Achilles this, bearing it to
him through the concourse of Argives, and stood by him
and said: "Lo now for thee too, old man, be this a treasure,
a memorial of Patroklos' burying; for no more shalt thou
behold him among the Argives. Now give I thee this prize
unwon, for not in boxing shalt thou strive, neither wrestle,

nor enter on the javelin match, nor race with thy feet; for grim old age already weigheth on thee."

Then he ordained prizes of the violent boxing match; a sturdy mule he led forth and tethered amid the assembly, a six-year mule unbroken, hardest of all to break; and for the loser set a two-handled cup. Then he stood up and spake a word among the Argives: "Son of Atreus and ye other well-greaved Achaians, for these rewards we summon two men of the best to lift up their hands to box amain. He to whom Apollo shall grant endurance to the end, and all the Acha-ians acknowledge it, let him take the sturdy mule and return with her to his hut; and the loser shall take with him the two-handled-cup."

Thus spake he, and forthwith arose a man great and valiant and skilled in boxing, Epeios son of Panopeus, and laid his hand on the sturdy mule and said aloud: "Let one come nigh to bear off the two-handled cup; the mule I say none other of the Achaians shall take for victory with his fists, for I claim to be the best man here. Sufficeth it not that I fall short of you in battle? Not possible is it that in all arts a man be skilled. Thus proclaim I, and it shall be accom-plished: I will utterly bruise mine adversary's flesh and break his bones, so let his friends abide together here to bear him forth when vanquished by my hands."

Thus spake he, and they all kept deep silence. And alone arose against him Euryalos, a godlike man, son of king Mekisteus the son of Talaos. Thus Tydeides famous with the spear made ready Euryalos for the fight, cheering him with speech, and greatly desired for him victory. And first he cast about him a girdle, and next gave him well-cut thongs of the hide of an ox of the field. And the two boxers being girt went into the midst of the ring, and both lifting up their stalwart hands fell to, and their hands joined battle grievously. Then was there terrible grinding of teeth, and sweat flowed from all their limbs. And noble Epeios came on, and as the other spied for an opening, smote him on the cheek, nor could he much more stand, for his limbs failed straightway under him. And as when beneath the North Wind's ripple a fish leapeth on a tangle-covered beach, and then the black wave hideth it, so leapt up Euryalos at that blow. But great-hearted Epeios took him in his hands and set him upright, and his dear comrades stood around him, and led him through the ring with trailing feet, spitting out clotted blood, drooping his head awry, and they set him down in his swoon among them and themselves went forth and fetched the two-handled cup.

Then Peleus' son ordained straightway the prizes for a third contest, offering them to the Danaans, for the grievous wrestling match: for the winner a great tripod for standing on the fire, prized by the Achaians among them at twelve oxens' worth; and for the loser he brought a woman into the midst, skilled in manifold work, and they prized her at four oxen. And he stood up and spake a word among the Argives: "Rise, ye who will essay this match."

Thus said he, and there arose great Aias son of Telamon, and Odysseus of many wiles stood up, the crafty-minded. And the twain being girt went into the midst of the ring, and clasped each the other in his arms with stalwart hands, like gable rafters of a lofty house which some famed craftsman joineth, that he may baffle the wind's force. And their backs creaked, gripped firmly under the vigorous hands, and sweat ran down in streams, and frequent weals along their ribs and shoulders sprang up, red with blood, while ever they strove amain for victory, to win the wrought tripod. Neither could Odysseus trip Aias and bear him to the ground, nor Aias him, for Odysseus's strength withheld him. But when they began to irk the well-greaved Achaians, then said to Odysseus great Aias, Telamon's son: "Heaven-sprung son of Laertes, Odysseus of many wiles, or lift thou me, or I will thee, and the issue shall be with Zeus."

Having thus said he lifted him, but Odysseus was not unmindful of his craft. He smote deftly from behind the hollow of Aias' knee, and loosed his limbs, and threw him down backward, and Odysseus fell upon his chest, and the folk gazed and marvelled. Then in his turn much-enduring noble Odysseus tried to lift, and moved him a little from the ground, but lifted him not, so he crooked his knee within the other's, and both fell on the ground nigh to each other, and were soiled with dust. And now starting up again a third time would they have wrestled, had not Achilles himself arisen and held them back: "No longer press each the other, nor wear you out with pain. Victory is with both; take equal prizes and depart, that other Achaians may contend."

Thus spake he, and they were fain to hear and to obey, and wiped the dust from them and put their doublets on.

Then straightway the son of Peleus set forth other prizes for fleetness of foot; a mixing-bowl of silver, chased; six measures it held, and in beauty it was far the best in all the earth, for artificers of Sidon wrought it cunningly, and men of the Phoenicians brought it over the misty sea, and landed it in harbour, and gave it a gift to Thoas; and Euneos son of Jason gave it to the hero Patroklos a ransom for Lykaon Priam's son. Now this cup did Achilles set forth as a prize in honour of his friend, for whoso should be fleetest in speed of foot. For the second he set an ox great and very fat, and for the last prize half a talent of gold. And he stood up and spake a word among the Argives: "Rise, ye who will essay this match."

Thus spake he, and straightway arose fleet Aias Oïleus' son, and Odysseus of many wiles, and after them Nestor's son Antilochos, for he was best of all the youth in the foot-race. Then they stood side by side, and Achilles showed to them the goal. Right eager was the running from the start, but Oïleus' son forthwith shot to the front, and close behind him came noble Odysseus, as close as is a weaving-rod to a fair-girdled woman's breast when she pulleth it deftly with her hands, drawing the spool along the warp, and holdeth the rod nigh her breast—so close ran Odysseus behind Aias and trod in his footsteps or ever the dust had settled there, and on his head fell the breath of noble Odysseus as he ran ever lightly on, rnd all the Achaians applauded his struggle for the victory and called on him as he laboured hard. But when they were running the last part of the course, forth-with Odysseus prayed in his soul to bright-eyed Athene: "Hearken, goddess, come thou a good helper of my feet."

Thus prayed he, and Pallas Athene hearkened to him, and made his limbs feel light, both feet and hands. But when they were now nigh darting on the prize, then Aias slipped as he ran, for Athene marred his race, where filth was strewn from the slaughter of loud-bellowing oxen that fleet Achilles slew in honour of Patroklos: and Aias' mouth and nostrils were filled with that filth of oxen. So much-enduring noble Odysseus, as he came in first, took up the mixing-bowl, and famous Aias took the ox. And he stood holding in his hand the horn of the ox of the field, sputtering away the filth, and spake among the Argives: "Out on it, it was the goddess who marred my running, she who from of old like a mother standeth by Odysseus' side and helpeth him."

So spake he, but they all laughed pleasantly to behold him. Then Antilochos smiling bore off the last prize, and spake his word among the Argives: "Friends, ye will all bear me witness when I say that even herein also the immortals favour elder men. For Aias is a little older than I, but Odysseus of an earlier generation and earlier race of men. A green old age is his, they say, and hard were it for any Achaian to rival him in speed, save only Achilles."

Thus spake he, and gave honour to the fleet son of Peleus. And Achilles answered him and said: "Antilochos, not unheeded shall thy praise be given; a half-talent of gold I will give thee over and above." He said, and set it in his hands, and Antilochos received it gladly.

BOOK XXIV

How the body of Hector was ransomed, and of his funeral.

THEN the assembly was broken up, and the tribes were scattered to betake them each to their own swift ships. The rest bethought them of supper and sweet sleep to have joy thereof; but Achilles wept, remembering his dear comrade, nor did sleep that conquereth all take hold on him, but he kept turning him to this side and to that, yearning for Patroklos' manhood and excellent valour, and all the toils he achieved with him and the woes he bare, cleaving the battles of men and the grievous waves. As he thought thereon he shed big tears, now lying on his side, now on his back, now on his face; and then anon he would arise upon his feet and roam wildly beside the beach of the salt sea. Nor would he be unaware of the Dawn when she arose over the sea and shores. But when he had yoked the swift steeds to his car he would bind Hector behind his chariot to drag him withal; and having thrice drawn him round the barrow of the dead son of Menoitios he rested again in his hut, and left Hector lying stretched on his face in the dust. But Apollo kept away all defacement from his flesh, for he had pity on him even in death, and covered him all with his golden aegis, that Achilles might not tear him when he dragged him.

Thus Achilles in his anger entreated noble Hector shamefully; but the blessed gods when they beheld him pitied him, and urged the clear-sighted slayer of Argus to steal the corpse away. So to all the others seemed it good, yet not to Hera or Poseidon or the bright-eyed Maiden, but they continued as when at the beginning sacred Ilios became hateful to them, and Priam and his people, by reason of the sin of Alexandros in that he contemned those goddesses when they came to his steading, and preferred her who brought him deadly lustfulness. But when the twelfth morn from that day arose, then spake among the Immortals Phoebus Apollo: "Hard of heart are ye, O gods, and cruel. Hath Hector never burnt for you thigh-bones of unblemished bulls and goats? Now have ye not taken heart to rescue even his corpse for his wife to look upon and his mother and his child and his father Priam and his people, who speedily would burn him in the fire and make his funeral."

Then in anger spake unto him white-armed Hera: "Even thus mightest thou speak, O lord of the silver bow, if ye are to give equal honour to Achilles and to Hector. Hector is but a mortal and was suckled at a woman's breast, but Achilles is child of a goddess whom I myself bred up and reared and gave to a man to be his wife, even to Peleus who was dearest of all men to the Immortals' heart. And all ye gods came to her bridal, and thou among them wert feasting with thy lyre, O lover of ill company, faithless ever."

Then to her in answer spake Zeus who gathereth the clouds: "Hera, be not wroth utterly with the gods: for these men's honour is not to be the same, yet Hector also was dearest to the gods of all mortals that are in Ilios. So was he to me at least, for nowise failed he in the gifts I loved. Never did my altar lack seemly feast, drink-offering and the steam of sacrifice, even the honour that falleth to our due. But verily we will say no more of stealing away brave Hector, for it cannot be hidden from Achilles, for his mother abideth ever nigh to him night and day. But I were fain that some one of the gods would call Thetis to come near to me, that I may speak unto her a wise word, so that Achilles may take gifts from Priam and give Hector back."

Thus spake he, and airy-footed Iris sped forth upon the errand and between Samothrace and rocky Imbros leapt into the black sea, and the waters closed above her with a noise. And she sped to the bottom like a weight of lead that mounted on horn of a field-ox goeth down bearing death to ravenous fishes. And she found Thetis in a hollow cave; about her sat gathered other goddesses of the sea, and she in their midst was wailing for the fate of her noble son who must perish in deep-soiled Troy, far from his native land. And standing near, fleet-footed Iris spake to her: "Rise, Thetis; Zeus of immortal counsels calleth thee."

And to her made answer Thetis the silver-footed goddess: "Wherefore biddeth me that mighty god? I shrink from mingling among the Immortals, for I have countless woes at heart. Yet go I, nor shall his word be in vain, whatsoever he saith."

Thus having said the noble goddess took to her a dark-hued robe, no blacker raiment was there found than that. Then she went forth, and wind-footed swift Iris led the way before her, and around them the surge of the sea was sundered. And when they had come forth upon the shore they sped up to heaven, and found the far-seeing son of Kronos, and round him sat gathered all the other blessed gods that are for ever. Then she sat down beside father Zeus, and Athene gave her place. And Hera set a fair golden cup in her hand and cheered her with words, and Thetis drank, and gave back the cup. Then began speech to them the father of gods and men: "Thou art come to Olympus, divine Thetis, in thy sorrow, with violent grief at thy heart; I know it of myself. Nevertheless will I tell thee wherefore I called thee hither. Nine days hath dispute arisen among the Immortals concerning the corpse of Hector and Achilles waster of cities. Fain are they to send clear-sighted Hermes to steal the body away, but now hear what glory I accord herein to Achilles, that I may keep through times to come thy honour and good will. Go with all speed to the host and bear to thy son my bidding. Say to him that the gods are displeased at him, and that I above all Immortals am wroth, because with furious heart he holdeth Hector at the beaked ships and hath not given him back, if haply he may fear me and give Hector back. But I will send Iris to great-hearted Priam to bid him go to the ships of the Achaians to ransom his dear son, and carry gifts to Achilles that may gladden his heart."

Thus spake he, and Thetis the silver-footed goddess was not disobedient to his word, and sped darting upon her way down from the peaks of Olympus. And she came to her son's hut; there found she him making grievous moans, and his dear comrades round were swiftly making ready and furnishing their early meal, and a sheep great and fleecy was being sacrificed in the hut. Then his lady-mother sate her down close beside him, and stroked him with her hand and spake to him by his name: "My child, how long with lamentation and woe wilt thou devour thine heart, taking thought of neither food nor rest? good were even a woman's embrace, for not long shalt thou be left alive to me; already death and forceful fate are standing nigh thee. But hearken forthwith unto me, for I am the messenger of Zeus to thee. He saith that the gods are displeased at thee, and that himself above all Immortals is wroth, because with furious heart thou holdest Hector at the beaked ships and hast not given him back. But come restore him, and take ransom for the dead."

Then to her in answer spake fleet-footed Achilles: "So be it: whoso bringeth ransom let him take back the dead, if verily with heart's intent the Olympian biddeth it himself."

So they in the assembly of the ships, mother and son, spake to each other many winged words. But the son of Kronos thus bade Iris go to holy Ilios: "Go forth, fleet Iris, leave the abode of Olympus and bear my message within Ilios to great-hearted Priam that he go to the ships of the Achaians and ransom his dear son and carry gifts to Achilles that may gladden his heart; let him go alone, and no other man of the Trojans go with him. Only let some elder herald attend on him to guide the mules and smooth-wheeled waggon and carry back to the city the dead man whom noble Achilles slew. Let not death be in his thought nor any fear; such guide will we give unto him, even Hermes who shall lead him until his leading bring him to Achilles. And when he shall have led him within the hut, neither shall Achilles himself slay him nor suffer any other herein, for not senseless is he or unforeseeing or wicked, but with all courtesy he will spare a suppliant man."

Thus spake he, and airy-footed Iris sped forth upon the errand. And she came to the house of Priam, and found therein crying and moan. His children sitting around their father within the court were bedewing their raiment with their tears, and the old man in their midst was close wrapped all over in his cloak; and on his head and neck was much mire that he had gathered in his hands as he grovelled upon the earth. And his daughters and his sons' wives were wailing throughout the house, bethinking them of all those valiant men who had lost their lives at the hands of the Argives and were lying low. And the messenger of Zeus stood beside Priam and spake softly unto him, and trembling came upon his limbs: "Be of good cheer in thy heart, O Priam son of Dardanos, and be not dismayed for anything, for no evil come I hither to forebode to thee, but with good will. I am the messenger of Zeus to thee, who, though he be afar off, hath great care and pity for thee. The Olympian biddeth thee ransom noble Hector and carry gifts to Achilles that may gladden his heart: go thou alone, let none other of the Trojans go with thee. Only let some elder herald attend on thee to guide the mules and the smooth-wheeled waggon to carry back to the city the dead man whom noble Achilles slew. Let not death be in thy thought, nor any fear; such guide shall go with thee, even the slayer of Argus, who shall lead thee until his leading bring thee to Achilles. And when he shall have led thee into the hut, neither shall Achilles himself slay thee, nor suffer any other herein, for not senseless is he or unforeseeing or wicked, but with all courtesy he will spare a suppliant man."

Thus having spoken fleet Iris departed from him; and he bade his sons make ready the smooth-wheeled mule waggon, and bind the wicker carriage thereon. And himself he went down to his fragrant chamber, of cedar wood, high-roofed, that held full many jewels, and opened fair lids of chests wherefrom he chose twelve very goodly women's robes and twelve cloaks of single fold and of coverlets a like number and of fair sheets, and of doublets thereupon. And he weighed and brought forth talents of gold ten in all, and two shining tripods and four caldrons, and a goblet exceeding fair that men of Thrace had given him when he went thither on an embassy, a chattel of great price, yet not that even did the old man grudge from his halls, for he was exceeding fain at heart to ransom his dear son.

Then he called unto his sons, chiding Helenos and Paris and noble Agathon and Pammon and Antiphonos, and Polites of the loud war-cry, and Deïphobos and Hippothoos and proud Dios; nine were they whom the old man called and bade unto him: "Haste ye, ill sons, my shame; would that ye all in Hector's stead had been slain at the swift ships! Woe is me all unblest, since I begat sons the best men in wide Troy-land, but none of them is left for me to claim, neither godlike Mestor, nor Troilos with his chariot of war, nor Hector who was a god among men, neither seemed he as the son of a mortal man but of a god:—all these hath Ares slain, and here are my shames all left to me, false-tongued, light-heeled, the heroes of the dance, plunderers of your own people's sheep and kids. Will ye not make me ready a wain with all speed, and lay all these thereon, that we get us forward on our way?"

Thus spake he, and they fearing their father's voice brought forth the smooth-running mule chariot, fair and new, and bound the body thereof on the frame; and from its peg they took down the mule yoke, a boxwood yoke with knob well fitted with guiding-rings; and they brought forth the yoke-band of nine cubits with the yoke. The yoke they set firmly on the polished pole on the rest at the end thereof, and slipped the ring over the upright pin, which with three turns of the band they lashed to the knob, and then belayed it close round the pole and turned the tongue thereunder. Then they brought from the chamber and heaped on the polished wain the countless ransom of Hector's head, and yoked strong-hooved harness mules, which on a time the Mysians gave to Priam, a splendid gift. But to Priam's car they yoked the horses that the old man kept for his use and reared at the polished crib.

Then the old man made haste to go up into his car, and drave forth from the doorway and the echoing portico. In front the mules drew the four-wheeled wain, and wise Idaios drave them; behind came the horses which the old man urged with the lash at speed along the city: and his friends all followed lamenting loud as though he were faring to his death. And when they were come down from the city and were now on the plain, then went back again to Ilios his sons and marriage kin. But the two coming forth upon the plain were not unbeheld of far-seeing Zeus. But he looked upon the old man and had compassion on him, and straightway spake unto Hermes his dear son: "Hermes, since unto

thee especially is it dear to companion men, and thou hearest whomsoever thou wilt, go forth and so guide Priam to
the hollow ships of the Achaians that no man behold or be
aware of him, among all the Danaans' host, until he come to
the son of Peleus."

Thus spake he, and the Messenger, the slayer of Argus,
was not disobedient unto his word. Straightway beneath his
feet he bound on his fair sandals, golden, divine, that bare
him over wet sea and over the boundless land with the
breathings of the wind. And he took up his wand wherewith
he entranceth the eyes of such men as he will, and others he
likewise waketh out of sleep: this did the strong slayer of
Argus take in his hand, and flew. And quickly came he to
Troy-land and the Hellespont, and went on his way in semblance as a young man that is a prince, with the new down
on his chin, as when the youth of men is the comeliest.

Now the others, when they had driven beyond the great
barrow of Ilios, halted the mules and horses at the river to
drink; for darkness was come down over the earth. Then the
herald beheld Hermes from hard by, and marked him, and
spake and said to Priam: "Consider, son of Dardanos; this
is matter of prudent thought. I see a man, methinks we shall
full soon be rent in pieces. Come, let us flee in our chariot,
or else at least touch his knees and entreat him that he have
mercy on us."

Thus spake he, and the old man was confounded, and he
was dismayed exceedingly, and the hair on his pliant limbs
stood up, and he stood still amazed. But the Helper came
nigh of himself and took the old man's hand, and spake and
questioned him: "Whither, father, dost thou thus guide

these horses and mules through the divine night, when other mortals are asleep? Hadst thou no fear of the fierce-breathing Achaians, thy bitter foes that are hard anigh thee? If one of them should espy thee carrying such treasures through the swift black night, what then would be thy thought? Neither art thou young thyself, and thy companion here is old, that ye should make defence against a man that should assail thee first. But I will nowise harm thee, yea I will keep any other from thy hurt: for the similitude of my dear father I see in thee."

And to him in answer spake the old man, godlike Priam: "Even so, kind son, are all these things as thou sayest. Nevertheless hath some god stretched forth his hand even over me in that he hath sent a wayfarer such as thou to meet me, a bearer of good luck, by the nobleness of thy form and semblance; and thou art wise of heart and of blessed parents art thou sprung."

And to him again spake the Messenger, the slayer of Argus: "All this, old sire, hast thou verily spoken aright. But come say this and tell me truly whether thou art taking forth a great and goodly treasure unto alien men, where it may abide for thee in safety, or whether by this ye are all forsaking holy Ilios in fear; so far the best man among you hath perished, even thy son; for of battle with the Achaians abated he never a jot."

And to him in answer spake the old man, godlike Priam: "Who art thou, noble sir, and of whom art born? For meetly hast thou spoken of the fate of my hapless son."

And to him again spake the Messenger, the slayer of Argus: "Thou art proving me, old sire, in asking me of noble Hector. Him have I full oft seen with mine eyes in glorious battle, and when at the ships he was slaying the Argives he drave thither, piercing them with the keen bronze, and we stood still and marvelled thereat, for Achilles suffered us not to fight, being wroth against Atreus' son. His squire am I, and came in the same well-wrought ship. From the Myrmidons I come, and my father is Polyktor."

And the old man, godlike Priam, answered him, saying: "If verily thou art a squire of Achilles Peleus' son, come tell me all the truth, whether still my son is by the ships, or whether ere now Achilles hath riven him limb from limb and cast him to the dogs."

Then to him again spake the Messenger the slayer of Argus: "Old sire, not yet have dogs or birds devoured him, but there lieth he still by Achilles' ship, even as he fell, among the huts, and the twelfth morn now hath risen upon him, nor doth his flesh corrupt at all, neither worms consume it, such as devour men slain in war. Truly Achilles draggeth him recklessly around the barrow of his dear comrade so oft as divine day dawneth, yet marreth he him not; thou wouldst marvel if thou couldst go see thyself how dewy fresh he lieth, and is washed clean of blood, nor anywhere defiled; and all his wounds wherewith he was stricken are closed; howbeit many plunged their points in him. So careful are the blessed gods of thy son, though he be but a dead corpse, for they held him dear at heart."

Thus spake he, and the old man rejoiced, and answered him, saying: "My son, it is verily a good thing to give due offerings withal to the Immortals, for never did my child—if that child indeed I had—forget in our halls the gods who inhabit Olympus. Therefore have they remembered this for him, albeit his portion is death. But come now take from me this goodly goblet, and guard me myself and guide me, under Heaven, that I may come unto the hut of Peleus' son."

Then spake unto him again the Messenger the slayer of Argus: "Thou art proving me, old sire, who am younger than thou, but thou wilt not prevail upon me, in that thou biddest me take gifts from thee without Achilles' privity. I were afraid and shamed at heart to defraud him, lest some evil come to pass on me hereafter. But as thy guide I would go even unto famous Argos, accompanying thee courteously in swift ship or on foot. Not from scorn of thy guide would any assail thee then."

Thus spake the Helper, and leaping on the chariot behind the horses he swiftly took lash and reins into his hand, and breathed brave spirit into horses and mules. But when they were come to the towers and trench of the ships, there were the sentinels just busying them about their supper. Then the Messenger, the slayer of Argus, shed sleep upon them all, and straightway opened the gates and thrust back the bars, and brought within Priam and the splendid gifts upon his wain. And they came to the lofty hut of the son of Peleus, which the Myrmidons made for their king and hewed therefor timber of the pine, and thatched it with downy thatching-rush that they mowed in the meadows, and around it made for him their lord a great court with close-set palisades; and the door was barred by a single bolt of pine that three Achaians wont to drive home, and three drew back that mighty bar—three of the rest, but Achilles by himself would drive it home. Then opened the Helper Hermes the door for the old man, and brought in the splendid gifts for Peleus' fleet-footed son, and descended from the chariot to the earth and spake aloud: "Old sire, I that have come to thee am an immortal god, even Hermes, for my father sent me to companion thee on thy way. But now will I depart from thee nor come within Achilles' sight; it were cause of wrath that an immortal god should thus show favour openly unto mortals. But thou go in and clasp the knees of Peleus' son and entreat him for his father's sake and his mother's of the lovely hair and for his child's sake that thou mayest move his soul."

Thus Hermes spake, and departed unto high Olympus. But Priam leapt from the car to the earth, and left Idaios in his place; he stayed to mind the horses and mules; but the old man made straight for the house where Achilles dear to Zeus was wont to sit. And therein he found the man himself, and his comrades sate apart: two only, the hero Automedon and Alkimos, of the stock of Ares, were busy in attendance; and he was lately ceased from meat, even from eating and drinking: and still the table stood beside him. But they were unaware of great Priam as he came in, and so stood he anigh and clasped in his hands the knees of Achilles, and kissed his hands, terrible, man-slaying, that slew many of Priam's sons. And as when a grievous curse cometh upon a man who in his own country hath slain another and es-capeth to a land of strangers, to the house of some rich man, and wonder possesseth them that look on him—so Achilles wondered when he saw godlike Priam, and the rest won-dered likewise, and looked upon one another. Then Priam spake and entreated him, saying: "Bethink thee, O Achilles like to gods, of thy father that is of like years with me, on the grievous pathway of old age. Him haply are the dwellers round about entreating evilly, nor is there any to ward from him ruin and bane. Nevertheless while he heareth of thee as yet alive he rejoiceth in his heart, and hopeth withal day after day that he shall see his dear son returning from Troy-land. But I, I am utterly unblest, since I begat sons the best men in wide Troy-land, but declare unto thee that none of them is left. Fifty I had, when the sons of the Achaians came. Now of the more part had impetuous Ares unstrung the knees, and he who was yet left and guarded city and men, him slewest thou but now as he fought for his country, even Hector. For his sake come I unto the ships of the Achaians that I may win him back from thee, and I bring with me untold ransom. Yea, fear thou the gods, Achilles, and have compassion on me, even me, bethinking thee of thy father. Lo, I am yet more piteous than he, and have braved what none other man on earth hath braved before, to stretch forth my hand toward the face of the slayer of my sons."

Thus spake he, and stirred within Achilles desire to make lament for his father. And he touched the old man's hand and gently moved him back. And as they both bethought them of their dead, so Priam for man-slaying Hector wept sore as he was fallen before Achilles' feet, and Achilles wept for his own father, and now again for Patroklos, and their moan went up throughout the house. But when noble Achilles had satisfied him with lament, and the desire thereof departed from his heart and limbs, straightway he sprang from his seat and raised the old man by his hand, pitying his hoary head and hoary beard, and spake unto him winged words and said: "Ah hapless! many ill things verily thou hast endured in thy heart. How durst thou come alone to the ships of the Achaians and to meet the eyes of the man who hath slain full many of thy brave sons? of iron verily is thy heart. But come then set thee on a seat, and we will let our sorrows lie quiet in our hearts, for all our pain, for no avail cometh of chill lament. This is the lot the gods have spun for miserable men, that they should live in pain, yet themselves are sorrowless. For two urns stand upon the floor of Zeus filled with his evil gifts, and one with blessings. To whomsoever Zeus whose joy is in the lightning dealeth a mingled lot, that man chanceth now upon ill and now again on good, but to whom he giveth but of the bad kind him he bringeth to scorn, and evil famine chaseth him over the goodly earth, and he is a wanderer honoured of neither gods nor men. Even thus to Peleus gave the gods splendid gifts from his birth, for he excelled all men in good fortune and wealth, and was king of the Myrmidons, and mortal though he was the gods gave him a goddess to be his bride. Yet even on him God brought evil, seeing that there arose to him no offspring of princely sons in his halls, save that he begat one son to an untimely death. Neither may I tend him as he groweth old, since very far from my country I am dwelling in Troy-land, to vex thee and thy children. And of thee, old sire, we have heard how of old time thou wert happy, even how of all that Lesbos, seat of Makar, boundeth to the north thereof and Phrygia farther up and the vast Hellespont—of all these folk, men say, thou wert the richest in wealth and in sons, but after that the Powers of Heaven brought this bane on thee, ever are battles and man-slayings around thy city. Keep courage, and lament not unabatingly in thy heart. For nothing wilt thou avail by grieving for thy son, neither shalt thou bring him back to life or ever some new evil come upon thee."

Then made answer unto him the old man, godlike Priam: "Bid me not to a seat, O fosterling of Zeus, so long as Hector lieth uncared for at the huts, but straightway give him back that I may behold him with mine eyes; and accept thou the great ransom that we bring. So mayest thou have pleasure thereof, and come unto thy native land, since thou hast spared me from the first."

Then fleet-footed Achilles looked sternly upon him and said: "No longer chafe me, old sire; of myself am I minded to give Hector back to thee, for there came to me a messenger from Zeus, even my mother who bare me, daughter of the Ancient One of the Sea. And I know, O Priam, in my mind, nor am unaware that some god it is that hath guided thee to the swift ships of the Achaians. For no mortal man, even though in prime of youth, would dare to come among the host, for neither could he escape the watch, nor easily thrust back the bolt of our doors. Therefore now stir my heart no more amid my troubles, lest I leave not even thee in peace, old sire, within my hut, albeit thou art my suppliant, and lest I transgress the commandment of Zeus."

Thus spake he, and the old man feared, and obeyed his word. And the son of Peleus leapt like a lion through the door of the house, not alone, for with him went two squires, the hero Automedon and Alkimos, they whom above all his comrades Achilles honoured, save only Patroklos that was dead. They then loosed from under the yoke the horses and mules, and led in the old man's crier-herald and set him on a chair, and from the wain of goodly felloes they took the countless ransom set on Hector's head. But they left two robes and a well-spun doublet, that Achilles might wrap the dead therein when he gave him to be carried home. And he called forth handmaids and bade them wash and anoint him when they had borne him apart, so that Priam should not look upon his son, lest he should not refrain the wrath at his sorrowing heart when he should look upon his son, and lest Achilles' heart be vexed thereat and he slay him and transgress the commandment of Zeus. So when the handmaids had washed the body and anointed it with oil, and had thrown over it a fair robe and a doublet, then Achilles himself lifted it and laid it on a bier, and his comrades with him lifted it on to the polished waggon. Then he groaned aloud and called on his dear comrade by his name: "Patroklos, be not vexed with me if thou hear even in the house of Hades that I have given back noble Hector unto his dear father, for not unworthy is the ransom he hath given me, whereof I will deal to thee again thy rightful share."

Thus spake noble Achilles, and went back into the hut, and sate him down on the cunningly-wrought couch whence he had arisen by the opposite wall, and spake a word to Priam: "Thy son, old sire, is given back as thou wouldest and lieth on a bier, and with the break of day thou shalt see him thyself as thou carriest him. But come let us, noble father, take thought of meat, and afterward thou shalt mourn over thy dear son as thou carriest him to Ilios; and many tears shall be his due."

Thus spake fleet Achilles, and sprang up, and slew a pure white sheep, and his comrades skinned and made it ready in seemly fashion, and divided it cunningly and pierced it with spits, and roasted it carefully and drew all off. And Automedon took bread and served it on a table in fair baskets, while Achilles dealt out the flesh. And they stretched forth their hands to the good cheer lying ready before them. But when they had put off the desire of meat and drink, then Priam son of Dardanos marvelled at Achilles to see how great he was and how goodly, for he was like a god to look upon. And Achilles marvelled at Priam son of Dardanos, beholding his noble aspect and hearkening to his words. But when they had gazed their fill upon one another, then first spake the old man, godlike Priam, to Achilles: "Now presently give me whereon to lie, fosterling of Zeus, that of sweet sleep also we may now take our fill at rest: for never yet have mine eyes closed beneath their lids since at thy hands my son lost his life, but I continually mourn and brood over countless griefs, grovelling in the courtyard-close amid the mire. Now at last have I tasted bread and poured bright wine down my throat, but till now I had tasted naught."

He said, and Achilles bade his comrades and handmaids to set a bedstead beneath the portico, and to cast thereon fair shining rugs and spread coverlets above and thereon to lay thick mantles to be a clothing over all. And the maids went forth from the inner hall with torches in their hands, and quickly spread two beds in haste. Then with bitter meaning said fleet-footed Achilles unto Priam: "Lie thou without, dear sire, lest there come hither one of the counsellors of the Achaians, such as ever take counsel with me by my side, as custom is. If any of such should behold thee through the swift black night, forthwith he might haply tell it to Agamemnon shepherd of the host, and thus would there be delay in giving back the dead. But come say this to me and tell it true, how many days' space thou art fain to make funeral for noble Hector, so that for so long I may myself abide and may keep back the host."

And the old man, godlike Priam, answered him, saying: "If thou art verily willing that I accomplish noble Hector's funeral, by doing as thou sayest, O Achilles, thou wilt do me grace. For thou knowest how we are pent within the city, and wood from the mountain is far to fetch, and the Trojans are much in fear. Nine days will we make moan for him in our halls, and on the tenth we will hold funeral and the folk shall feast, and on the eleventh we will make a barrow over him, and on the twelfth we will do battle if need be."

Then again spake the fleet noble Achilles unto him, saying: "All this, O ancient Priam, shall be as thou biddest; for I will hold back the battle even so long a time as thou tellest me."

Thus speaking he clasped the old man's right hand at the wrist, lest he should be anywise afraid at heart. So they in the forepart of the house laid them down, Priam and the herald, with wise thoughts at their hearts, but Achilles slept in a recess of the firm-wrought hut.

Now all other gods and warriors lords of chariots slumbered all night, by soft sleep overcome. But not on the Helper Hermes did sleep take hold as he sought within his heart how he should guide forth king Priam from the ships unespied of the trusty sentinels. And he stood above his head and spake a word to him: "Old sire, no thought then hast thou of any evil, seeing thou yet sleepest among men that are thine enemies, for that Achilles spared thee. Truly now hast thou won back thy dear son, and at great price. But for thy life will thy sons thou hast left behind be offering threefold ransom, if but Agamemnon Atreus' son be aware of thee, and aware be all the Achaians."

Thus spake he, and the old man feared, and roused the herald. And Hermes yoked the horses and mules for them, and himself drave them lightly through the camp, and none was aware of them.

But when they came to the ford of the fair-flowing river, then Hermes departed up to high Olympus, and Morning of the saffron robe spread over all the earth. And they with wail and moan drave the horses to the city, and the mules drew the dead. Nor marked them any man or fair-girdled woman until Kassandra, peer of golden Aphrodite, having gone up upon Pergamos, was aware of her dear father as he stood in the car, and the herald that was crier to the town. Then beheld she him that lay upon the bier behind the mules, and thereat she wailed and cried aloud throughout all the town: "O men and women of Troy, come ye hither and look upon Hector, if ever while he was alive ye rejoiced when he came back from battle, since great joy was he to the city and all the folk."

Thus spake she, nor was man or woman left within the city, for upon all came unendurable grief. And near the gates they met Priam bringing home the dead. First bewailed him his dear wife and lady mother, as they cast them on the fair-wheeled wain and touched his head; and around them stood the throng and wept. So all day long unto the setting of the sun they had lamented Hector in tears without the gate, had not the old man spoken from the car among the folk: "Give me place for the mules to pass through; hereafter ye shall have your fill of wailing, when I have brought him unto his home."

Thus spake he and they parted asunder and gave place to the wain. And the others when they had brought him to the famous house, laid him on a fretted bed, and set beside him minstrel leaders of the dirge, who wailed a mournful lay, while the women made moan with them. And among the women white-armed Andromache led the lamentation, while in her hands she held the head of Hector slayer of men: "Husband, thou art gone young from life, and leavest me a widow in thy halls. And the child is yet but a little one, child of ill-fated parents, thee and me; nor methinks shall he grow up to manhood, for ere then shall this city be utterly destroyed. For thou art verily perished who didst watch over it, who guardedst it and keptest safe its noble wives and infant little ones. These soon shall be voyaging in the hollow ships, yea and I too with them, and thou, my child, shalt either go with me unto a place where thou shalt toil at unseemly tasks, labouring before the face of some harsh lord, or else some Achaian will take thee by the arm and hurl thee from the battlement, a grievous death, for that he is wroth because Hector slew his brother or father or son, since full many of the Achaians in Hector's hands have bitten the firm earth. For no light hand had thy father in the grievous fray. Therefore the folk lament him throughout the city, and woe unspeakable and mourning hast thou left to thy parents, Hector, but with me chiefliest shall grievous pain abide. For neither didst thou stretch thy hands to me from a bed in thy death, neither didst speak to me some memorable word that I might have thought on evermore as my tears fall night and day."

Thus spake she wailing, and the women joined their moan. And among them Hekabe again led the loud lament: "Hector, of all my children far dearest to my heart, verily while thou wert alive dear wert thou to the gods, and even in thy doom of death have they had care for thee. For other sons of mine whom he took captive would fleet Achilles sell beyond the unvintaged sea unto Samos and Imbros and smoking Lemnos, but when with keen-edged bronze he had bereft thee of thy life he was fain to drag thee oft around the tomb of his comrade, even Patroklos whom thou slewest, yet might he not raise him up thereby. But now all dewy and fresh thou liest in our halls, like one on whom Apollo, lord of the silver bow, hath descended and slain him with his gentle darts."

Thus spake she wailing, and stirred unending moan. Then thirdly Helen led their sore lament: "Hector, of all my brethren of Troy far dearest to my heart! Truly my lord is godlike Alexandros who brought me to Troy-land—would I had died ere then. For this is now the twentieth year since I went thence and am gone from my own native land, but never yet heard I evil or despiteful word from thee; nay, if any other haply upbraided me in the palace-halls, whether brother or sister of thine or brother's fair-robed wife, or thy mother—but thy father is ever kind to me as he were my own—then wouldst thou soothe such with words and refrain them, by the gentleness of thy spirit and by thy gentle words. Therefore bewail I thee with pain at heart, and my hapless self with thee, for no more is any left in wide Troyland to be my friend and kind to me, but all men shudder at me."

Thus spake she wailing, and therewith the great multitude of the people groaned. But the old man Priam spake a word among the folk: "Bring wood, men of Troy, unto the city, and be not anywise afraid at heart of a crafty ambush of the Achaians; for this message Achilles gave me when he sent me from the black ships, that they should do us no hurt until the twelfth morn arise."

Thus spake he, and they yoked oxen and mules to wains, and quickly then they flocked before the city. So nine days they gathered great store of wood. But when the tenth morn rose with light for men, then bare they forth brave Hector, weeping tears, and on a lofty pyre they laid the dead man, and thereon cast fire.

But when the daughter of Dawn, rosy-fingered Morning, shone forth, then gathered the folk around glorious Hector's pyre. First quenched they with bright wine all the burning, so far as the fire's strength went, and then his brethren and comrades gathered his white bones lamenting, and big tears flowed down their cheeks. And the bones they took and laid in a golden urn, shrouding them in soft purple